The Rise and Fall of the
EMERALD TIGERS

The Rise and Fall of the EMERALD TIGERS

Ten Years of Research in Panna National Park

Raghu Chundawat

SPEAKING TIGER PUBLISHING PVT LTD
4381/4 Ansari Road, Daryaganj,
New Delhi–110002, India

First published by Speaking Tiger in hardback 2018

All photos in the book courtesy Joanna Van Gruisen

ISBN: 978-93-86582-65-2
e-ISBN: 978-93-86582-66-9

10 9 8 7 6 5 4 3 2 1

Typeset in Adobe Jenson Pro by Jojy Philip
Printed at Sanat Printers, Kundli

Contents

Foreword

India is filled these days with self-styled tiger experts, both foreign and domestic. Anyone with the price of park entry, a mobile phone and a presence on Facebook feels qualified to weigh in on how best to protect the National Animal.

Raghu Chundawat, the author of this rich and compelling book, is the real thing. The son of a forest officer who showed him his first tiger at the age of five or six, he had already conducted a pioneering survey of the ecology of snow leopards when, in 1996, he launched what still remains the longest-lived study ever made of Indian tigers in the wild.

Panna Tiger Reserve, where he chose to work, is one of the most beautiful protected areas in Central India; no one who has seen the clean, clear Ken River twisting its way through the forest or experienced Panna's spectacular plateaus, gorges and seasonal waterfalls is likely to forget them. But Chundawat did not pick it for its beauty. He wanted to study tigers where they were most threatened, and Panna's tiger population was then dwindling; it was home to no more than fifteen of the great cats in a landscape ideally suited for many more. He was determined to find out why, hoping to learn scientific lessons that could be applied to struggling tiger populations elsewhere in the country.

Over the course of the next ten years, Chundawat, his wife—the writer-photographer Joanna Van Gruisen—and a team made up of research students and local people with intimate knowledge of the forest managed to radio-collar and monitor five female and two male tigers, and to follow closely the daily lives of several other tigers as well.

Nature doesn't make such a study easy. Summer heat routinely reaches 50° C and sparks fast-moving fires in the tinder-dry grassland.

Pre-dawn winter wind-chill often dips below freezing just when the researchers head out on elephant-back to monitor tiger kills. Monsoon rains render forest roads impassable and yield clouds of mosquitoes that carry cerebral malaria—from which Chundawat once nearly died. The rigours of scientific study in the field are demanding, too: walking transects in every kind of weather to estimate the density of prey; picking through redolent scat to catalogue precisely what tigers have been snacking on most recently; waiting anxiously to see whether a tranquilized animal recovers fully (they always did); struggling to make sense of mountains of accumulated data on an astonishing ninety-five tiger years of observations, including uncollared tigers and cubs.

Chundawat's account of his findings, and how they came about, will fascinate weekend wildlifers and serious students of ecology alike. Panna's tigers, he writes, were at once, 'vulnerable' and 'resilient, temperamental, trusting—and contrary to popular perception—peaceful.' And, thanks to close cooperation between Chundawat's team and an especially able Field Director, P. K. Chawdhry, who appreciated good science and understood the anti-poaching impact of constant monitoring on foot and elephant-back, the tiger population more than doubled to thirty-five tigers in just five years.

Then began a slow-moving but unrelenting disaster. Chawdhry was transferred. The new management proved wary of outsiders, jealous of its prerogatives and eager to provide elephant rides for the wave of tourists newly attracted by Panna's tigers. Monitoring from elephant-back ended. Researchers reported seeing animals with wire snares around their necks—evidence that without monitoring poachers had free reign—but were told by park management it was none of their business. A collared tigress went missing. Another was found dead in a snare. When the Field Director failed to act, Chundawat wrote to the authorities in Bhopal and Delhi to tell them what was happening.

His account of the six hard years that followed is admirably free of bitterness but surely represents one of the most shameful chapters in the history of Indian conservation. Unable or unwilling to face the real problem—the ease with which poachers were now moving in and out of the forest which were supposed to be protected—officials, both on the state and federal level, chose instead to focus their ire on the man who first brought it to their attention. When nothing was done, Chundawat dared go public with the story. He was maligned as an alarmist with a private axe to grind. He was harassed, threatened, accused of collaborating with poachers, and made the target of frivolous court cases. His vehicle was seized. His research project was shut down. He was barred from entering the forest, even as a fee-paying visitor.

He continued to speak out, nonetheless, and tigers continued steadily to disappear. The cover-up continued: as late as June 2008, a Forest Department official was still reassuring the public that 'nothing is lost in Panna,' that the 'tiger density in the park has never been better.'

By the following January, every one of the tigers Chundawat had come to know had vanished along with all their offspring. Panna Tiger Reserve had no tigers at all.

The following year, five tigers—four females and one male—from three other parks in Madhya Pradesh were translocated to Panna, and over the intervening years the park's population has returned to near pre-disaster levels. But Chundawat worries that without a coherent, science-based strategy, tragedy could strike again at any time. In his final chapter he spells out in crisp detail his ideas for how Panna, and by extension all of India's wildlife enclaves, could be more closely and creatively safeguarded.

Chundawat's love for the tiger and the forest in which it lives infuses every page of this book. So does the courage of his convictions. Over the years, the tiger has been fortunate to have had a number of extraordinary champions, tiger-wallahs like Billy Arjan Singh, Fateh Singh Rathore and Ullas Karanth, willing to risk everything rather than abandon their mission. On the evidence of this book, Raghu Chundawat belongs in that remarkable company.

Geoffrey C. Ward
co-author of *Tiger-Wallahs*

Introduction

I do not remember my first ever tiger sighting but some of my earliest memories are of watching tigers with my father in Kanha in the late sixties. I remember riding elephants in the Kanha meadows, following tigers in the tall grass and sitting next to the mahout. I was five or six years old when father was posted to the South Mandla forest division and Kanha was one of the ranges under his charge. I was fortunate that my father, who had earlier been a keen hunter, had by this time stopped hunting and spent most of his time watching wildlife and trying to protect it. Instead of hunting, a conservation philosophy was therefore imprinted in my subconscious. I sometimes imagine with dread what would have been the impact if I had grown up in an environment where hunting instead of watching wildlife was the important outdoor activity. I feel very lucky to have grown up listening to his tiger stories and to have accompanied him in the field, where at an early stage in my life I learned to respect these creatures. What I failed to acquire from my father was his extraordinary talent for telling stories. His friends would bring their friends and relatives just to listen to his amazing tales. I miss this very much now because after thirty years of wildlife research I, too, have accumulated quite a lot of experience and some very interesting observations. It would have been delightful to share these with him. It is during these moments I miss his presence very much. I therefore dedicate this book to him.

I've found it extremely hard to share my experiences: not because I do not want to but because I find people are more interested in telling their stories than in listening to others. They start by asking me some questions about my work but, very quickly, I find myself listening to somebody's fleeting encounter with a tiger ten years ago, with an interpretation of what they saw putting any expert to shame. No wonder people in India think that there are more tiger experts in the subcontinent than tigers; it may be so! Sometimes these random observations are presented as scientific facts and this tendency has circulated many myths about the tiger; when repeated often enough the myths become truth in general perceptions. That is why it is important for a researcher to write down his experiences with proper factual information so that such unfounded theories and hypothetical explanations may be dispelled.

Brief History

Hunting of tigers was a popular sport up to the 1960s and lots of books were written to cater to this interest. Most of our natural history knowledge of the time comes from these hunting books, which are still enjoyed today. For instance, most of us have grown up reading Jim Corbett's stories about hunting man-eating tigers. These books, with their sensational hunting stories, further fuelled interest in sport-hunting. One of the lowest points came around the turn of the twentieth century, between 1875 and 1925, when sport-hunting decimated our abundant tiger population. According to the well known historian Mahesh Rangarajan, close to 80,000 tigers (along with 1,50,000 leopards and 2,00,000 wolves) fell to sport hunting during those fifty years (Rangarajan, 2001). His estimate may just be a fraction of the actual tigers killed during this period. But even by this estimate, at least 1,600 tigers were shot every year, and if this harvest was anywhere between 5–10 per cent of the population, it suggests that the population of tigers in India would have been somewhere in the range of 16,000 to 32,000. Some folks estimate that India had a population of 40,000 tigers or more at the turn of the twentieth century; this may not be very far from the truth.

There were a few individuals at the time who did not glorify such killings. For instance, Captain Forsyth was among the first who wanted to stop them (Forsyth, 1889). Gilbert, Russell and several others were early proponents for ending the bounty for killing a tiger. Reginal George Burton wrote *The Book of The Tiger* in 1933, one of the first comprehensive documents about natural history and tiger behaviour. Jim Corbett also campaigned hard to save tigers. F.W. Champion picked up a camera instead of the gun, taking nature photography to a new level. He developed the technique where a tiger could take its own picture. Through his classical images of tigers, he created a new cult of nature photography in India and helped bring to light a different side of the tiger in the popular imagination. However, sport-hunting of tigers continued until the 1960s. Concerned by this decline, many voices, like those of E.P. Gee, P.D. Stracey, and later Kailash Sankhala and Billy Arjan Singh, spoke and wrote extensively about wildlife conservation in the subcontinent. Though much was written at the time, there was very little in the way of good scientific literature on the tiger. George Schaller's *The Deer and the Tiger* (1967) was the first book that was based on original scientific work on tigers in India.

The 1970s brought a watershed moment when the Wild Life (Protection) Act, 1972 was enacted and Project Tiger was launched. Project Tiger spawned a whole movement across the country by creating a network of tiger Reserves to protect tigers and their habitat. The early successes of Project Tiger halted the decline and all seemed well until the late 1980s, when an unexpected threat took a heavy toll on the tiger population. Unexpected because, somehow, for decades India had managed to remain free from the illegal trade in tiger body parts arising from the demand by traditional medical practices of Southeast Asian countries. Stracey had warned of this earlier but the warning had been forgotten. As early as 1968, he wrote that the tiger in India was 'not exposed to any great extent to persecution resulting from superstitious fancy in regard to the alleged value of its various parts for medicinal purposes.' However, he noted that the cult was 'highly developed' among the Malays and the Chinese especially and wondered how this would affect the survival rate of the tiger. Comparing the already apparent drain on the rhino population for its horn, he said, 'On this analogy alone there seems no future for the tiger in south-east Asia' (Stracey, 1968). In India, few took notice of Stracey's warnings amidst the glories of Project Tiger.

The loss of tigers in the late '80s and '90s was largely due to the demand for tiger bones, mainly for Traditional Chinese Medicine (TCM). Ten years later, it was the demand for tiger skins from Tibet. If this trend continues and we allow tiger populations to be impacted by one crisis after another, the tiger may survive only in a few places, in forests that provide larger, more secure landscapes. We have already lost a huge gene pool.

The total extinction of tigers in Sariska by 2004 and in Panna by 2009 is worrying because it tells us that even within our protected areas they are not safe. Such incidents expose some of the fundamental problems in tiger conservation—problems besides poaching and human disturbances, that are not ecological or biological in nature. They relate to the functioning of the management system of the tiger Reserves, which have been unable to evolve a proper understanding of tiger ecology. This is obvious from the repeated crises that have beset tigers since the 1990s, with the Sariska and Panna extinctions happening within the space of five years and under the leadership of the National Tiger Conservation Authority.

This Book

To cater to the enormous interest tigers have generated, a very large number of coffee table books have been published. Most books on tigers are either based on anecdotal, secondary information or on brief field experiences. There have been works by individuals from the scientific community, but these are accounts of personal experience in the field that throw some light on the tiger's natural history. There are also books on tigers by non-scientists that are based on extensive natural history observations but there are none from a single study on the tiger. This is mainly because there have hardly been any long-term studies on the tiger in India. Prior to our work in Panna no research had continued beyond two-three years. *The Rise and Fall of the Emerald Tigers* aims to fill this gap by providing authentic scientific research from the field in the hope that it will enhance our understanding of the species.

Over the duration of our study, we followed one of the best recoveries of a tiger population from 1996 to 2001. We also witnessed the unique event of a tiger population eventually suffering a local extinction. This gave us the chance to identify the ecological and biological factors responsible for the loss. We were able to document the systemic failures that allowed this tragic event to happen. This is a story with many lessons for tiger conservation.

Moreover, this book documents observations made on the multiple generations of tigers that we monitored in a Tropical Dry Forest. There were many exciting times but unfortunately it ended as a very tragic tale, as all the tigers with whom we had worked were lost by 2009. We had known some of them from the time they were born, till they had babies of their own. Losing all of them was like losing a part of one's family; it was a heartbreaking experience. I could no longer be a dispassionate scientist, as we are told to be. One tigress, the matriarch of the Panna tigers, whom we called 'Baavan', meaning 'fifty-two', became a favourite of ours. She was the only tigress we knew that managed to survive through all the ups and downs of the Reserve. Through her struggle to survive, we understood why tigers are so vulnerable in the Dry Forests of the subcontinent. We also learned how resilient, temperamental, trusting and—contrary to popular perception—peaceful these creatures are. In this book, I wish to share the knowledge we accumulated during eight years of tracking different tigers. I hope to provide the reader with scientific research in an accessible manner and facilitate a greater understanding about tiger ecology.

After a general introduction and description of the area, the book will first cover the science. The aim has been to try to present the information not only as reference material for the scientific community, but to make it accessible to managers of tiger Reserves and tiger fans interested in knowing more about the animal's natural behaviour. The last three chapters of the book discuss the politics surrounding tiger conservation and the systemic failures that allowed the extinction to occur. They document our collective failure to save the original tiger population. It is important to learn from such failures so that their repetition is prevented. When the tigers in Sariska went extinct very little was learnt since no one had documented the decline or studied in detail why and how it happened. In Panna, however, we were there to witness this undesirable event and could document the inability of the system to react appropriately to the situation. It is from documenting such failures that pertinent corrective measures can be understood and implemented for the future. Further, based on our findings, we propose some innovative strategies to revitalize the wildlife conservation effort in the country.

This book will not only be useful for tiger conservation in India but has relevance for the entire tiger range across Asia. It should add to a growing body of knowledge about managing large carnivore populations around the world.

1

Tigers in the Subcontinent:

An Overview

Among wild animals, the tiger has always attracted considerable attention across the world. But despite the overwhelming number of supporters and well-wishers, the population of this feline predator has been deteriorating. Recent estimates indicate that tigers now survive in only 7 per cent of their former range (Dinerstein et al., 2007). We have already lost three subspecies—Bali, Caspian and Java tigers (*Panthera tigris balica, P.t. virgata,* and *P.t. sondaica*). The South China tiger (*P.t. amoyensis*), according to some experts, does not have a sufficient breeding population to survive in the wild (Nowell and Jackson, 1996). Populations of three subspecies, Amur, Sumatra and Indo-Chinese tigers (*P.t. altaica, P.t. sumatrae* and *P.t. corbetti*), are holding on against great odds. Only the Royal Bengal tiger (*P.t. tigris*) is performing relatively better. According to All-India Estimates from 2014, we are left with only about 2,200 tigers, and it is sad to realize that what survives now in India is close to the number of tigers that were shot every year when sport hunting was at its peak. Could the situation have evolved differently? I believe we could have done better if the problem had been dealt with when early warning signs were given.

In the short span of my life, I have seen vast changes. I remember when travelling with my father in the Mandsaur district, Madhya Pradesh, in the mid-'70s, he pointed towards a large tree and told me that this was the tree from where his elder brother had shot his first tiger. He had been sitting with him. But what was shocking was that thirty-forty years later there was no forest to be seen in the neighbourhood. The nearest forest cover (now without any tigers) was over 20 kilometres away. This is just an example to show how much of the tiger's home we have lost in the recent past. In this case, the tiger habitat was the casualty of a large dam. We not only lost tiger habitat due to the submergence but entire villages were relocated here after clearing the forest. It is not that we were not aware of the number of tigers we lost when it was happening, but early warnings were ignored. Nothing has changed even now as we continue to ignore the warnings and facts.

There were still plenty of tigers by the time India gained independence. My parents told me that in the early fifties my father, who was a forest officer, was posted at Bhopal and resided in a place called Roshanpura *naka* (i.e. checkpost). People who know Bhopal will know the location, it is now in the heart of the city and New Market dominates the place. I was told that once they had lost a calf to a tiger from there. Even in the sixties, I remember how often I was woken up to be shown a tiger on the road when driving through the central Indian landscape. The unfortunate thing is how quickly we forget what the past was like—for the younger generation the current situation has become the new baseline, and in the absence of documentation we fail to understand what has been lost. Some describe this as 'conservation amnesia'. I had no idea until my mother told me about it. So, a tiger appearing on the outskirts of Bhopal should not be a surprise, though it does surprise many of us now. Unfortunately, due to poor understanding of our conservation history, with every new generation the baseline continues to shift; it moves forward and we fail to recognize how much has been lost. An example of such conservation amnesia is when we celebrated the estimate of 1,700+ tigers in 2010–11, hardly remembering that four decades ago, when India had 1,800 tigers (All-India Census, 1970), we felt it was drastic enough to launch Project Tiger. The figure of 1,400 tigers from the 2008 estimate became the new norm for tiger conservation and 1,700 tigers was considered a great achievement.

In 1969, it was Mr Kailash Sankhala who, at an IUCN (International Union for Conservation of Nature) Congress, suggested that India may have only 2,500 tigers left. This shocked the entire conservation community and changed the world for tigers in India. Through his presentation, Sankhala convinced the world about the dire state of tigers in India. He sought an international effort to save the tiger from extinction. Thereafter, the tiger was included in the Red Data Book and declared an endangered species. From a healthy 40,000 tigers at the turn of the century to less than 2,000 was a drastic decline and needed an immediate response. India rose to the occasion—tiger hunting was banned in 1970. In 1972, a complete ban on hunting of wild animals was enacted with The Wild Life (Protection) Act, 1972. Project Tiger was launched in 1973 with a commitment to restore the tiger population to its original glory. There were many individuals who played very important roles in this campaign. Mrs Indira Gandhi, then prime minister of India, played a particularly crucial role with very able support from Dr Karan Singh and Kailash Sankhala. Project Tiger was provided the funds needed for tiger conservation in the field. The World Wild Life Fund (WWF) joined hands, providing more funding and support. Kailash Sankhala became the first director of the uniquely Indian initiative of Project Tiger. Under this project a series of important tiger habitats were set aside for tiger conservation and notified as 'Tiger Reserves'. Sankhala identified key individuals and posted them as Field Directors of these Reserves. Creating a hardworking team with the right talent was key to the success of Project Tiger and allowed the tiger population to recover. I was fortunate enough to know and work with some members of this glorious team of foresters-turned-tiger-conservationists, including Shri Sanjay Debroy, Fateh Singh Rathore, H.S. Panwar, and M.K. Ranjit Sinh from Indian Administrative Services, whose contribution has remained unmatched so far. The 1970s and early 1980s seemed to be golden years for the tiger in India. Ranthambhore, Corbett, Kanha, Bandhavgarh, Bandipur and Manas Tiger Reserves became popular destinations for a different kind of traveller in India, who came to see and admire the beauty of the tiger and all its co-denizens in the forest.

We now have a new generation of tiger conservationists who have devoted their life to working for tigers in different capacities. A few names stand out in my mind—Valmik Thapar, who fought a hard battle to save the Ranthambhore tigers early on but later became a champion for tigers all over India. Belinda Wright and the late Ashok Kumar risked their lives to expose the illegal trade in tiger body parts. Debbie Banks from the London-based Environmental Investigation Agency has also been a strong support, working with Indian NGOs in this regard. Bittu Sahgal launched *Sanctuary*, the oldest wildlife magazine of India still in circulation, which created a support base for wildlife in India. He also began a children's issue, working tirelessly to instill an appreciation and knowledge of wildlife and conservation in the younger generation. His success has been immense. In fact I too was inspired by the photographs and articles I read in the magazine. Dr Ullas Karanth took a different path, working scientifically to gather information on the tiger, which was desperately needed for success in saving the tiger. He pioneered new population monitoring methods and has also been an outstanding inspiration and trainer for subsequent generations of conservationists. In the 1980s and '90s we were extremely fortunately to have Dave Fergusson from the US colloquial Fish and Wild Life Service, USA. I do not think there was any wildlife research project in India that did not benefit from his support. Whether it was academic collaboration, research equipment, special clothing for high altitudes, grants or institutional support. He personally knew most of us, interacting and providing personal support. His contribution to wildlife conservation in any field from tigers to birds to high-altitude creatures was enormous and unconditional. These diverse talents, along with extremely dedicated field staff and their leaders, all worked hard. Most of them continue to fight, and succeed. The results can be seen in the enormous number of tiger fans we now have in every field, be it science, journalism, politics, business, film or tourism. One does not stand alone for the tiger. This is good news for the species and its co-inhabitants.

But despite this support base, the 1990s and the decade that followed it were turbulent years, witnessing the extinction of tiger populations from two tiger Reserves. As a result of these losses, one cannot feel as confident as we did in 1970s and '80s. We no longer have a team such as the one Sankhala was able to put together. Local extinctions from two highly protected areas of Sariska (2004) and Panna (2009) are worrying because it says that even within our Protected Areas tigers are not safe. A quick review of literature suggests that major threats to tigers include poaching of tigers, habitat loss and loss of habitat quality caused by depletion of prey due to poaching or other forms of human disturbances and development activities (Panwar, 1982; Seidensticker, 1986; Wemmer et al., 1987; Johnsingh et al., 1991; Sahgal and Thapar, 1996). But one major limiting factor that is not included, which I consider important, is the failure to incorporate science in the management of tiger Reserves. The total extinctions also exposed other fundamental problems that are not ecological or biological in nature but relate to the functioning of the system. Why was our management system not able to learn from Sariska? Had they done so, a repetition in Panna could not have occurred. I had a front row seat for the tiger extinction in Panna. This book reports on the tiger ecology learnt from my long-term research there and discusses this loss in the hope that we can learn lessons and prevent any recurrences.

Since the 1970s, when the world woke up to the need of protecting the tiger, the Royal Bengal tiger (*P.t. tigris*), found in the Indian subcontinent, has provided hope for the future of the species. The foremost chance of saving tigers for posterity rested with the Indian subcontinent because it supported 60 per cent of the world's wildlife population. However, recent estimates based on the National Tiger Conservation Authority of India (NTCA) census in 2014, place tiger numbers in the country closer to 2,226. With such small numbers, I would describe the future of this population as precarious, despite the fact that we have arrested the decline somewhat. My main concern is that tiger populations in India are divided into numerous small populations, many of which are isolated and being pushed towards extinction (Johnsingh et al., 1991; Jhala et al., 2011).

The extinctions of Sariska and Panna shocked the nation, but apparently not the managers. The complete loss of a tiger population exposed the fact of a fundamental flaw in the management system which allowed it to happen, not once but twice in a single decade. Aggressive development plans created an environment unsuitable for the survival of a large predator like tiger. The situation is worse outside the Protected Area network. Organized poaching for illegal trade is the biggest nail in the coffin for tigers. We have already lost most tigers outside the protected areas and are now swiftly losing populations inside these areas as well. This loss must be stalled. Sariska and Panna were warning signals.

Though the government of India has made considerable efforts for conservation, the repeated occurrence of tiger crises indicates that we have not done enough and our efforts may have been imperfectly directed. Much more needs to be done to save wild tigers in India. When we lost tigers from Sariska and Panna, we did not *lose* Panna and Sariska. The habitat and prey remained intact. This shows that the management actions were able to protect tiger habitat and prey but failed to protect the tiger. The management needs to understand this—its methods are working for some things but not for the tiger (Panwar, 1982, 1987; Wemmer et al., 1987; Jonsingh et al., 1991; Karanth, 1991).

Since tigers occupy diverse habitats, different conservation approaches are required but the current management only has a one-size-fits-all approach. We need different conservation models with new ideas to address different challenges and these can only come when we have a better understanding of the ecosystem. When the decline was happening we were not prepared enough to react immediately and now, when tigers are dispersing, we have no plans to use this opportunity to establish new, connected breeding populations. We can only be prepared if we develop a better understanding.

My Study

A better understanding of the ecosystem can only come from ecological study. Unfortunately, very few studies have been conducted on the ecology of tigers, with even fewer long-term studies. In the absence of substantive reliable information, management actions remain dependent on personal whims which may have very little relevance to reality. At the policy level, we need to know where our 'viable' populations (i.e. ones capable of producing surplus individuals) are, and we need to know how they can be connected to each other. Their connectivity is important for the long-term viability of a larger meta-population. At the field level, it is important for management to know how these habitats are utilized. How do we identify and manage these habitats to optimize tigers' reproductive potential? These are some of the more important questions we need to answer in order to achieve our conservation goal. With so much to learn, I never expected it would be so difficult for me to get a research project approved.

The idea that such a study on tiger ecology was needed came to me in 1993, after spending over two months in Ranthambhore. As soon as I joined the faculty of the Wild Life Institute of India (WII), I was given my first assignment: to provide training to the Ranthambhore Tiger Reserve staff in conducting tiger census using pugmarks and plaster casts. It was the year following the exposure of illegal trade in tiger bones and body parts for TCM which had shocked the nation and the world. The loss of tigers was more visible in Ranthambhore than in any other tiger habitat because it had always attracted visitors to its beautiful valleys and lakes. When tigers were poached here it was noticed. Though we had lost tigers in almost every corner of the country, the headlines were focused on Ranthambhore. Several petitions were filed to address the crisis facing the nation.

This was the first time I became involved in tiger conservation. The Supreme Court had asked the WII to train and supervise the census exercise in Ranthambhore and I was one of those sent to do this. It was my first exposure to the pugmark-based census and the controversy associated with tiger numbers. I came to know how fanatically some defend the pugmark method while others dismiss it with equal aggression. I was neutral on the issue at the time, maybe leaning towards the pugmark method because it was taught at WII and I had participated in several training programmes. But what I saw in Ranthambhore completely changed my outlook.

Picture a large hall with three walls divided into sections marked 1, 2, 3, 4 and 5. Plaster casts of forty-two different individuals were arranged in neat heaps in front of the numbered sections. Forty-two was the number of tigers claimed to be still in the Reserve, hence the precise number of piles. The then director of WII, H.S. Panwar had come to supervise the analysis. By direction of the Supreme Court, Valmik Thapar and Fateh Singh Rathore had joined us to witness the evaluation. What we saw in the next two days was no less than chaos, despite desperate and sincere attempts by everybody to sort the pugmarks and give them definite 'IDs'. Some of the pugmark casts went through twenty or more ID assignations of individual tigers. When taught in the classroom, it sounds simple to look at differences and resolve any confusion by the date, time and direction of travel. However, reality is very different. It was shocking to see experts of the pugmark method struggle to identify tigers from the completely mixed-up piles of plaster casts. This confusion continued till late in the evening and we left for the night with unfinished work at hand. The next day was no different. I was stunned to see people walking in circles, picking up the same plaster casts from different piles and putting them in yet another pile. I was not thinking. I was not supposed to, the experts were there. This charade continued till around 8 p.m. until we had had enough and took a break. Our task was almost finished, or so I thought. We had to catch a train the next morning, so work started very early the next day. But we were still very far from reaching any conclusive figure. Desperate messages were sent to change our reservations to an afternoon train and we continued. When we left for the train the census analysis was still not over. But when we finally boarded the train, one of the Range Officers joined us and the final number of Ranthambhore's tigers was decided there. The report was completed and as soon as it was handed over, the Range Officer jumped out at the next station to take it back to Sawai Madhopur.

I was too shocked and disgusted to show much interest in what was being written and how we came to the magic number of thirty-five tigers. It is all a blur in my memory and I am thankful for that, because what I had seen was enough to destroy my belief in the integrity and functioning of the system. Prior to this, an independent assessment had been done by an expert nominated by the Chief Wild Life Warden, but those results were not accepted as they suggested a figure of only seventeen tigers. It was now up to this new evaluation to save the authority from this low number. During my three months' stay in the Reserve, I saw tigers only twice. Where people regularly recorded over ten different sightings of tigers in one drive, now even finding a pugmark was difficult. In this situation, the reported figure of over thirty-five tigers was a conspiracy as far as I was concerned. An honest assessment was required so that immediate corrective measures could be taken and political will mobilized. Instead, by not reporting the real situation, we were encouraging complacency: the Park staff was reassured that, whatever happened, senior officers would save the situation for them. This is exactly what happened during the 2005 census in Panna which directly led to the loss of all the tigers there.

It seemed that the authorities protected those who failed to save the tigers. This charade has happened too often and its only victim is the tiger. Dismayed by what I had witnessed in Ranthambhore, I started reading and collecting literature, making a comprehensive review of the status of the tiger. I developed what I thought was a sound research proposal. But soon I learned how difficult it was to get a tiger study sanctioned. There seemed to be a general belief that we didn't need to study tigers because we already knew a lot about them. It was astonishing for me to hear this from the head of a scientific institution. There were only two studies after *The Deer and the Tiger*, one conducted in Chitwan National Park in Nepal and the other by Dr Ullas Karanth in Nagarahole, Karnataka. The latter had unfortunately come to an abrupt end. I made several attempts to get a tiger study approved but failed. Every rejection helped me develop a better proposal but the failure of my sixth attempt left me highly dejected. The experience changed my relationship with the then head of the WII forever. After a long defence, I was told that whatever I would write after ten years of study, he could write then and there in half an hour. I had never expected such a reaction. Like many young scholars, I had held him in the greatest respect and worshipped him as my role model. I, and others too, could have written a viable proposal in a month but that was not the point—we needed reliable scientific information, not anecdotal fiction. Further discussions were turning bitter so I decided to let it go. It was only after a change of guard at the institute that I submitted a tiger study proposal again. It was promptly approved and I finally had a grant to launch the study. These episodes epitomize the attitude that exists in the system and is one of the major reasons why tigers, indeed wildlife as a whole, is suffering.

My struggle did not end with the grant. I was in touch with a very keen and bright student and wanted him to join the research project for his PhD. After a formal interview with the faculty, we felt that he would be a perfect candidate for the project. He was of Indian origin, but we learned that he held a British passport. Therefore, he was advised to apply for his work permit to the Ministry of Environment, Forest and Climate Change (MOEFCC). After a long delay, we finally received a communication from the head of wildlife at the MOEFCC rejecting the application. The letter said that tiger conservation in India was a controversial issue and one could not ensure in this case that there will not be dissemination of sensitive information! I still cannot understand why tiger conservation is considered such a controversial issue and why ecological information on tigers is so sensitive that it cannot be shared with the rest of the world. I therefore had to find a new candidate. I knew I wanted to work in Tropical Dry Forest habitats and had to find one that suited the study. My next biggest challenge was to procure permissions for fieldwork in a Protected Area and for the radio-collaring of tigers.

2

The Place: Emerald Forest of Panna

I fell in love with what I saw from the roof of the Bargadi inspection hut on my very first morning in the Reserve in October, 1995 when visiting with H.S. Pabla. As far as the eye could see it was all grassland. I felt strongly attracted to the park and found it one of the most beautiful places in central India that I had seen so far.

The Panna Tiger Reserve is located on the northern edge of the Vindhyan mountain range where the hills give way to the Gangetic plains to the north (Figure 2.1). It is one of the most valuable tiger habitats of the Tropical Dry Forests of India (Pabla, 1984; Chawdhry, 1997). I wanted to work in Tropical Dry Forest habitats and had had Pench, Tadoba and Satpura in mind. Ranthambhore had been dropped earlier because it was a place with lots of tourists and radio-collaring tigers there would generate unnecessary controversy.

Later that first day we drove around the Reserve and this strengthened my first instinctive feeling that Panna would be an ideal place for my study. Its unique topography—a series of gorges, high escarpments and stepwise plateaux—creates a terrain that is friendly for a telemetry-based study. We also saw plenty of prey, a lone wild dog and a few signs of tiger. It seemed like the ideal site—it had an extensive road network, elephants for tracking and a tiger population that was suffering from all the problems that we needed to study.

When I decided on Panna as my study site, friends threw up their hands in horror, believing it was not the best place since the tiger population was so low. Though I understood their concern, I also knew that my objective was to study tigers where they were most threatened. This would allow us to understand the reasons for their decline. Information from such a study would be more useful in managing tiger populations than that gathered from optimal habitats like Bandhavgarh or Kanha. I knew it would not be possible for me to radio-collar many tigers simultaneously and track them but I was prepared for the long haul—a study extending over several years that allowed us to gather information on several individual tigers.

History

Panna Tiger Reserve and the adjoining territorial forests provide a fairly large contiguous habitat for tigers all along the Vindhyan ranges. Some of these forests were protected as private game Reserves of the erstwhile princely states of Bijawar, Chattarpur, Ajaygarh and Panna. The Park area had been a favourite hunting ground for the maharajas of Panna and their guests for centuries. These forests are known for their light-coloured leopards and cheetahs—known as the *sandela* cheetah i.e. sandalwood-coloured. There were many records of the *sandela* leopards too, and one well-preserved specimen is still with the erstwhile royal family of Ajaygarh. In fact, many of the tigers in Panna were pale with very few or faint, almost brownish stripes, almost like *sandela* tigers! In addition to the light colouration, their unusual body shape and size made this population morphologically unique. Many experienced tiger experts frequently mistook some of the females for male tigers.

The Panna forest attained the legal status of 'Protected Forest' in 1948. A part of these forests was declared a National Park in 1981 and designated as 'Panna Tiger Reserve' (PTR) in 1994. The Panna National Park (PNP) included a major part of the existing Gangau Wild Life Sanctuary. Strangely, the Gangau Wild Life Sanctuary, which was notified prior to Panna's National Park was lost to records for a long time. It was only by chance that a major portion of the Sanctuary was notified as a National Park in 1981. Twenty-nine compartments or forestry management units of the Gangau Sanctuary were left out completely, while many of them were only partly included in Panna National Park. Confusion over the status of these compartments continued for a long time. They were managed as territorial forests till as late as 2004 when, finally, the Forest Department found the lost sanctuary in their records, and these forest areas were handed over to the management of the Panna Tiger Reserve. It now forms a very important part of the Reserve that is designated as the 'Critical Tiger Habitat' (CTH or 'core') of the Reserve.

In addition to this, another large portion of habitat surrounding the CTH has been earmarked as a 'Buffer Habitat'. After amendments to the Wild Life Protection Act (1972) in 2006, it was made mandatory for all tiger Reserves to have a CTH and a buffer. A 'buffer' is described as a multiple use area, where people and tigers coexist and the local population is permitted to have forest rights and concessions as prescribed in the Forest Conservation Act (1980) and the Wild Life Protection Act. Within the CTH, the aim is to create inviolate spaces for the tiger and other wildlife, and all human settlements are to be relocated elsewhere after due settlement of rights and monetary compensation. The total area of the Panna Tiger Reserve according to the government notification is 1,688.37 km^2, which includes 576.13 km^2 of CTH and 1,021.98 km^2 of buffer.

Topography

According to Panwar and Rogers' 1988 report, these forests fall under Zone 6 E, which is described as the 'Central Highlands' of the Deccan Peninsula. This location is significant as from this point onwards the forest of the Vindhyan ranges gives way to the Gangetic plains dominated by humans and agriculture, marking the end of the tiger habitat towards the north. Here forest cover is classified as 'Northern Dry Deciduous Teak Forest' (5 B C/2) and the most common vegetation type is described as 'miscellaneous forest' which is interspersed with small grasslands (Champion and Seth, 1968).

The topography of the area is very interesting. It is like a tableland in steps—the two upper plateaux are extensive, forming the bulk of the tiger habitat, while the last plateau drops into the Ken valley. The fall between the upper-middle plateau and the Ken river valley is steep and forms 10-80 metre high escarpments. This creates a series of gorges, cliffs and overhangs. The escarpments along the river provide excellent views and the vista of the Ken river gorge from Sakra is incredible. I have spent many hours sitting on the edge of the cliff, watching the sun set after a long hard day, admiring the beauty of this unique Bundelkhand landscape.

The series of escarpments create unique microhabitats and are characterized by caves and rock shelters, springs and patches of thick forest cover in the gorges. The Vindhyan strata in this region are known for their poor water retention capacity, mainly due to the large number of fractures and faults. As a result, most of the surface water percolates down very fast, leaving streams, nallahs and pools dry almost as soon as the monsoon is over. Nevertheless, the faults do create a few springs that remain perennial. While most streams are seasonal, Ken and Shyamri (a tributary of Ken) are perennial rivers. The Ken flows for about 55 kilometres through the park, before joining the Yamuna in Banda district in Uttar Pradesh.

Climate

The landscape is dotted with large seasonal waterfalls. These waterfalls are dry most of the year but they are an amazing sight during monsoon, when they are flowing at their peak. In fact, Panna is most beautiful soon after the monsoon when the lush green cover is interspersed with flowering *Saccharum munja* grasslands. These grasslands and the forest gradually dry up and by February-end the grass cover is bone dry. Its beauty then is in the gold and pink hues, though it lacks nutritional value, as most of the nutrition moves below ground; only biomass and fibres are left above ground. This dry grass biomass becomes a major source for forest fires during the peak summer months. Some of these fires are pretty unmanageable, especially when coupled with strong winds. Once, I remember a fire moved so fast that it covered eight to nine kilometres in two hours flat. We had temperature data loggers

The geological formations that create deep gorges are locally called 'Seha'. The Panna landscape is dotted with these. The waterfalls here dry up soon after the monsoon, but the lush habitat and caves at the base of the escarpments provide much-needed shelter for tigers escaping from the extreme heat of the summer months.

placed in the field and despite a mad dash in a four-wheel-drive vehicle and a motorcycle we could not recover them. Fire in these dry forests plays a very significant ecological role.

The climate of Panna is typically semi-arid with three distinct seasons. Summer begins in March and lasts until the first shower of the monsoon, i.e. the first week of June. The forest turns brown and completely leafless by mid-April. Though this is not the hottest month, the forest appears at its driest. By mid-May many trees and shrubs start sprouting and the new flush of green foliage dots the forest, and the dry landscape looks very different once again. These trees provide much-needed shelter from the scorching sun as well as nutritious forage for the animals. One can see wild animals spending most of their day resting under the shade created by the new flush. Though May is the hottest and driest month of the year, it appears amazingly alive.

This new growth provides excellent nutritive forage for the wild herbivores who, till then, have mostly survived on poor quality forage

The dry forest of Panna Tiger Reserve is characterized by dry river-beds with a few perennial springs. These waterholes are important resources and centres of activity during the hot summer months (April and May) before the monsoon rains arrive in June.

since winter. This growth also coincides with the fruiting season. Mahua (*Madhuca longifolia*), achar (*Buchanania lanzan*), ghont (*Ziziphus xylopyrus*) and tendu (*Diospyros melanoxylon*) provide high-energy supplements. Ghont is a lifeline for the ungulates in times of food scarcity. Not just its new sprouts, which sometimes get delayed due to the lack of moisture in such a drought-prone region, but the dry fruits of ghont and its dry leaves are also a source of nutrition. Walking through these forests one can see small piles of ghont kernels regurgitated after rumination. These are difficult months for all the life forms. On a very hot day temperatures can frequently touch 47°C and on surfaces exposed to the sun can easily cross 50°C.

Once the sun is out, the temperature soars quickly, touching 40°C by 9 a.m. Heat waves prevail, blowing hot dry air throughout the day. These conditions continue for weeks and take a huge toll on the energy requirements of wild animals. Any weak or unhealthy individual is less likely to survive through these testing times. Water, which was abundant once, is now restricted to a few perennial springs and drying river pools. These are now the major centres of activity. Some animals are so badly hit by this heat that they cannot even make it to these water points and they die. I have only occasionally seen this in Panna but this is a common occurrence in other dry forest areas such as Sariska.

If you sit in a hide (a camouflaged shelter used to observe wildlife at close quarters) near one of these waterholes, there is never a dull moment. Animals and birds of all shapes and sizes come throughout the day and night for a quick drink and vanish. They don't want to hang around for long because the place is also frequented by predators like tigers and leopards. These waterholes, therefore, become very important and sensitive micro-habitats during the summer months. These sites are not only activity centres for animals but for the poachers, too. Poachers make full use of the increased animal activities at these sites. Many times we found traps and snares around these water points. Around some waterholes we even found machans built by poachers. We had to visit some of these sensitive areas on a regular basis, especially the ones which were visited by the radio-collared tigers regularly, to remove and destroy poachers' traps or snares. Waterholes close to and outside the boundary of the Tiger Reserve were more vulnerable to poachers.

The heat wave continues into June but not for long, as moisture-laden westerly winds bring the first pre-monsoon showers, giving immediate relief from the severe heat. The weather quickly changes from dry and hot, to hot and humid. If the monsoon is not delayed, the first rains occur around the first week of July. During the monsoon, the landscape changes very quickly. The dry leafless forest magically turns into a lush emerald dream. This is a season of plenty—water everywhere, food in abundance, very little fluctuation between minimum and maximum temperatures. Many waterfalls cascade during this period. They don't last long but, at their best, they offer the most breathtaking sights in the forest.

Unfortunately, this is a time when the roads are almost inaccessible. This hampers research activities a great deal. More than anything though, this is a time when the mosquito menace is at its peak.

The mixed forests of Panna are rich in plant diversity. Sambar and nilgai are predominantly browser herbivores and the browse-line shows the plant diversity on which they feed. The mixed nature of these Tropical Dry Forests is one reason why they can support fairly high wild herbivore densities.

Almost everyone on our research team has suffered from malaria during the monsoons. The worst is cerebral malaria, caused by the *falsiperium*, which could be fatal. I once got infected and it took the doctors two weeks before they could even diagnose it as *falsiperium* malaria. I remember the awful experience of quinine infusion more than anything else.

The average annual rainfall for this region is approximately 1,100 mm—fairly high for an arid region. But over 70 per cent of the rainfall happens during July and August only. By the end of September the monsoon fury subsides and vegetative growth reaches its peak; the grass grows tall and flowers bloom. It is during this period between late September and early October that Panna is at its most beautiful. A long dry spell follows the monsoon.

Mornings in November can be cool and misty—it is the beginning of a relatively short winter in Panna. During December and January, the temperatures regularly fall below 5°C and frost is a common feature in open habitat. What I learned from the temperature data loggers (recording temperatures every hour) was a revelation—the temperature was at its lowest between 0600 and 0700 hours in the morning, just as the sun was rising, not in the early morning hours before sunrise, as we all generally believed. This was when usually we went out in the open jeep for wildlife viewing. With the wind-chill factor, the weather is equivalent to several degrees below freezing. No wonder we felt so cold in the mornings!

Fauna

Panna's forest supports a fairly diverse community of both small and large carnivores. Other than the tiger (*Panthera tigris tigris*), co-predators are the common leopard (*Panthera pardus*) and the wild dog or *dhole* (*Cuon alpinus*). Leopards are fairly common and sighted regularly throughout the Reserve.

The number of carnivores in the Reserve has increased considerably in the last few decades. The wild dog population is seen with increasing frequency. The largest pack I ever saw in the Reserve consisted of fourteen animals near Jhalar village, though a pack of eighteen dogs has also been reported. Wild dogs mostly occupy the short grassland habitat and are relatively less shy than other predators.

Sloth bear (*Melursus ursinus*) and hyena (*Hyaena hyaena*) are common in the area but the wolf (*Canis lupus laniger*), another large predator, is seen only occasionally. The forests of Panna support a fairly sizeable population of sloth bears according to a detailed ecological study conducted by Yoganand (2005). Though both the sloth bear and hyena are common, they are seen only occasionally during the daytime as they are nocturnal species.

The forests of Panna are rich in biodiversity and provide food for bears throughout the year, making them one of the most important habitats for bears in central India. Yoganand's study provides new information on the bears' food requirements, ranging pattern and social organization (Yoganand, 2005).

During the flowering of the mahua tree (*Madhuca longifolia*) in

April, when a large human population spreads out across the forest to collect its flowers, the bear-human conflict reaches its peak.* Many cases of maulings are reported during this time.

We know very little about the other large carnivore—the hyena. They are major scavengers and feed on the kills of tigers and leopards after they have finished. They also feed on domestic livestock carcasses. They share these with other carnivores like jackals, wild cats and, most significantly, domestic dogs. It is this sharing of the carcasses with domestic dogs and other wild predators such as tigers and leopards that is important to monitor, as it is the source of the exchange of disease between the domestic and wild carnivore population.

I had once seen a hyena, jackals, domestic dogs and a rusty spotted cat (*Prionailurus rubiginosus*)—all sharing the same carcass one after the other, in the space of a few hours. It is in a situation like this that disease transfer occurs. Currently we have no idea what kind of catastrophe this can cause in our wild carnivore populations. We must be careful here, as we know from the African example that a large population of lions in the Serengeti disappeared in just a few months (Craft et al., 2011). Despite knowing the consequences of such a phenomenon, here in India we are waiting for disaster to happen. We need a better insight, perhaps through a pilot project, into this aspect of veterinary science. This is important because it is a very common phenomenon in almost every Protected Area in the country and we are not equipped to deal with its horrific eventuality.

Smaller Cats

My first two sightings of the rusty spotted cat were quite bizarre and equally interesting. The rusty spotted cat is considered rare, and though I knew they were found in the region, I never saw one for years. But when I did finally cross paths with it, I saw three different cats on separate occasions on a single drive. It was late June and soon after a sharp early monsoon shower, I had left Panna town in the late evening.

---

* The leaf litter burnt under these fruiting trees (to make it easy for collection) is another common cause of large-scale forest fires every year during this month.

By the time I reached the outskirts it was dark. As I was passing by a forest nursery I spotted a tiny kitten crossing the road. My initial thought was that it was a domestic cat but when I saw it sitting still next to the road, I turned the vehicle around to get a better look in my headlights. Looking through my binoculars I was pleasantly surprised to see the distinctive stripes of the rusty spotted cat on its forehead. I had a good look at it for over five minutes before it disappeared into the hedge.

Later, one after another on the same drive, I saw two more rusty spotted cats. I could not believe my luck! Though, strangely enough, I never saw one on the road again for several years. I did spot them on several occasions but never in my headlights, despite all the driving at night while tracking the radio-collared tigers.

In 2010, however, the monsoon brought an explosion of grasshoppers which were attracted to my headlights in huge numbers. I saw several rusty spotted cats in those days. Since then, we spotted these cats on the roads every monsoon. Curiously, all of my sightings were close to human settlements and never deep in the forest.

The other smaller cat, which I never believed existed in the Reserve, is the desert cat (*Felis sylvestris*). Yoganand once told me he saw one on the Talgaon plateau but at the time I was not very convinced. So it came as a surprise when I saw one myself. This was also a very strange encounter: we were tracking one of the radio-collared tigers and, to get a better radio signal, one of my assistants went up on the roof of a large watchtower called 'mahua pani tower'. On his return, after taking the radio locations of at least five other radio-collared animals, he told me that he had seen a wild cat, which he thought was sick. I immediately went up to have a look. What I saw hiding in one corner was a desert cat. I rushed back to the jeep to pick up my camera. When I went up there again the cat was still there, but the moment I pointed my camera at it, it got up, ran past me and jumped straight into a twelve-foot-deep ravine, disappearing into the forest. I still have no explanation for why it did not move all the time we were taking radio-locations— the noise from the receiver did not disturb it—but left the moment we made eye contact and pointed the lens at it. This was the only sighting I had, though other naturalists working in the Ken River Lodge have reported seeing this species on several occasions in the Reserve and also in the adjoining forest during night safaris in the buffer zone.

The other small cats found in the forest are the jungle cat (*Felis chaus*) and the Caracal (*Caracal caracal schmitzi*). The jungle cat is the most common wild cat in the region. The best time to see it is soon after monsoon when the grass on the roads is cleared. These roads become the only open space in the sea of tall grass for these tiny creatures. We saw the jungle cat on the roads more often in September and October than at any other time of the year. Sometimes we saw up to four-five cats in one drive through the Reserve. In addition to these wild cats, the forests of Panna are home to several species of mongooses and civets, also otters, jackals (*Canis aureus*) and the Indian fox (*Vulpes bengalensis*). The very rare caracal is rarely spotted.

Antelopes

The extensive open thorny forests with the short grassland of the Reserve are the ideal habitat for the three antelope species: the chousingha or four-horned antelope (*Tetracerus quadricornis*), the nilgai (*Boselaphus tragocamelus*) and the chinkara (*Gazella bennettii*).*

Typically on a drive in the Reserve one can easily see several small groups of nilgai almost everywhere, though most often they are found in open forest habitats. Chinkaras are not as widely distributed and are mainly seen in smaller groups on flat ground with short grasses. I was told by the staff and villagers, who have been around in these forests much longer, that both the chinkara and the nilgai were present in much larger numbers at the time Panna Tiger Reserve was created, than they are now (especially the chinkara). As the protection status of the forest improved and pressure from the migratory livestock, which used to move in from the neighbouring forest in large numbers (30,000–40,000) lessened, habitat recovery was quick (Pabla, 1984).

---

* Koustubh Sharma conducted a detailed study on chousingha here (Sharma et al., 2013).

Another large tiger prey, the nilgai is an antelope species and, unlike sambar, is partial to open, drier spaces. They achieve highest abundance in these areas. But the nilgai is a highly adaptable species and is very widely distributed in all habitats of Panna, ranging from open to thick forests.

This modified the habitat into extensive tall grasslands that were unsuitable for the chinkara. Thus, they gradually disappeared from this area. Chinkaras now survive only in the short grass habitats and the forest outside the Reserve, where grazing livestock keep the grasses short and the more open habitat suits them. A similar trend is also reported for nilgai, but because of their adaptability in various habitat types, they survived better this change in habitat quality. They are widely distributed in the Reserve but occupy the open habitat in greater abundance. On the whole, both species have suffered a population decline as per general views of the old staff and other locals.

Ungulate species that benefitted early on as result of the increased protection measures are the sambar (*Cervus unicolor*)—the largest deer and a major prey of the tiger in India, along with the chousingha. When I first arrived in Panna in 1995–96, it was the frequency of the sightings of sambars that led to my selecting the site for research. I had never seen them in such high numbers anywhere else, other than Sariska and Ranthambhore. Instantly, I felt that with such a high prey density in Panna there was no doubt that the tiger could do better than its current status. On a single twenty-kilometre drive in the forest, one easily saw twenty or more sambar and at least three-four chousingha.

But we hardly saw any chital (*Axis axis*) or wild pigs (*Sus scrofa*) those days. We considered ourselves lucky if we saw one or two herds of chital or encountered a wild pig. But this changed soon and fast—by the end of the study in 2005, chital were the most numerous tiger prey in Panna. This recovery of the chital population started from abandoned villages and cattle camp sites. Three villages and two cattle camps were rehabilitated very early on in the 1980s. These open areas transformed into large grasslands and the chital population thrived. But there were still thirteen villages inside the Tiger Reserve with a total human and cattle population of approximately 2,500 and 9,500 respectively (in 1996–97). Many of these villages were located along the river Ken and their main occupation was agriculture and cattle rearing. Before we started our study the four villages that were resettled outside the National Park were Bargadi, Khemariya, Kheraiya and Bhadar, the last of which was a large cattle camp rather than a village.

Sambar, a large prey for tigers, is a deer species that prefers forest habitat. As a student, whenever I went to a new area for a survey with Dr A.J.T. Johnsingh, our beloved teacher, every sambar sighting was exciting for him, because it meant that there was a possibility of tigers in the area. Our study explains why the sambar is such an important tiger prey in the subcontinent.

Three families from Khemariya did not leave and stayed on. These vacated spaces recovered into very productive grassland and benefitted the chital population the most.

In Bargadi, villagers left behind their cattle and this population had grown into a free-ranging herd of about 175 when we began our study. They returned to Khemariya every evening for the night and developed a seasonal pattern of returning to the Bargadi grassland for grazing in late January or early February. These feral cattle opened up the grassland by grazing on the coarse grass and soon chital followed. Facilitated by the cattle herds, the chital population recovered fast. During early monsoon in 1996–97, we recorded an aggregation of about 100–150 but by 2002, it had increased several fold. I counted over 580 chital, from a single herd in those early monsoon aggregations in 2000. We noticed a similar trend in the Bhadar grassland as well as Kheraiya but not on the same scale.

In relatively drier meadows, grasses dried fast and by November-December it flowered and seeded. We know that as soon as grass seeds are dropped, most of the nutrition of the plant is moved to the biomass below ground. The above ground biomass is then composed mainly of fibres. The Bargadi and Bhadar grasslands, which are relatively moister, provide more nutritive value up to March, just prior to their peak rutting activity in April. No wonder chital population exploded more in these two regions than anywhere else in the Reserve. The chital then dispersed from here to other areas. Now they occupy most of the Reserve and are seen regularly.

Human Demographics

During the years of my study, three more villages on the banks of Ken river were rehabilitated outside the tiger Reserve and, after 2005, another four villages were relocated. Now only three villages remain within the CTH, but a much larger human population of the buffer zone surrounds the highly protected core. This group of villages is dependent on the forests and its natural resources for their daily needs (grazing, fuel wood and non-timber forest produce). We conducted a socio-economic survey of seven such villages located at the periphery of the Reserve. This survey was done to assess the dependence of the local population on the tiger habitat. The villages: Bador, Bakchur, Darera, Hinauta, Kaimasan, Madaiyan and Umrawan (Figure 2.1). The total population of these seven villages was 3,239 individuals, belonging to 602 families. The average family size in these villages ranged between 4.8–6.2 family members (Figure 2.2). On the whole, tribal families are generally smaller. The sex ratio (953:1000) is also better than the country average, which is a very healthy sign for the region. Tribal form the largest community (52%) in these villages, followed by OBCs (Other Backward Castes, 30%).

From this survey we found that labour, in some form or other, was the main source of employment for almost 69 per cent of the population (Figure 2.3). The community was mainly dependent on the projects carried out by the Forest Department and other government

Unlike sambar and nilgai, chitals are not browsers. They use open grassland areas for feeding and the adjoining forest cover for other purposes. They are seen in greater abundance in such ecotone habitats.

bodies. What surprised us was that contrary to general belief, only a very small percentage of the population was dependent on dairy for a living, despite all villages hosting a large cattle population. Only the OBCs, mainly represented by the Yadavs in this region, largely depend on livestock and its related occupations. Most of their milk production is consumed locally. The tribal community, which forms the bulk of the workforce, mainly depends on income from labour and agriculture. Unlike OBCs, they do not pursue dairy and government jobs.

Dependence on the Forest

Most of the people in these villages and other neighbouring settlements use fuel wood for cooking, which they either collect from the neighbouring forest or purchase as head loads.* Only a very small number of families have alternate energy sources like LNG cooking

* A 'head load' is the amount of dead firewood that a person can carry from the forest for personal consumption and this is legally allowed in specific parts of the forest.

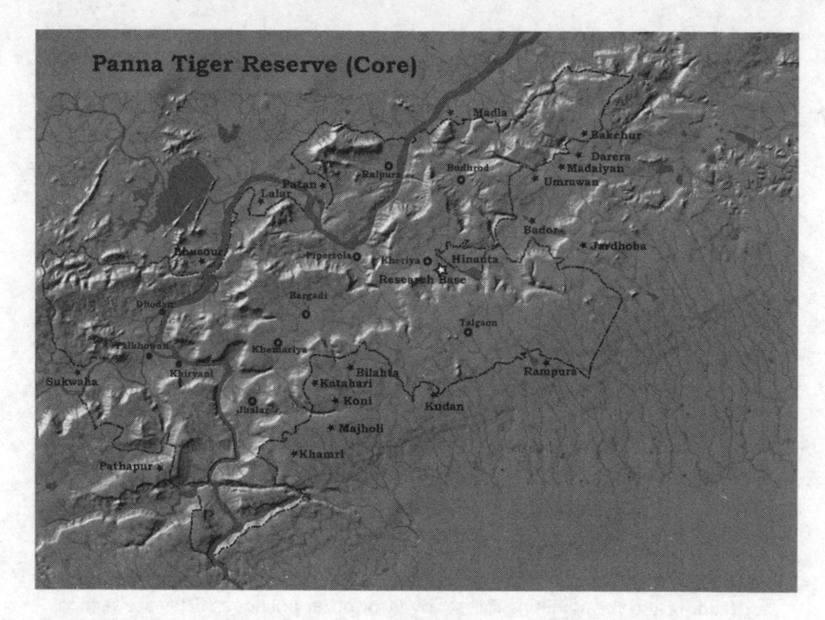

Figure 2.1 Map of the Panna Tiger Reserve showing village locations and topographic details.

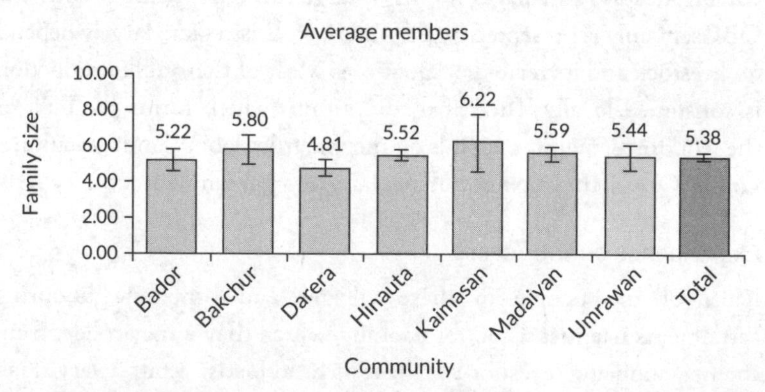

Figure 2.2 Average family size in the surveyed villages.

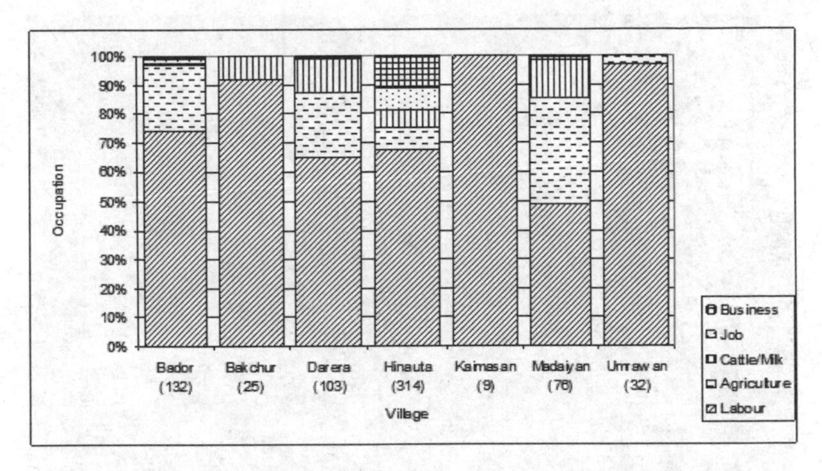

Figure 2.3 Village-wise occupation in the surveyed villages (the figure in brackets indicates sample size).

gas. The pressure on the forest for fuel is tremendous and it increases sharply during the winter months. About twenty-five tons of wood is used every week in these seven villages, according to our estimates. We also noticed that fuel consumption did not vary across communities but it did vary with occupation.

Along with fuel wood, the locals also collect Non-Timber Forest Produce (NTFP) or Minor Forest Produce (MFP) and this constitutes a significant chunk of their annual income. This is the other main source of income, besides labour. Over 60 per cent of the families are involved in MFP collection. MFP includes mahua flowers and seeds (flowers for food, fodder and brewing alcohol; seed for oil), aonla/amla fruits (*Emblica officinalis*) for medicinal purposes and savoury snacks, Achar (*Buchanania Lanzan*) fruits or chironji (as dry fruits), and tendu patta or bidi leaves. People collect these major MFP items in large quantities. Tendu patta is the largest and most organized MFP collection activity in the region. Almost all the population is involved in its collection, which lasts for a maximum of two weeks in May. It is organized and collected for the government.

From this survey we estimated that over 5,700 kg of achar, 36,500

The flowers and seeds of mahua (*Madhuca longifolia*) are important non-timber forest produce (NTFP). The economic gain from three-four large mahua trees is equal to one acre of non-irrigated land. No wonder this tree is revered so much by forest-dwellers!

kg of mahua flowers and 58,800 kg of aonla (all dry weights) are collected by the seven villages from the forest. The cumulative income from these, according to our conservative estimates, is in the range of Rs 34,35,000 which is equivalent to ₹5,981 per family.

One can tell from these numbers that the forest contributes substantially to the local economy every year and its inhabitants are heavily dependent on it for sustenance. When these forests were set aside as national parks and sanctuaries for nature and wildlife conservation purposes, the locals were officially cut off from their main source of livelihood. While villages within the notified areas were relocated, settlements on the peripheries continued to collect fuel wood and MFP from the forest.

Even though these settlements have been historically dependent on the forests for their sustenance, very little effort has been made to provide alternatives for the economic losses they have to suffer. MFP collection is an important issue for the Reserve management.

An appropriate plan has to be formulated for alternative sources of income so that dependence on the forest gradually becomes redundant within a cost-benefit scenario.

With the continued reliance of the peripheral settlements on forest resources, these areas are especially conflict-ridden. Crop damage by wild animals makes agriculture in these areas unsustainable and farmers are forced to take extreme steps such as installing live electric wires. Unfortunately, throughout India, this has led to many accidental electrocutions of tigers and leopards. While these accidents are a definite blow to wildlife conservation in the area, the consequences for the farmers are also dire—killing protected species like the tiger can lead to life imprisonment.

Leaf litter burning in the mahua season in April can also lead to large-scale, fast-spreading forest fires.

Such incidents do not augur well for either the wildlife or the peripheral local communities. The latter have been perennially neglected by the management. In the beginning, when protected areas were first established, the focus was entirely on stabilizing the wildlife population within the boundaries. This took a long time and in the meanwhile proper rehabilitation of the peripheral communities, including providing alternative livelihoods, was ignored. Now these communities regard the management as an anti-people programme of the government.

It is clear that the survival of these settlements is tied to the forest. However, one cannot ignore the adverse impact this has had on the wildlife of the park. We can no longer afford to have an unfriendly environment at the periphery. Instead of merely condemning the locals' dependence on the forest there needs to be a concerted effort to understand their situation and to work towards formulating alternative sources of income.

The future success of these protected populations of the Reserve largely depends on how well we manage these peripheral communities' interests and their sentiments towards wildlife.

3

Research Methods

I revisited Panna in December 1995 to make a preliminary assessment of the study site and evaluate its suitability for conducting a radio-telemetry-based study in more detail. I spent almost five weeks there conducting pilot studies. These studies included walking transect lines to make prey estimates. Transect lines are long straight lines in the forest (1–2.5 km) that are walked repeatedly and from which tiger prey are counted. The species, numbers, and distance from this line are recorded. This is also known as distance sampling.

I also tested how well I could track tigers using radio-telemetry. For this, I placed radio-collars at various places to review their signal strength. Radio-collars are special collars fitted with a small radio-transmitter that constantly sends radio signals at a specific radio frequency. The radio frequency for each collar is unique so that we can identify individual collars and animals.

I have been asked many times why we need to radio-collar animals to study them. Many find it ugly and invasive. I fully sympathize with these feelings but I also know that to understand the tiger's ecological needs, this is the best way to gather information. When we see a tiger in the field, we can only observe it for a short time—a few minutes or an hour at the most. We learn very little from these brief and random observations. If we don't have a systematic record of information from before and after this period, we can only extrapolate the behaviour of the tigers from these random observations. It is here that we inevitably end up speculating a great deal and making mistakes. Radio-telemetry allows us to track on a systemic schedule and, in this way, gather full and accurate data excluding any speculation.

The Team

Once I had decided on Panna as the site, the systematic fieldwork began. We started in October 1996 when Neel Gogate joined the project as a field biologist. He was soon joined by Abi Tamim Vanak, who came to work on his MSc dissertation on tigers. A few years later, Koustubh Sharma came to Panna for his PhD work on the four-horned antelope. We collaborated extensively, conducting animal counts and all of them helped me in analyzing the data collected. We put together a field team and a systematic schedule for monitoring tiger movements, estimation of tiger prey, habitat evaluation, studies to determine tiger food habits and an assessment of human pressures on the tiger habitat. Our field team members were locals from Hinauta village. The late Kalyan Singh Yadav and Sataru were the first two

I had a great field team and the success of this research is due to these extremely devoted individuals. Here Mahadev Yadav (with antenna) is seen with Banshgopal Yadav (at the back) and Dayaram Yadav.

members of the team. Sataru was a cattle herder. We needed a person who knew the area well and he was the perfect choice. He knew every inch of the Reserve and his sense of direction was impeccable. We used to joke that he was our live GPS. His navigational skills rescued us many times.

Once, my rucksack containing a camera and other equipment had been left behind in the field and, by the time I realized this, it was dark. There were too many precious things in my bag that I could not afford to lose. Unfortunately, it also had the flashlight we needed to search in the dark. Sataru said he could find the place, so we decided to go back to fetch it. It was pitch dark and we had a long way to go. I had no clue about where we were going—we were following Sataru blindly. But after about thirty minutes' walk he stopped and said that there, under that tree was where we were sitting, and indeed he found the rucksack there for me. Coming back was easy as we had the flashlight.

Even later, when we had the GPS for navigation, his skill was still an invaluable asset. He was the only person who noticed when we arrived at the wrong spot in one of the plots located on several parallel lines. We then found that we had entered one of the x or y coordinates incorrectly. His navigation skills were phenomenal. He also knew every waterhole in the area—not only the perennial ones but also seasonal waterholes. His knowledge was crucial in developing a waterhole map for the Reserve. He worked with us for about five years before joining the Reserve management staff.

Kalyan remained with us till the end of our project, working with us in various capacities. He was a great support in whatever we did and the best field assistant I ever had. He was a great taskmaster, leader, a fantastic tracker, and a sincerely hardworking person, on whom one could rely totally. When I took charge of the project several others joined us.

Suresh Yadav, Kalyan's younger brother joined us along with Banshgopal, Hargovind and Mahadev. When we did a training session with MSc students, we realized how good our team's field skills were. We placed a few radio-collars in different places and asked the students to obtain their location using the triangulation method. Our assistants turned out to be far more accurate than the students, even though several of them had not gone beyond Class 8 in their education.

We radio-collared several tigers and Neel monitored them from late 1996 to mid-1999. I decided to enlarge the scope of the study when I took over the fieldwork and continued with the project. After arriving at Panna, our first task (1999–2005) was to replace the old radio-collars with new ones. We also radio-collared several new tigers. In addition, we radio-collared the tiger's major prey species—the sambar and chital. We wanted to radio-collar the nilgai too, but we couldn't do it in time.

I had hoped that the project would run as a continuous long-term study on the tiger. There were hardly any such studies in India, besides the one conducted in Nagarahole by Ullas Karanth and his team. Such studies are important because they provide information and understanding that cannot be gained from short-term studies lasting two-three years. This is because short-term studies are samples of observations within a short window of time, whereas long-term studies can record most variations over a much longer period and therefore provide a much-needed in-depth understanding. However, for extraneous reasons, the research work began to falter from 2003–04, and came to an abrupt halt in December 2004. Thereafter, politics intervened and hampered the research project, with adverse consequences for the tiger. I will elaborate on that part of the story in the last two chapters.

Radio-Telemetry for Monitoring of Animals

Contrary to popular belief, the tiger remained one of the least studied species in India until the mid-nineties. The focus of most of the studies that had been done (without telemetry) was on density estimation, predator-prey relationships and food habits. Understanding the space need of a tiger population is one of the fundamental pieces of information needed for managing a viable population. Space need for tigers can vary in different ecological environments. For example, in temperate climes, the space need for an individual tiger could be as big as several hundred square kilometres whereas, in the terai, a tropical environment, their need could be many times smaller, about 15–20 square kilometres. The space need determines the density and size of a population within a given protected area. It is therefore important to understand the need for space of a viable population. There were a few such studies conducted in Nepal but none in India. Our Panna study filled this gap. It was the first time that the tiger's space need in a Tropical Dry Forest was studied.

The study of wild animals is quite a tedious job—wild animals are shy, and difficult to find and observe in a forest habitat over a long period of time. It is also not always possible to identify individual animals. Moreover, locating an identified free-ranging individual in the wild on a regular basis is almost impossible. But to understand behaviour one needs repeated observations of an individual. Therefore, it is essential to identify and follow individual animals on a regular basis. This way one can generate a series of observations and create a database from which to draw reliable conclusions. Radio-collars are the key to achieving this. Occasional observations of wild animals cannot show a trend and conclusions thus reached could be highly misleading.

This is where the scientific approach differs from casual and anecdotal natural history knowledge building. Unfortunately, we suffer from this kind of a knowledge base. If we really want to strengthen the wildlife management of the country we must create an environment where it is based on rigorous and long-term scientific research.

So, for example if we want to know how much space is required by a tiger or by its prey in a Dry Forest, we must be able find the individual animal on a regular basis so as to track its movements. Since it is impossible to locate a wild and free-ranging tiger on a regular basis, we radio-tag a particular tiger. Radio signals from the transmitter provide us with information on its whereabouts as and when we require. From such radio-tracking, one can determine its home-range size, movement patterns, use of habitats, activity patterns and behaviour. This information is essential for effective management of the tiger.

The challenge for us was to *place* the radio-collars on the animals.

To attach a collar, one first needs to capture the animal. In India, one requires several permissions for a chemical capture, even for radio-collaring purposes. They are extremely difficult to obtain especially when the target animal is a tiger. I was one of the few who got permission for radio-collaring from the government of Madhya Pradesh and the MOEFCC.

We were able to radio-collar a total of seven tigers (though several were collared more than once over the nine years), five sambars and two chitals in Panna. I have always believed that tranquillization or 'chemical capture' is an expert's job, in the same way that anaesthesia for human beings is, in surgery. Many of my colleagues disagree with me on this subject, and many tranquillizations are not done by experts. Anyone who is trained can calculate drug doses for a healthy animal from published literature and someone who shoots well can use the dart gun, but expertise is required when an animal is drugged. As long as the tranquillization goes smoothly, as it does most of the time for carnivores, all may be well. However, when complications crop up during sedation, an amateur will be at a complete loss and the animal may die. For an endangered species like the tiger, this is too big a risk. Thus, all our chemical restraint operations were conducted under professional veterinary supervision.

Working with my veterinary colleagues, I was impressed to learn that they handled the animals like human patients. This was far from what I had seen in many other tranquillization operations. I learned so much from these masters—how we should treat these animals with utmost respect and care, and how we should ensure that animal well-being is paramount.

Of course, this inevitably meant that we missed many opportunities to capture animals. In certain situations they were let go in the interest of their well-being. These were occasions that frustrated me a bit when I was keen to collar an animal but was strongly advised against it by the experts. I felt like we were missing good opportunities, but now, looking back, I know that we made the right decisions. We avoided any chance of putting the animals in danger or discomfort. As a result we never lost a tiger during our operations.

Chemical Restraints of Tigers

The first job was to identify a tiger and locate it. This was a big task in Panna, especially early on, when the density there was so low. It would take us many days to find one. This was the most stressful part of the job because our tranquillization experts were only available twice in a year for about ten-twelve days. To increase our chances, we targeted a couple of tigers for every visit. There were times when the team went back without conducting tranquillization. Finding a known tiger was like looking for a needle in the hay. But once a tiger was located, a team of veterinary professionals, including the wildlife medicine expert, Dr Pradip K Malik, Dr Peshin (an anaesthesia expert) and his supporting team, cautiously approached the animal on the back of a trained elephant.* In addition to this, we also placed a few observers on trees, at vantage points, to keep an eye on the tiger's movements after the drug was injected. The elephant with the veterinary doctors approached the animal to within 25–30 metres to assess its size and approximate weight. Then the wait began—the animal needed to provide us with a good and clear view for darting.

We preferred the Tele-inject equipment for darting (a gun that uses adjustable air pressure to shoot the dart) and the new but effective and safe drug called "Meditomedine" (trade name Zalopine) in combination with Ketamine. Antisedan was used to reverse the effect of the tranquillization. Only on one occasion did we use the standard combination of Rompun and Ketamine. Good darting is not only science but a skill, and Dr Malik was a master. There is a delicate balance to be struck, as the impact of the dart had to be enough to pierce the skin and release the drug but not so much that it should cause trauma to the animal. We learned that the distance an animal moves from where it was darted depends on how hard the dart hits the animal. Dr Malik ensured that the pressure on the projectile was kept at the minimum required, to avoid trauma. Our main worry was

---

* In case of a new animal or when replacing a non-functional collar, we invariably used two elephants. But when we were replacing the old collar with a new one, we only needed one elephant to approach the animal.

Chemically restraining animals to place a radio-collar is always risky, but this risk is minimized by inviting veterinary experts. Dr Malik, my good friend, seen in this photograph with me, is the best in the business.

losing the animal in a sea of grass, which, if not found quickly, could put its life in danger. So, the priority was to reduce the trauma from the hit. But to achieve this we had to wait for the right opportunity. By minimizing the impact of the dart, the impact trauma for the animal was kept at the lowest possible. We further reduced disturbance by shooting the dart only when the tiger was not looking directly at us and by not making excessive movements. After the prick, when the animal would look up at us surprised, it would not see any reaction from us. Not knowing where the dart came from, it would remain calm and settle down immediately. In most cases, it would move no more than a few metres. Occasionally, it would move a little further but would inevitably find suitable shade nearby and lie down.

Sometimes we had to wait a long time for the appropriate moment to dart an animal, even as long as an hour. This waiting could make our elephant fidgety, making aiming for the shot very difficult. We always needed a good, clear view to avoid the dart getting deflected by obstacles. Even a blade of grass could cause a deflection and result in disaster. One can easily imagine that it was not easy to get all these things to fall into place all the time. I certainly needed to learn a lot of patience. But the results were fantastic and, on a couple of occasions, the tiger did not bother to move even five metres from where it was darted; on most occasions it remained within our sight.

The great advantage of this was that it allowed the research team and the vets to monitor the animal throughout the induction time of the drug. We noticed that they started showing signs of the drug within six minutes, and within only ten-twelve minutes, the animal's head rested on the ground. We always approached the tranquillized animals cautiously from behind and first checked their reflexes. We gently pulled on the tail. If it showed no reaction to the pull, the animal was properly sedated. Once its status was properly determined, members of the research team quickly moved in to fix the radio-collar on the animal and take the morphometric measurements (body measurements like length, height at shoulder and weight). In the meantime, the veterinary doctors monitored the health of the animal. On an average, we took less than twenty minutes to finish collaring along with the other procedures. As soon as we finished and had taken some photographs, the research team moved away from the animal. The doctor would then inject a dose of antidote intra-muscularly at two-three places, and monitor its recovery from the elephant's back. When using Meditomedine and Antisedan, the tiger's recovery took only ten-fifteen minutes and it walked away with coordinated steps within twenty minutes after the injection of the antidote. However, when the combination of Xylezine and Ketamine was used, it took longer to recover. We had to monitor the animal very intensively for the next six to eight hours and intermittently for twenty-four hours after it had recovered, to ensure its safety after tranquillization.

Radio-collaring Prey Species

We wanted to understand tiger prey as much as the tiger itself, which is why we decided to collar a few of its major prey species. Some sambar and chital were tranquillized using the same drugs and equipment that we used for the tiger. In this case, we approached them from an open vehicle and darted them from a distance of 25-30 metres. Occasionally, we also used hides. After darting, the animals never moved more than 50–60 metres. We kept a close watch and observed their behaviour from a distance. It usually took six to eight minutes for them to go down. Once down, the research team would wait for another twelve to fifteen minutes before approaching closer, giving it sufficient time to be fully sedated. From 10 metres, the animal's status was assessed again before it was approached and touched. Immediately a dark cloth was used to cover the eyes and the radio-collar was attached. After recording the measurements, the antidote was administered and recovery was observed from a distance of 20–30 metres. The animals took fifteen to twenty minutes to recover after which they would walk in a well-coordinated, proper manner. Once, however, there was an exception—one large male sambar had an explosive recovery. It seemed to have gotten prematurely disturbed by the noise of footsteps on dry leaves made by one of the observers and it leapt up and bolted away at full speed. We followed it for 300 metres, after which it sat down again for half an hour, before moving away calmly. We also kept a continuous watch on these animals for six to eight hours and on an hourly basis for the next twenty-four hours, in the case of the tigers, to help eliminate any chance of predation post-tranquillization.

Monitoring of Radio-collared Animals

We tracked each radio-collared animal on a systematic schedule to monitor its movements. Whenever we could see the animal we logged its location using the GPS. However, when it was away from the road and not visible to the naked eye, we used the triangulation method (Heezen & Tester, 1967; Springer, 1967; Zimmerman, 1990; Saltz, 1994; Mech, 2002). For this method, whenever a strong signal is received on the radio, we use our directional antennae to determine its direction, and a compass to obtain the bearing and record the observers' location with GPS. We repeat this procedure from three or four different points. Later this data set is used to determine the animal's location.

Earlier, GPS equipment was not so common, and the project did not have one of its own. However, for some time we were able to use one that belonged to the WII. I took this opportunity to mark the entire road network at 500-metre intervals, in some places every 250 metres. Coordinates for each of these points were recorded and we developed a key with which to identify these locations. This was a major job, as it took months to mark all the roads that we used for tracking radio-collared animals. In addition to these, several vantage locations were also keyed in. From these marked sites we took radio-locations. Once GPS sets were easily available we could tag locations quite easily.

Also, working with GPS and reference points meant we were able to obtain a series of locations on a regular schedule to log locations of every radio-collared animal at least twice a week. We were thus able to build an unbiased data set of the animals' movements to determine home ranges, movement patterns, habitat use and social organization; we could also identify kills and kill sites. When we wanted to *see* the animals for observations, we could home in on foot for the prey species but for the tigers we went on elephant-back.

In addition to this, at least once a month we monitored the animals continuously through the full 24-hour period over several days. This gave us additional information about their daily activity patterns, movements and habitat use on an hourly basis. We obtained locations of the tigers every hour and their activities were recorded every fifteen minutes. Their radio-collars had built-in activity sensors, which meant that when the animal was active, its pulse rate was signalled by the increasing frequency of beeping on our monitors. A fast rate told us that the animal was active, while a slower rate indicated that it was resting.

Study Population

We intensively monitored tigers for eight years, from 1996 to 2004. Later, between 2004 and 2005, our monitoring was irregular, and by March 2005, all observations had come to an end. During these nine years we accumulated an enormous amount of information. We radio-collared seven different tigers (five females and two males), monitoring them for varying lengths of time, cumulatively clocking forty-one tiger years of data. When we include other known tigers (not radio-collared but monitored regularly) and their cubs, it amounts to a staggering ninety-five tiger years of observations. We ourselves were amazed by these statistics, as we had not imagined accumulating such a huge bank of knowledge when we set out to learn about tiger ecology.

Our results were primarily based on our observations of five adult male tigers (two radio-collared), eight breeding females (five radio-collared) and fourteen litters (over thirty-one cubs, collared and uncollared). Among these, one tiger really became a part of our lives; she was a tigress whom we named 'Baavan' meaning 'fifty-two'. The 'rise' of the emerald tigers of Panna at this time was largely thanks to her.

4

Tiger Prey

Group Dynamics, and Estimation of Animal and Biomass Density

The tiger is very widely distributed in Asia and it occupies a variety of habitats (Sunquist et al., 1999). In Asian forests it has evolved as a specialist predator of large herbivores, mostly large deer species such as sambar, chital, elk, sika deer, wild boar, wild cattle such as gaur, and other large ungulates of tropical and also temperate forests (Hayward et al., 2012). Wild ungulate prey availability is one of the most important ecological factors that govern tiger abundance (Sunquist and Sunquist, 1989; Karanth et al., 2004). This is one reason why tigers can achieve higher abundance in forests that are characterized by high wild prey densities. Outside our protected areas, the prey base has significantly decreased. This is why we have lost tigers from a large part of their range (Jhala et al., 2011). Globally the tiger now survives mainly in the protected habitats that still harbour a fairly good population of prey (less than 7% of its former range) (Sunquist et al., 1999; Dinerstein et al., 2007). This trend is also obvious from the recent all-India Assessment conducted by the NTCA (Qureshi et al., 2006; Jhala, 2008; Jhala et al., 2011). If our goal is to manage a demographically viable population of tigers, then it is important that in our protected areas and other conservation landscapes the tiger's prey base is managed intensively, in addition to other ecological parameters. In this context effective management of large herbivore populations is an important conservation issue. But despite its high conservation significance very little quantitative information on prey ecology, other than abundance, is available, and almost none from the Tropical Dry Forests.

Panna's tiger habitat is highly fragmented and like other tiger habitats it suffers every year from forest fires, poaching, livestock and loss of habitat and habitat quality (Panwar, 1987; Karanth, 1991; Debroy, 1996; Seidensticker, 1997; Wikramanayake et al., 1998 Chundawat, & Gogate, 2001). Every wildlife biologist who has worked with tigers understands the importance of prey populations for the tiger. Since very little is known about prey ecology, during our study considerable research effort was invested in understanding the ecological requirements of large ungulate prey. The tiger's major wild prey species in Panna Tiger Reserve are sambar, chital and nilgai but other prey of the area include wild pig, langur and, occasionally, four-horned antelopes and chinkara. During our study we observed significant changes in prey populations.

Counting Tiger Prey

One of the most essential aspects of understanding tiger ecology is to gauge the size of its prey base. Therefore, in Panna we began by finding out how many sambar, chital, nilgai and other prey species were present in the tiger Reserve; also how they were distributed and how they used the forest spatially (various habitats) and temporally (seasonally). This information helped us understand the tiger's ecological needs and its relationship with the space it uses. The first set of our investigations, therefore, were entirely devoted to answering these questions and this formed a major part of the study. From the outset we had established a system for monitoring the tiger's prey population. We used a technique known as 'distance sampling' through line or 'transect' surveys (Burnham et al., 1980; Buckland et al., 1993). In recent years this method has been widely and successfully used in several tropical forests of the subcontinent like Nagarahole (Karanth and Sunquist, 1992), Gir (Khan et al., 1996), Pench in MP (Biswas and Sankar, 2002), Bhadra (Jathanna et al., 2003), Ranthambhore

(Bagchi et al., 2003) and several other places (Karanth and Nichols, 2002). More recently, the all-India assessment of the tiger and its prey was also based on this technique (Jhala et al., 2011). Before this method was introduced in India, protected area management estimates were based on total counts. One of the major assumptions of this obsolete method is that field staff conducting the survey can locate and count all the animals within the sampled area. This is actually impossible even in a very ideal field situation. Imagine a small group of people trying to locate and count all the animals in a forested habitat—inevitably some animals may be seen and counted twice while others will be present in the area but not detected. Such attempted counts therefore do not provide a very reliable estimate. It is likely that most of the population estimates for tiger prey were gross underestimates. The approach of distance sampling takes non-detections (missing animals) into account and gives equal importance to these in estimating population size. The basic assumption is that as the distance from the observer increases, the probability of seeing an animal in a forest will decrease, and that of missing an animal will increase. A sample of sighting distances during line surveys allows us to calculate this probability. From these estimates one can calculate non-detections.

For estimation of prey populations in Panna, we established eleven transect lines randomly in different types of habitats. Transect lines are 1–2 km straight lines established in the forest by marking regular intervals of 40–50 metres to provide a guide. Vegetation at this line is very carefully cleared to assist us in smooth and silent walks during our count surveys. We make sure that we clear just enough so as not to significantly change the habitat for our study animals and we maintained these transect lines every year. We conducted our count surveys by walking the lines on a very systematic schedule every year for over nine years. During the walk, we counted the number of animals we detected and meticulously recorded information about the species and number of animals seen, their sex and age class. Additionally, we used very precise laser range finders to estimate the radial distance from the line and also used a very precise compass to determine the radial angle from the line to calculate the perpendicular distance. We trained the field staff who were soon able to use equipment to determine the required details and note it on the prescribed data sheet.

We also conducted surveys using vehicles and roads as lines so as to cover a much larger area. These roads were monitored regularly, twice or sometimes thrice every month. Since roads are not straight lines in these surveys, instead of calculating perpendicular distance using radial angle and distance, we calculate perpendicular distance directly. But these counts were mainly used for gathering demographic data on group size and population structure (age and sex class) of the prey population from a large part of the park. Because these counts were conducted on a regular basis our demographic data was of much better quality than those that are collected opportunistically. We used the computer software programme 'Distance 4' for the calculation and analysis of this data to arrive at an estimate of population densities (Laake et al., 1994).

Neel Gogate had conducted preliminary surveys that provided a baseline for comparisons and for determining population trends. When I began field work in 2000, we intensified the prey monitoring. By the end of 1999, when Neel had completed his work, we had established a network of transect lines. I modified the network by dropping a few lines and creating new lines to cover a much larger area. We also used this opportunity to test some methodological questions by running the lines at different schedules. We experimented with the different designs that are in use in the Indian subcontinent to compare the results so that, from our experience, a standardized protocol could be developed.

In 2000 and earlier, we would walk the transect lines only during morning hours and twice every month from October to June. This is one of the most common approaches used in many studies. We modified this in 2001; that year we surveyed all the lines simultaneously every morning and evening but within a small window of fifteen days in March. In 2002 we did not conduct surveys but modified the 2001 protocol for the 2003 survey. This time, instead of walking all the lines simultaneously, only three lines were walked every morning and evening. Each line therefore was repeated every fourth day in February and March. So, in 2003 we repeated the survey in the evening on the same line but only after a gap of three days. This was done to minimize the disturbance caused by repeated walks for two weeks in the mornings and evenings. This way, in total twenty-four (12 days × 2 times a day) temporal replicates for each line were completed. Later in 2005, another modification was made: we did not repeat the line survey on the evening of the same day but repeated it in the afternoon after four days' break. In this survey the three lines that were surveyed in the morning were not repeated in the evening; instead three different lines were surveyed. In 2004 we did not conduct foot transects but prey was monitored by vehicular survey. The data from these surveys was then analyzed to determine the best design approaches, the appropriate season for surveys in tropical forests where visibility changes considerably with the season, and how repeated walks on the line affect density estimates. I hope that these discussions can help new studies to design future surveys appropriately to achieve their desired objectives most effectively and reliably. There are very few long-term studies that have done such extensive surveying and certainly none from a Tropical Dry Forest. Most are short duration studies, limited to one survey, and only a few are of two-three years' duration, though without the luxury of experimenting with study designs.

Running transect lines every month by a research team of three-four persons is a full-time job and leaves little time for other work. Under this protocol it is also not easy to achieve the required sample size. We followed a similar protocol during the year and the total transect length covered by the team and the number of animals sighted were much less than in the more intensive surveys we did in the later years. Moreover, the research team was completely occupied by this activity for at least two weeks every month in our earlier approach. As a result, we had fewer days to complete other tasks. When we concentrated our efforts to complete the survey in six to eight weeks we were able to gather more data and had plenty of time left for other activities in the year. The only limitation was that for this protocol we needed a larger team for a short duration, which is logistically very possible. In 2001 we had a team of volunteers who helped conduct the survey. These volunteers were trained in surveying by Ullas Karanth and Samba Kumar of the Centre for Wild Life Studies, Bangalore, and it was they who had organized this help. We conducted the next few surveys by training local youths and hiring them for three-four weeks. It was fun working with the local boys and it also helped them understand the importance of the work being done in their neighbourhood. They also realized how much hard work we were putting in to understand our natural heritage. By participating in the field exercise they had a chance to get involved directly, and learned their first conservation lessons. They felt they were having an experience of a lifetime that they said they would never forget. Through them I could spread the conservation message to a wider audience. This partnership helped break barriers, making it much easier to communicate with them. Plus they all had such exciting encounters with wild animals that it made the work very enjoyable for them. They kept asking me when we would next call them for a survey. Unfortunately, we could not continue with our research after 2005, when it came to an abrupt end. The survey had to be abandoned halfway because our research permits were not renewed.

In this book, animal densities and biomass densities of ungulate prey calculated from the 2003 survey data were used for comparing the result with other habitats in the Indian subcontinent.

Population Structure and Group Size

In addition to the line transect surveys, we also monitored the prey populations for demographic parameters on a very systematic schedule throughout the year. This we did by driving through the Reserve and recording every sighting of animals. We used the forest roads as the transect lines and these roads were monitored twice or thrice every month. It was almost impossible to drive during the monsoon months, so at that time we reduced the frequency and drove only when there was a break in rains and roads were motorable. Efforts were to cover all the roads at least once a month. Whenever we saw an animal, we recorded information about the species—the number seen together (i.e. the group size), age, sex, and the perpendicular distance from the road; along with this the date, time, activity and transect number were also noted. From this simple data set, we are able to extract most of the demographic details of the prey population. This process takes very little effort but can provide a wealth of information for managers.

Making Sense of the Data

For density estimates and related analyses concerning variance (variation in animal abundance in a given landscape), the nine transect lines that we walked on a systematic schedule were considered as 'spatial replicates'. Spatial replicates covering various habitats are essential for reliable estimates: they need to represent most of the variation that occurs in the study area. For example, if we take the case of nilgai in the Reserve: it is distributed widely but occurs in varying abundance in different forest types. They occupy open and savannah forest in higher abundance than the dense forest patches where they are found in much lower abundance. Our replicate, therefore, covered most of these variations so that our results provided a good overall estimate of the population. The coefficient of variance (CV) of an estimate illustrates the variability that the estimated mean represents. A high CV suggests that the estimate comes from a population that is distributed in highly variable abundances.*

Information gathered from the temporal replications (repeat surveys on the same line at different times) on particular transect lines were pooled. We followed the standard procedures for our analysis (Buckland et al., 2001; Thomas et al., 2002). Cluster sizes (group size of the animal being counted) were estimated using size bias regression method by regressing the natural log of cluster size against estimated probability of detection at distance x, g(x). Whenever the regression was not found significant at alpha level of 0.15, mean of cluster sizes was used to estimate density. Both manual as well as automatic pooling

* For other factors involved here refer to *Monitoring Tigers and Their Prey: A Manual for Researchers, Managers and Conservationists in Tropical Asia* (Karanth and Nichols, 2002).

functions were used in Distance 4.0 to fit the detection curve at the lowest possible value of c^2 (Chi-square). This is important because in forest habitats it is easier to detect a large herd than a small herd and, if sampling is biased by this phenomenon, density estimates can be affected.

We also wanted to compare our results from different seasons and from morning-evening surveys. We tested density and other available estimates and their respective standard deviations by one factor, ANOVA (Analysis of Variance) (Zar, 1984). Changes in other parameters like seasonal group size and radial distance were also tested using the same factor. But the trends were tested for accuracy with the help of maximum R^2 value and with Student's t-test for testing the significance of a regression.

Results

Population Structure and Group Size

Group size

We were interested in knowing the group size of tiger prey because when a tiger is hunting, its encounter with prey and success of making a kill depend on group size and density. Obviously, there are several other factors such as stalking cover and wind direction. that also work simultaneously, but group density and size are very important. When prey is distributed in larger numbers but in smaller groups, probability of the tiger encountering a prey is high compared to a population that forms larger and fewer groups. Larger groups are a form of anti-predatory behaviour—it is simply more eyes for better vigilance. This has been studied extensively. Since we also know that group size can be a reflection of the productivity of the ecosystem, it is indicative of the quality of the habitat. The prey that we surveyed included sambar, chital, nilgai, four-horned antelope, chinkara, wild pig and also a non-ungulate prey, the langur. We recorded data for over 14,372 animals that were seen in 3,981 groups between 2000 and 2002 (Table 4.1). But out of these sightings, we could age and sex only about 80 per cent of the animals (11,592 prey animals). This data set does not include transect line data from 2003 and 2004 along with the data collected in 1996–1999. During this early period we also recorded information from 12,697 animals of which 9,761 were aged and sexed. We use the 2000–02 data sets for comparison only and to detect a trend.

We noticed that chital formed larger groups (average 5.6 ± 0.29 chitals; n=788) among all prey populations but nilgai and sambar, two ungulates with similar body size, were surprisingly seen in similar group sizes in Panna (sambar=3.1 ± 0.085; n=937 and nilgai=3.1 ± 0.088; n=1358). It was surprising because nilgai are generally seen in larger social groups elsewhere in the subcontinent. Other smaller ungulates like chinkara and four-horned antelopes were mostly seen in smaller groups (four-horned antelope=1.4 ± 0.05; n=285 and chinkara=1.8 ± 0.06; n=392) but wild pigs formed larger groups (4.5 ± 0.34; n=120). When we compare these group sizes with our observations from 1996–99 (Table 4.2), we notice a slight decline in group size for nilgai but an increase in sambar and almost no change in the chital group size.

Groups sizes of most prey species do not change with seasons though chital and wild pigs are seen in larger groups during the monsoon months. In fact, we found two peaks for larger groups in chital—one during monsoon and another during the mating season in March/April (Figure 4.1). When we look at the frequency of group size in a little more detail, it is very obvious from the data that four-horned antelopes are mostly solitary (73%). But we have occasionally seen up to seven individuals together during our surveys. These were rare sightings as they were congregations near mahua trees during the flowering season. Group sizes are more evenly distributed in chital and nilgai, whereas sambar are often seen in small groups of two or three (see Table 4.1). In sambar population these are often small family groups of a mother with her fawn and an accompanying yearling. A detailed population structure of the prey population that was surveyed is given in Table 4.3.

Comparison of the observations above with other studies conducted in more productive tiger habitats of the subcontinent

Table 4.1 Details of group sizes of tiger prey in Panna Reserve from the 2000–02 sample.

Species	*Animal Sighted*	*Group sighted*	*Mean Group size*	*Range*	*Percent occurrence of group size*			
	n=14372	*n*=3981			*1*	*2–3*	*4–10*	*>10*
Sambar	2929	937	3.1	1–24	27.6	40.8	29.6	2
Chital	4448	788	5.6	1–80	23.1	32.6	32.9	11.4
Nilgai	4163	1358	3.1	1–50	38.4	33.7	25	2.9
Four-horned Antelope	427	285	1.4	1–7	73	24.2	2.8	0
Wild pig	542	120	4.5	1–20	34.2	11.7	50	4.2
Chinkara	725	392	1.8	1–12	48	45.4	6.4	0.3
Langur	1138	101	8.0	1–50	9.4	0	59.7	30.8

Table 4.2 Comparison of group size of tiger prey between the 1996–99 and 2000–02 samples.

Species	*Mean Group size*	
	1996–99	*2000–02*
Sambar	2.9	3.1 ± 0.09
Chital	5.7	5.6 ± 0.29
Nilgai	3.5	3.1 ± 0.09
Four-horned Antelope	1.4	1.4 ± 0.05
Wild pig	Na	4.5 ± 0.34
Chinkara	2.0	1.8 ± 0.06
Langur	Na	8.0 ± 0.75

Table 4.3 Population structure of tiger prey in Panna TR from 2000–02 sample.

	N	*Number per 100 females*		
		Males	*Yearlings*	*Fawns*
		Chital		
Monsoon	436	66.1	22.0	11.9
Summer	1498	40.6	14.5	32.0
Winter	1295	46.6	9.1	38.2
Annual	3229	46.2	13.3	31.8
		Sambar		
Monsoon	166	46.3	34.1	22.0
Summer	1380	33.0	16.3	45.1
Winter	1158	51.3	15.5	49.3
Annual	2704	41.2	17.1	45.3
		Nilgai		
Monsoon	438	25.1	20.4	13.8
Summer	1637	56.3	15.9	46.7
Winter	2020	52.8	21.7	42.0
Annual	4095	50.3	19.3	39.8
		Four-horned Antelope		
Monsoon	26	90.9	27.3	18.2
Summer	247	48.8	7.9	37.8

	N	*Number per 100 females*		
		Males	*Yearlings*	*Fawns*
Winter	160	50.6	10.4	46.8
Annual	433	51.6	9.8	40.0
		Chinkara		
Monsoon	113	50.7	2.8	5.6
Summer	262	73.1	6.7	15.7
Winter	350	60.9	5.4	6.9
Annual	725	63.1	5.4	9.6
		Wild Pig		
Monsoon	24	55.6	0.0	111.1
Summer	201	58.7	26.7	82.7
Winter	158	63.1	13.8	66.2
Annual	383	60.4	19.5	77.2

suggests that the wild ungulates formed smaller groups in Panna (Karanth and Sunquist, 1992; Khan et al., 1996; Biswas and Sankar, 2002; Karanth and Nichols, 2002; Bagchi et al., 2003; Jathanna et al., 2003). This phenomenon is more pronounced in the chital population. Though we saw a very marginal increase in group size in chital from 1997 to 2004 with increase in density, it still remained small relative to other areas. Group size could be an important indicator for poor resource availability and quality, and this can affect reproductive success (Jarman, 1974). The smaller group size is an important observation for a Tropical Dry Forest and can be a response to prevailing ecological conditions. Factors limiting herbivore group size in this habitat would make an interesting study. Monsoon is a time of abundance of important resources such as water, food, cover and optimal temperature, and we expected to see larger group size in this time of plenty; however our data does not show a change in pattern for group size across different seasons in the two larger prey, sambar and nilgai. Only with the chital population did we see larger groups during the monsoon as well as during the rutting season (Figure 4.1).

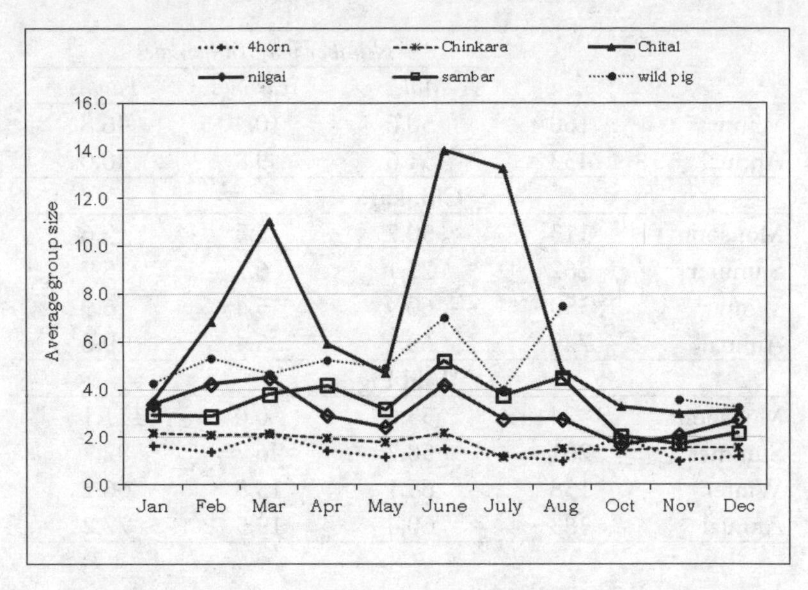

Figure 4.1 Monthly average group size of tiger prey in Panna Tiger Reserve (2000–02)

In addition to the group size we also noticed that the female-to-fawn ratios were small at the end of the breeding year for all prey species in Panna. Again the comparison was most noticeable among the chital populations from other habitats (Karanth, 1993; Khan et al., 1996; Kumar, 2000; Mishra, 1982). During our monitoring of tigers we saw high predation on young chital fawns. This is an important issue in managing the prey population because it limits the recruitment. Our observations not only indicate poor recruitment but high mortality in the yearling age class too (12–24 months old). Panna, a Tropical Dry Forest, has an extensive intermix of open grassland to dense forest cover. This provides a range of suitable habitats for chital with a high abundance of grass. But with the long dry spell that follows the monsoon, grass growth stops soon after it flowers in October and November. After December, the dead, above-ground biomass of grass provides very poor-quality forage in terms of nutrition. This occurs when the chital population requires quality nutrition, prior to their readiness for rut in March and April. Can this be a reason for the low fawn ratio in Panna other than predation? We need more detailed studies to look into these important issues. In our study, we were focusing mainly on the group size in order to understand the predation ecology of tigers. Other reasons could be additional or cumulative predation on these young animals from various predators such as leopards, wild dogs and jackals. A similarly high mortality is also noticed in the sambar population—from a healthy ratio of more than 40 fawns for every hundred females soon after fawning between September and November, to less than 20 yearlings (12–24 months old) for every 100 females. Since sambar is a preferred prey species of tigers in the subcontinent (Karanth, 1993; Chundawat et al., 1999; Biswas and Sankar, 2002; Bagchi et al., 2003; Hayward et al., 2012), it is important that the dynamics of this high mortality of sambar fawns be further studied and understood.

Distance Sampling

The observations above gave us information on group sizes and population structure. From the distance sampling survey we gathered crucial information on prey availability (group density) and number of prey in a unit area. Information on both parameters is crucial for assessing the tiger's ecological needs and its response. But the information on group density provided quantitative information on encountered rates of prey. When the tiger is searching for a prey, it is more likely to encounter species that have the highest density of groups.

During the monthly survey in 2000, we walked a total of 233.6 kilometres and sighted 339 animal groups. In this survey, we walked all the lines in the mornings. Later we modified our approach and conducted more intensive surveys in 2001, 2003 and 2005. With these modifications we could gather better quality data and test several methodological questions.

We pooled the 2000 distance sampling data in bi-monthly groups for analysis purposes, to detect changes in encounter rates, group sizes and sighting distances, and their likely effect on density estimates. We observed that encounter rates of all the prey species changed between bi-monthly groups (Figure 4.2). We also noticed a similarly significant variation in ungulate density. We can see in Figure 4.2 that cumulative encounter rates of most prey species reached a high during February and March.

This was the main reason we modified our survey protocol to conduct later surveys during February and March to maximize efficiency. In 2001, in a fifteen-day-long survey, the total length covered was 520.7 km and we recorded 1,014 groups. In 2003, on a survey lasting forty-five days we walked 466.06 km, recording 1,023 groups. In addition to this we conducted a smaller survey in 2005, to look for an answer to a specific question. In these surveys we could cover a much greater distance in relatively short durations, and collected much larger data sets than during the monthly surveys of 2000. However, we needed a much bigger field team.

I found a significant shift in encounter rates between the morning and evening surveys of 2001 and 2003 for most species (Figure 4.3a, b & c). These encounter rates were consistently low in the evening, significantly affecting our density estimates for some species whose morning and evening data is pooled together (one-tailed tests for Nilgai^{2003}: F=16.63, p=0.001; Sambar^{2001}: F=11.03, p=0.005).

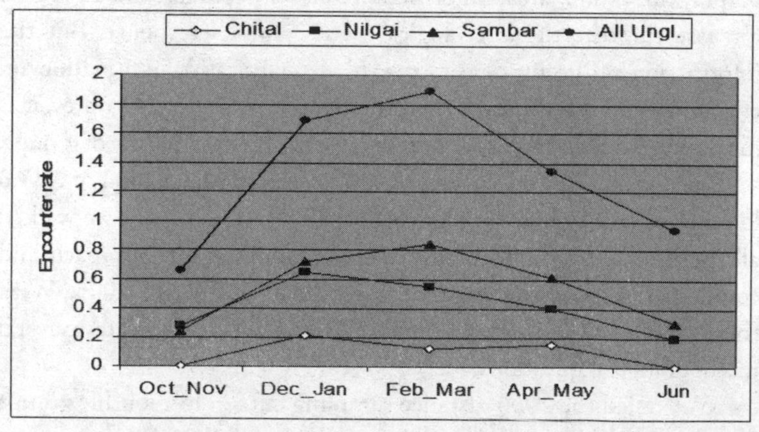

Figure 4.2 Bi-monthly (pooled) encounter rates of major prey species of tiger during the 2000 survey in Panna Tiger Reserve. (Chital: $F=3.538$, $p<0.05$; Nilgai: $F=7.494$, $p<0.001$; Sambar: $F=5.049$, $p<0.005$).

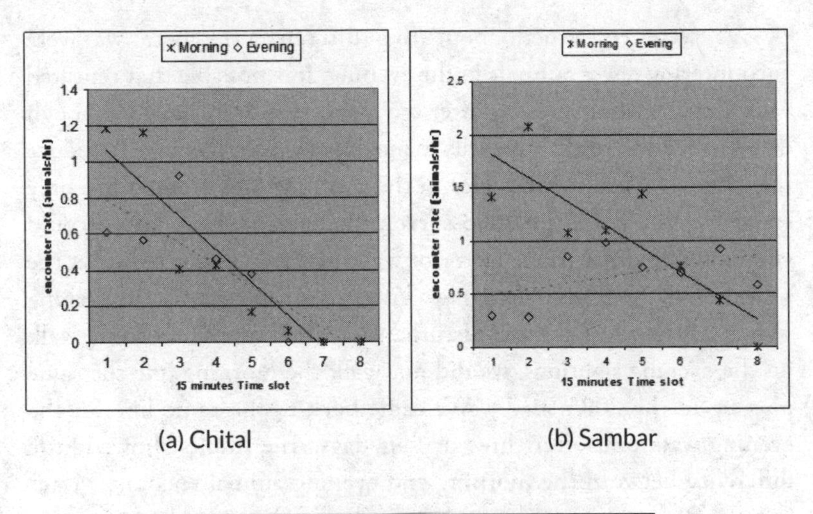

(a) Chital

(b) Sambar

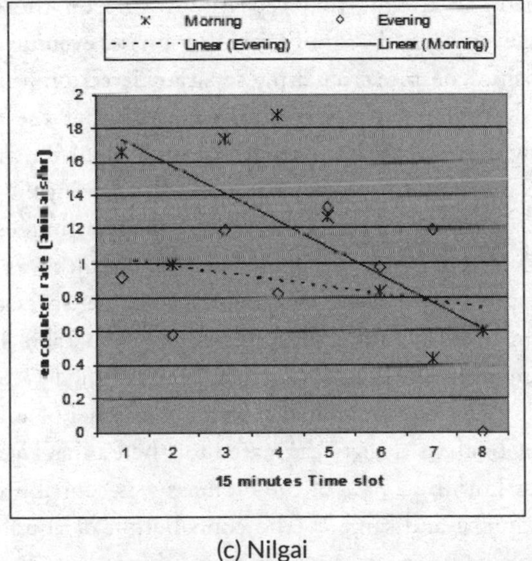

(c) Nilgai

Figure 4.3 Encounter rates (animal group sightings/hour) pooled for every 15-minute-interval of three major species of tigers during the walk on the line in the morning (between 6.45 and 8.30 am) and evening (between 16.30 and 18.15 pm), in Panna Tiger Reserve (2001 survey). Straight dotted lines indicate the trend for evenings and the continuous line for mornings. (a) chital; (b) sambar and (c) nilgai.

We were concerned about this discrepancy, where we were encountering fewer animals in the evening. It is possible that repeated walks on the same line day after day may have been causing enough disturbance and forcing animals to move away from the line. To reduce this effect, we walked the lines in the morning and evening but only every fourth day for the 2003 survey. This way we thought we could eliminate the disturbance factor of walking the line regularly. But the results from 2003 were similar—a lower encounter rate in the evening walks. So, to eliminate the disturbance caused by the morning walk on the evening sightings, we did not walk the morning line the same evening in the 2005 survey. We came back to the same line for the evening walk only after three or four days. The results showed little difference between the morning and evening animal encounter rates but confirmed our doubts that repeating a line on the same day, morning and evening, had a significant effect on the evening encounter rate and densities, despite calculating separate detection functions for morning and evening surveys. We also noticed that the encounter rate gradually declined with the length of time spent on walking the transect line, except in the case of sambar in the evenings.

For all discussion purposes we used the density estimates from the surveys conducted in 2003. The pooled prey abundance was estimated to be 46.32 prey/km^2 (excluding langur). Prey densities and other relevant parameters from different counts are given in Table 4.4. Chital, nilgai and sambar are the dominating tiger prey in Panna Tiger Reserve. Chital is the most abundant animal in terms of number of animals. The ungulate prey biomass density estimated for the Panna Tiger Reserve was 4,444 kg/km^2. But, 77% of the biomass was contributed by two prey species, nilgai and sambar. The contribution of chital was only 18% and smaller prey species was less than 5% (not including langur).

Interpretation of the Observations on Prey Estimation

Prey Density

We calculated density of tiger prey from the count conducted in 2003, mainly because this was the most complete count. Contrary to general perception, the density estimate of 46.4 ungulate preys/km^2 in

Panna Tiger Reserve is fairly high for the Tropical Dry Forests of the subcontinent (Karanth and Sunquist, 1992; Khan et al., 1996; Biswas and Sankar, 2002; Bagchi et al., 2003). If we include langur, the prey density is over 60.22 prey per square kilometre (Table 4.4). In most of the subcontinent, chital and sambar are the most numerous wild prey. But in the terai region (floodplains of the Himalaya), chital, hog deer and swamp deer are the dominant prey species. In terms of number of animals per square kilometre, chital is the most abundant animal in Panna. Contribution of smaller prey (<25 kg, including langur) is 10%; medium-sized prey, which includes chital and wild pig, is 39.3% and large prey (including sambar and nilgai) is 50.6%. Nilgai was the most frequently encountered prey (highest group density in 2003 sample) in the Reserve, followed by sambar and chital (Table 4.4).

The contribution of chital and wild boar, the tiger's most common and major prey throughout the subcontinent, is only 20 per cent. Contribution from other smaller prey species was minimal. Biomass densities from various tiger habitats indicate that, on average, medium-sized prey (54.6 %) contribution to prey availability was higher than large prey (35 %). When looked at in terms of number of animals in these habitats, medium-sized prey such as chital, wild pig and hog deer contribute, on average, over 70 per cent of prey availability. But Panna's prey structure was different—the contribution by chital and other medium prey is small, both in terms of biomass density (20%) and number of animals (39.03%).

The low abundance of chital, one of the tiger's major prey species, could be an important factor in the tiger ecology in Panna. Being the only grazing wild herbivore (Eisenberg and Seidensticker, 1976; Khan et al., 1996), chital is particularly susceptible to the grazing pressure of domestic livestock populations (Khan, 1996 and Jathanna et al., 2003). A large population of over 9,000 domestic cattle (prior to relocation of villages) within the Reserve and extensive accidental fires could be the reasons that limited the chital population here. Despite their low nutritive value, chital prefer grasses even during the dry summer months (Khan, 1996). Dry season fires are devastating in Panna, completely eradicating grasses from the burnt areas. In

Table 4.4 Animal (number of animals /km^2) and biomass density (kg/km^2) estimates of tiger prey in Panna Tiger Reserve from 1998, 1999, 2000, 2001 and 2003 surveys.

Species & wt.	*Year*	*N*	*D*	*D CV%*	*Encounter rate*	*Group size*	*D group*	*Dg CV*	*Biomass density*
Chital	1998	13.0	4.1	73.8	0.2	2.8	1.5	69.0	
47 kg	1999	20.0	7.6	63.6	0.2	5.1	1.5	59.3	
	2000	27.0	4.7	62.1	0.1	3.5	1.3	60.9	
	2001	231.0	11.0	52.9	0.5	3.9	3.1	52.5	
	2003	229.0	16.7	51.9	0.5	6.0	3.1	51.3	784
Sambar	1998	50.0	16.0	51.4	0.7	2.1	7.5	50.2	
175 kg	1999	65.0	16.6	46.8	0.7	1.8	8.8	46.0	
	2000	140.0	18.7	34.9	0.6	2.6	7.2	34.2	
	2001	240.0	8.8	37.2	0.5	2.3	4.0	36.9	
	2003	212.0	10.4	34.1	0.5	2.6	4.0	33.7	1813
Nilgai	1998	36.0	13.3	35.9	0.5	3.5	3.8	32.5	
125 kg	1999	49.0	8.2	32.9	0.5	2.3	3.6	31.5	
	2000	102.0	11.4	29.1	0.4	3.1	3.6	26.0	
	2001	307.0	6.3	37.2	0.6	2.7	2.7	37.0	
	2003	316.0	13.1	26.0	0.7	3.0	4.4	24.5	1639
Four-horned Antelope	1998	13.0	2.4	33.7	0.2	1.4	1.7	31.5	
21 kg	1999	15.0	4.2	47.9	0.2	1.6	2.8	46.0	

Species & wt.	*Year*	*N*	*D*	*D CV%*	*Encounter rate*	*Group size*	*D group*	*Dg CV*	*Biomass density*
	2000	31.0	3.0	31.9	0.1	1.6	1.9	29.5	
	2001	106.0	4.0	19.2	0.2	1.2	3.3	19.0	
	2003	78.0	2.7	20.6	0.2	1.2	2.2	20.2	57
Wild pig	1998								
34 kg	1999								
	2000								
	2001	39.0	1.4	46.5	0.1	3.3	0.6	42.6	
	2003	19.0	1.5	57.8	0.0	4.1	0.4	52.1	51
Chinkara	1998	19.0	2.7	44.2	0.3	1.5	1.7	42.1	
20 kg	1999	13.0	2.2	92.5	0.1	1.5	1.5	91.5	
	2000	24.0	2.3	50.3	0.1	1.9	1.2	49.4	
	2001	52.0	0.9	42.1	0.1	1.6	0.7	41.6	
	2003	81.0	2.0	45.5	0.2	1.8	1.1	45.1	40
Langur	1998	10.0	7.4	78.6	0.1	8.7	0.9	66.4	
9 kg	1999	14.0	25.9	56.5	0.2	17.9	1.4	53.5	
	2000	40.0	25.3	37.8	0.2	11.2	2.3	36.4	
	2001	142.0	20.7	26.7	0.3	8.2	2.5	25.6	
	2003	62.0	13.9	0.2	0.1	11.6	1.2	16.6	125

Table 4.5 Comparison of biomass (kg/km^2) and animal density ($animal/km^2$) obtained from Panna Tiger Reserve with other prey populations. Medium prey includes chital, hog deer, wild pig and large prey includes sambar, nilgai, barasingha, gaur and wild buffalo. In average estimation Panna is not included.

Tiger Reserve	*Biomass*	*Biomass density (%)*		*Animal*	*Animal density (%)*	
	Density	*Medium*	*large*	*Density*	*Medium*	*Large*
Panna	4444	20.2	77.7	46.4	39.3	50.6
Kanha[1]	4980	52.7	37.8	65.4	81.4	18.6
Nagarahole[1]	3347	45.7	52.7	41.7	74.3	18.2
Bhadra[1]	2114	146.8	1.2	22.8	52.2	28.1
Kaziranga[1]	4136	13.9	35.4	58.1	70.9	29.1
Ranthambhore[1,2]	4788	23.9	25.4	60.6	69.3	28.5
Pench[1,3]	4607	44.8	58.6	63.8	81.7	17.2
Average	3995	54.6	35.1	51.3	71.6	23.3

Sources: Karanth and Nichols, 2000; Bagchi et al., 2003; and Biswas and Sankar, 2002.

the recent past, rehabilitation of several villages and intensive fire protection measures have created extensive grasslands and restored them as suitable habitats for chital. As a result, the chital population is recovering, mainly in areas recently made free from human pressure (Karanth and Sunquist, 1992; Khan, 1996).

Smaller ungulate prey, such as barking deer, four-horned antelope, mouse deer, chinkara, wild pig and other less abundant animals, are important prey for a host of smaller co-predators of tigers. But, most of the discussion on tiger prey focuses on prey abundance and biomass, and not so much on prey diversity. We know from many examples that chital do respond very quickly to management interventions such as opening up of habitat, addition of new grasslands as a result of village rehabilitation, controlled burning and the creation of water holes, and can reach very high abundance. Once such a herbivore community attains super-abundance, it can alter the habitat, also supporting an artificially high density of a range of predators (Hobbs, 1996). Chital, from fawns (few kg) to adult males (>80 kg), provide a suitable sized prey to a host of predators such as jackals, wild dogs, leopards and tigers. Chital can sustain predation pressure due to their high abundance. However, other prey that exist in lower abundance may not be able to sustain such heavy predation. We have seen such a trend in Panna too: with the increase in chital population there was a steady decline in four-horned antelopes and sambar. The impact of chital on the ecology of sympatric ungulate species could be another interesting subject for future investigation. Though increasing chital abundance in response to management intervention may appear very encouraging, it can turn our national parks and wildlife sanctuaries into chital parks and we may lose the natural equilibrium. I would prefer to see a park with a greater diversity of prey in the system.

Density estimates of tiger prey from Pench, Ranthambhore, the Gir forest of Gujarat and Panna Tiger Reserve indicate that Tropical Dry Forests—the largest tiger habitat in India—can support fairly high prey biomass, provided the habitat is adequately protected (Eisenberg and Seidensticker, 1976; Karanth and Sunquist, 1992; Khan et al., 1996; Karanth and Nichols, 1998; Wikramanayake et al., 1999;

Biswas and Sankar, 2002). The forests of Panna support ungulate populations that have evolved in two different environments—some evolved in open habitats and others in a forest mosaic. Nilgai and chinkara represent a prey population partial to open habitats, whereas chital, sambar and four-horned antelopes are forest and forest-edge dwellers (Schaller, 1967; Eisenberg and Seidensticker, 1976; Prater, 1988). Because tigers have evolved as specialized forest-edge predators following the cervid radiation in Asia (Sunquist et al., 1999), its survival and hunting strategies are more cued to cervids than the other prey species that occupy open habitats, such as nilgai. Therefore, in Dry Forests, the high abundance of prey such as nilgai in open habitats may not necessarily translate entirely into tiger prey availability.

In the tropical forests of the subcontinent, ecological conditions vary drastically over time and space and this can affect animal distribution and detection (Thomas et al., 2002). Soon after the monsoon, visibility in forest habitats gradually increases with loss of foliage with the onset of the long dry season. Loss of foliage not only makes it easier to detect animals but they can now be sighted from longer distances, significantly increasing the radial distances. In addition to this, the changes in group size over the seasons affect the number of animals encountered as well as the encounter rate of the groups. Moreover, during peak summer months when water is available only at a few sites, most of the ungulates congregate near these points. In these changing ecological circumstances, monthly surveys do not provide a reliable estimate of ungulate densities in the Tropical Dry Forest of Panna Tiger Reserve. Pooling data from the surveys conducted over several months are therefore likely to be prone to limitations such as those encountered during our monthly surveys in 2000.

It is clear from the monthly surveys in 2000 that the highest encounter rates of detection for most ungulate prey are obtained during February and March. Moreover, group sizes during these months are also closer to the mean estimated for the year. Therefore, for estimation of wild herbivore populations in a Tropical Dry Forest, February–March appears to be the most suitable time. Walking transect lines simultaneously and repeatedly every morning and evening maximized the efficiency of the surveys (Karanth and Nichols, 1998). By conducting these surveys within a short time span (ranging from 15-40 days), the error associated with varying encounter rates, change in group sizes, and effect of visibility on radial distance and ESW (effective strip width) is minimized effectively in this study.

Low encounter rates during the evening count on the same line on the density estimation is a possibility because of repeated walks on the same line every day. We believe that this may have caused enough disturbance for animals to move away from the line; this not only affected the evening encounter rates, but the distances at which animal groups were sighted from the line.

Another factor could be the activity pattern of prey species. It is generally assumed that most of the animals are active during the early morning and evening (Karanth and Sunquist, 1992). Our radio telemetry study of sambar in Panna indicates that the activity pattern of herbivores is a likely factor in the low detection and density estimate in the evening for sambar (Figure 4.4). The first half of the morning surveys coincide with the peak activity period, which declines gradually. Similarly, increasing encounter rates in the case of sambar towards the end of the evening coincide with its increase in activity. The effect of repeated walks on the encounter rate was tested in 2005 by conducting an experimental exercise, mentioned earlier, where lines are walked only once in a day to see the effect of the disturbance caused by the previous walk. I suspect that in the 2001 and 2003 data sets, variations in the evening and morning count possibly caused underestimation of prey population.

These trends were consistent during all the surveys we conducted. They also highlight that counting animals for more than two hours can have a significant effect on encounter rate and density estimate because of the shift in activity pattern. This potentially limits the length of transects, which will depend largely on length, visibility, terrain and number of detection. To minimize the errors encountered in morning and evening counts in the shorter, intensive 2001 and 2003 surveys a new survey design is needed. A sampling period (as short as possible)

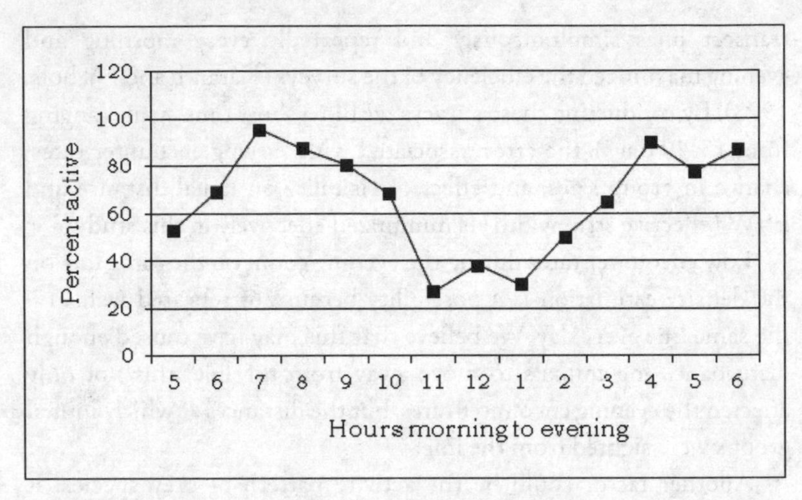

Figure 4.4 Activity pattern of sambar during the day in the months of February and March 2003, as determined from monitoring radio-collared sambars (n=5).

with more lines, which are walked once a day and repeated after three or four days, can minimize the errors encountered during the surveys. We also feel that because we obtain animal density of multiple species from a single protocol, it increases CVs for the resultant density estimate. For example, chinkara—a habitat specialist—is found in a certain habitat, but if we are using data from the habitats where it is absent or occurs in very low densities it creates high variation in CVs. In such a protocol we will need a greater number of lines to control the CVs. My studies in Panna show that we will need over 250 lines to have an acceptable CV. Since these are logistically difficult propositions, we must improve protocol to overcome these problems. These will require more experimental designs and testing in the field for improved and reliable estimates.

5

Tiger Society:
Solitary Existence but Social Living

Carnivores show a great diversity in their social organization and behaviour (McDonald, 1983; Gittleman, 1989). Many of them are solitary while some live in highly developed social units. Among these, felids (the cat family) have a highly specialized social system (Kleiman and Eisenberg, 1973). Their social organization and behaviour reflects a response to prevailing environmental and ecological factors as well as their con-specifics (other members of the same species). Whether they are solitary or live in groups depends on various factors. A balance between energetic cost incurred and benefits accumulated determines a particular way of life. A certain behaviour or strategy which results in benefits (i.e. reproductive success) and which also exceeds costs, increases the fitness of the population. For example, a pride of lions can not only defend its territory more effectively than a solitary lion, it can also catch much larger prey by cooperation in hunting (Gittleman, 1989). Such behaviour has its costs and benefits, and the balance of these can change in different circumstances or ecological conditions. Through such responses, animals adapt to varying ecological conditions. Further, by studying such behaviours we can map out the ecology of a species and plan conservation efforts accordingly.

Tigers largely appear to spend most of their time alone, they even hunt for food alone (Schaller, 1967; Sankhala, 1977; Sankhala, 1978; Sunquist, 1981; Smith, 1984). However, they are not alone in the forest: each individual tiger is part of a highly organized and peaceful society and they are in constant communication with each other (Schaller, 1967; Sankhala, 1977; Smith, 1984; Sunquist and Sunquist, 2002). Roaring, claw raking, spraying, and body rolls are some of the common means of communication to express reproductive status, establish social hierarchies, demarcate territories and sometimes also to announce a challenge. Tigers encounter these communication signs when travelling or patrolling their space. Adult tigers' association with other tigers are generally brief though longer associations happen while mating or sharing a kill (Schaller, 1967; Sankhala, 1977; Thapar, 1989; Sunquist and Sunquist, 2002). Outside of these activities, males and females occasionally do get together but these are brief meetings which usually go unnoticed, and very little has been written about these secret interactions.

Most of the information about the tiger comes from hunting records, anecdotal natural history notes and, more recently, from books like *The Deer and the Tiger* (Schaller, 1967). Schaller recognizes the lack of factual information, stating that 'the natural history of the tiger has been studied predominantly along the sights of a rifle...' I can now add: 'Also through the camera lens'. After four decades of tiger conservation in India, we know very little about a tiger's secret life through scientific understanding.

In the following chapters, we present our systematically recorded observations on social interactions, space-use patterns, communication techniques, dispersal, survival and mortality, resource use and food habits of the Panna tigers. Further, we analyze the effect of poaching on the viability of the population.

Since breeding males and females follow different strategies, their space needs and use also varies (Logan and Sweanor, 2001; Jedrzejewski et al., 2002). Females spend enormous amounts of time and energy in raising cubs. Therefore, they require resource-rich areas for good cover and prey availability, where they can successfully raise a litter (Sandell, 1989). A male's tenure as the dominant leader is short and follows a very different strategy. A dominant male tiger focuses his energy on his mates and on their growing cubs, providing security from other challenging males. To maximize his breeding potential, his range usually covers several female ranges (Schaller, 1967; Sankhala, 1978; Smith, 1984; Sunquist and Sunquist, 2002; Goodrich et al., 2010; Hojnowski et al., 2012). The size of the home ranges of females depends on many factors, including prey availability.

The extent of a tiger's range also depends on its environment. In Siberian temperate forests, tiger prey density is low and the climate is extreme and seasonal (Hornocker et al., 1995). Tiger ranges, in such climates, are several times larger than those in a very productive tropical forest system such as the terai or moist deciduous forests (Sunquist, 1981; Smith, 1984; Chundawat et al., 1999; Karanth and Sunquist, 2000; Goodrich et al., 2010). In the tropical forests tigers are found in much higher density. Thus, in different environments we expect different population responses from tigers. It is through such behavioural and population responses to the prevailing environment and through constant communication that tigers organize themselves into a very intricate, stable and successful society.

The Tiger Family

Baavan

Out of all the tigers that we studied, one really became a part of our lives; she was a tigress whom we named 'Baavan' (fifty-two). She was named so because her eyebrow markings resembled the numerals '5' and '2' (page 78).

I realized this quite late. In fact, it was during a massive search operation to locate her when her first collar had failed, that I came to know about her unique markings. Those were early days of the study in 1996, when my research student, Neel Gogate, was monitoring the radio-collared tigers. Prior to this radio-collar failure, we had lost one of our other radio-collared tigers due to suspected poisoning, so everyone was being extra careful. There was a lot of criticism in the media and naysayers were asking why we had collared a mother with three cubs. There was also a lot of tension in the air, because ours was only the second telemetry study on tigers in two decades. Our main

Note the markings above her eyes which can be read as '5' and '2'. These marks were unique and made her very identifiable. This is why we called her 'Baavan'.

fear was that tiger mortality would put an end to this study—as had happened to Dr Karanth's tiger study in the 1990s.

Baavan was the second tigress we had radio-collared. We monitored her for nine months until one day we failed to receive signals from her collar. This loss of radio-signals triggered panic at the forest headquarters in Bhopal. I tried my best to calm everyone but no explanation was good enough. I ended up leaving all my teaching assignments at the WII in Dehradun to spend several weeks in Panna searching for this female.

I was convinced that the loss of signal was more likely due to a failure in the functioning of the radio-collar than anything else. We had no evidence to indicate mortality and moreover we were regularly observing tracks within her area. Fortunately, we had a very capable and cooperative field director, P.K. Chawdhry, who was also convinced by the evidence that she was alive. I enjoyed my stay in Panna but it was frustrating because the pressure from the state capital had stopped all research activity, giving way to a mad search operation.

I had to leave Panna eventually, but the search continued and a week later our field staff confirmed Baavan's presence on a kill. I asked if they had seen her collar. When their answer was negative, I asked how they were so sure that it was the same individual. Kalyan, one of our more experienced trackers, told me that he knew her by the eyebrow markings that formed the number '52'. Not convinced, I asked them to go back the next day to try to see the collar. They did and not only confirmed that it was the tigress we were searching for, but also showed her to the senior staff of the Reserve. This good news was communicated to Bhopal.

Thus, all the drama ended and I was able to relax a bit. I hoped that this incident might build the Forest Department's confidence in the research team and lessen the problems when seeking fresh permissions for radio-collaring. After the incident, I gathered all the photographs I had of the tigress and looked more carefully at the markings on her eyebrow. Indeed, they actually looked like a '5' and '2'. From that day onwards, we called the lady with unique markings 'Baavan'. We replaced her collar twice after this. Her last collar continued to transmit signals up to 2005, even though our fieldwork had ended by then.

Our association with her lasted for over nine years and much of our knowledge of tiger ecology came from observing her and her family. Through her cubs and their cubs, she contributed over twenty tigers to Panna National Park. She and her family became an integral part of our life and the years I spent watching them are some of the most treasured moments of my life. I was not a dispassionate scientist anymore. During this time we spent hours, day after day, watching her and her family, unable to think of doing anything else. Our experience and understanding of tiger life in the dry forests is nothing but the story of Baavan and her neighbours as seen through the magnifying glass of rigorous science.

Identifying Individuals

Positive identification is the first step in developing an understanding of what happens in a tiger society. To ensure this I always took pictures so that it was possible to identify the animal later by matching it with our photo records. Joanna, who is the photographer in the family, kept an album of all the known tigers from our video and still pictures (this was in the pre-digital era). Knowing each individual from the photographs helped our research staff and encouraged an understanding of the importance of correct identification. Incorrect identification naturally leads to an inaccurate understanding of tiger behaviour. Joanna had developed a set of key characteristic markings for 'positive IDs'. Our first task for every observation was to establish a positive ID of the tiger.

Many times, the identification of a tiger is influenced by prior knowledge about the specific areas occupied by specific tigers. In following this conviction however, mistakes can be made, especially when a new tiger is encountered in the area of another known tiger. On our visits to other parks like Bandhavgarh, Kanha and Ranthambhore, we had noticed how casually and quickly a resident 'expert' identified individual tigers, from distances that always amazed us. But we soon realized how often their IDs could be incorrect even for animals they knew well. This taught us to be very cautious in our own identifications.

Actual IDs, in many circumstances, can only be confirmed when referred to photos. In going through this process we realized just how easy it could be to make mistakes. Identification was much easier if an individual had markings as distinctive and obvious as Baavan's but, unfortunately, this was not always the case and often these specific markings may not always be visible when catching a glimpse of a tiger through thick forest cover or among tall grass

I cannot stress enough the care and discipline required for identification in the field as misidentification can result in wrong conclusions and lead to an 'understanding' that may be way off the mark. Therefore, in our analysis we have discarded all observations where there was any reasonable doubt about the ID. This limited our data but its quality ensured reliability.

The New Tiger Neighbourhood: The Success Story

Baavan or F-123 was the second tiger that we radio-collared. Her first litter of three female cubs (the siblings were named 'F-111', 'F-120' and 'F-113') were also radio-collared while they were establishing their own territories or after they had established them, in spaces adjoining their natal area (Figure 5.1). The numerals in their names refer to the frequency of their collars, helping us to remember where to tune into them. 'F' indicated the females and 'M' signified the males.

During the first year of the study, we could identify only a total of four adult tigers within our study area of 250 km^2. They were two territorial females and two males. Both females were raising cubs. As mentioned, Baavan, who occupied the best habitat in the Reserve in the Chapner and Bhadar region, was raising a litter of three cubs that had been born in late April 1996. We radio-collared her in January 1997. The other female, whom we dubbed 'Bargadi', occupied the Bargadi region west of Baavan. She was raising a litter of two larger cubs, though they were also less than a year old at that time. She was one of the identified but not collared individuals.

In April 1996, we radio-collared the large dominant male, M-91, who patrolled the territories of both these females and beyond. We found no evidence of any other resident male within M-91's territory, except for a very old male who had occupied an area south of it. Thus, our estimate for 1996 was four adult tigers in an area of 250 km^2. This indicated an approximate density of two to three adult tigers for every 100 km^2, including two thirteen to fourteen months-old cubs but excluding the three cubs of Baavan, who were less than a year old.*

Extrapolating from this figure, one could estimate that there were maybe eleven to sixteen tigers in the entire Reserve but this would very likely be an overestimation.

Baavan's first litter of three female cubs all survived to adulthood and dispersed to establish territories adjoining their mother's. While Bargadi's cubs—one male and a female—died early at fifteen to sixteen

* When calculating tiger density, it is customary to only include animals above 12 months of age.

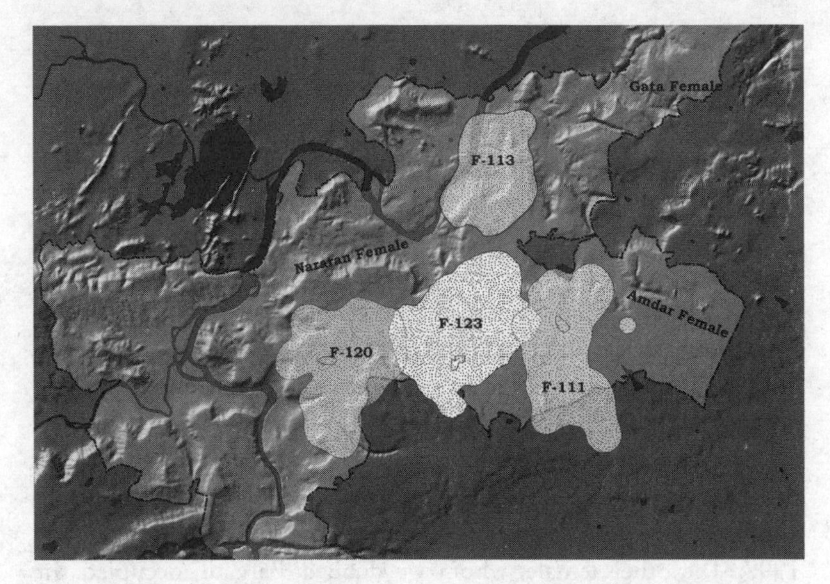

Figure 5.1 Home ranges of female F-123 and her three daughters F-111, F-120 and F-113, and locations of other females that were not radio-collared but known to the field team.

and twenty-two months, respectively. Bargadi was an old tigress, who had already lost a canine and some of her claws. She was displaced by one of Baavan's dispersing female cubs.

In mid-1997, the dominant M-91 had a territorial fight with a new male. We named this new challenger 'Madla' (after the area where we first saw him). Later, after collaring, he was also known as 'M-125'. In all the years of our study in Panna, this was the only fight between male tigers that we saw. It was quite intense, and continued for several days. M-91 was hurt quite severely and he lost the northern part of his range along the river Ken up to Madla village.

Thus, by the end of 1999, we positively knew that there were four adult females—Baavan and her three adult cubs, F-120, F-113 and F-111—within the study area, and two dominant males (M-91 and M-125). This increased the density to over three to four tigers per 100 km^2.

From 1996 to the end of 1998, the number of breeding females in the area doubled from two to four, mainly because of the three female cubs who occupied the vacant spaces around Baavan. By the end of 2001, we had evidence of seven resident tigresses—Baavan and her three offspring (settled and breeding) and three new tigresses who had moved into the area. Although we observed only one fight between males during the entire study, we saw fighting between females three times. One of the new females fought with F-120 a couple of times, but the latter held on to her territory. The three new breeding females identified by us (but not radio-collared) became known as 'Amdar', 'Gata' and 'Nararan', based on the areas they occupied (Figure 5.1). We had no photographic evidence of these clashes but suspected that it was the Nararan female who had tried her luck with F-120. She finally settled in the area north of F-120's range.

Between 1996 and 2002, Baavan gave birth to four litters and her daughters, females 111, 113 and 120, each had two or three litters. As a result, the number of floaters and sub-adult animals increased considerably. By early 2002, we were monitoring seven resident breeding females (each with a litter of various ages), two territorial males and four or five other unknown tigers (mainly males, some of them were identified).

By early 2002 the tiger population in Panna had reached its peak. All seven tigresses had a litter; this included Baavan with a litter of three cubs, and the other females—111, 113, 120, Amdar, Gata and Nararan—each had two cubs. Altogether, this accounted for fifteen cubs in an area of approximately 400 km^2 in tiger Reserve. This meant that there were nine breeding tigers that we knew of—two territorial males and seven territorial females—along with three or four other adult tigers and fifteen cubs of various ages. Together this made for a total population of over 28 tigers in the area that we were monitoring intensively (now 400 km^2). It was fascinating for us to be documenting such a remarkable recovery of a tiger population, especially at a time when tiger populations elsewhere, in all parts of the world, were showing a declining trend. Therefore, this recovery was a pleasant surprise and attracted worldwide attention as one of the finest success stories in tiger conservation.

Between 1996 and 2004, we identified and monitored a total of forty-one different tigers in Panna, including adult resident breeding tigers, non-territorial young adults, non-breeding animals and cubs over one year of age. Around December 2000, Hairy Foot, a new male tiger appeared and took over M-91's territory, establishing himself as the new dominant male. We continued to see occasional evidence of M-91's presence in the area for a while, but he disappeared from the scene by the end of February 2001.

Hairy Foot was an elusive male with huge front paws that were so hairy that one rarely saw a clear outline of his toe-impressions, hence his moniker. He evaded our radio-collaring efforts and we rarely saw him. The only good photograph we got was through a camera trap. Joanna had set a camera attached to an infrared beam device on one of his known paths. After weeks of trying, she finally caught one photo of him as he passed by early in the morning. Sadly, his tenure as the dominant male did not last long. He was found dead in the summer of 2003 under very bizarre circumstances. His partly decomposed body was found in a well, with only just enough skin visible to identify him by his unique stripe pattern that could be matched to Joanna's photographs. Could he really have fallen in? Or was he found dead and dumped there in the hopes that his body would not be found? We will never know for certain.

M-125 moved into a small part of Hairy Foot's area by the monsoon of 2003. By 2004, he had occupied the other's territory almost entirely, vacating most of his own territory in the north, his original Madla range. Another young male tiger dubbed as 'Broken Tooth', for his missing lower canine, had been seen as a floater animal since January–February 2003. He moved into the rest of Hairy Foot's territory not used by M-125 and the area vacated by the latter in the monsoon of 2003.

At the beginning of monsoon in 2002, within the two dominant male territories (of M-125 and Hairy Foot) we knew there were seven breeding female territories. Out of seven females and two males, we radio-collared four and one, respectively. For others, we had photographic evidence. Hairy Foot's predecessor, M-91, was radio-collared from April 1996 to September 2000.

In addition to breeding individuals, the tiger population mainly comprised of pre-dispersal adult cubs and a few other adult individuals, which are described as 'floaters' or 'transients'. The transient/floater population or non-territorial individuals in Panna were mainly young adults from previous litters, though a few floater males were not from our known population. Actually, none of the dominant males, including Madla, Hairy Foot and Broken Tooth were among the monitored Panna tigers. Most likely, they came from the neighbouring habitats. Two of the breeding females we identified later, in 2001–02 were also not from the population of cubs we knew from Panna. This indicated that there were other breeding populations outside the boundaries of Panna Tiger Reserve up till 2002. Many of the female cubs survived to adulthood and, as expected, established territories next to their natal area. But some of the females were not seen in the neighbourhood.

There were a few exceptions: a couple of Baavan's male cubs remained in the area and mated with F-113 and F-111 (sisters from a previous litter) and one of the male cubs took over from Broken Tooth in 2006. This male was Panna's very last remaining tiger. When he disappeared, the authorities were forced to admit in January 2009 that not a single tiger remained in the Reserve. The other was a female cub of the Amdar female. The daughter occupied the mother's territory after her death though, unfortunately, she too did not survive long and died due to poisoning, along with her first litter, in May 2006.

Sex Ratios

We were able to positively identify thirty-nine tigers by both sex and age, and found that the tiger sex ratio almost conformed to unity (19 females: 20 males). In the literature, the sex ratio is generally skewed towards the females—ranging from 3:1 to 5:1—but this refers only to the breeding animals (Goodrich et al., 2010; Karanth, 2001; Smith, 1984; Sunquist, 1981; Sunquist and Sunquist, 2002). In our case, it refers to all tiger cubs and adults. In Panna, the sex ratio of breeding individuals appeared very similar to that of other studies, where only territorial males and females were considered (Schaller, 1967; Sunquist and Sunquist, 2002). However, we noticed that within the two dominant male territories, several other resident but non-territorial adult males operated regularly. The territorial females mated with these non-territorial males frequently. If we include these males in the breeding population, the ratio is not as biased, though it still remains in the favour of females (1.4:1). This ratio differs significantly from previous studies.

In Panna in 2002, the tiger population in the intensively monitored area consisted of 31 per cent breeding individuals, 51 per cent cubs and sub-adults, and the remaining 18 per cent, non-territorial adults. Though the non-territorial adults are traditionally excluded from the breeding population, we observed these 'floaters' mating with resident breeding females. Therefore, we consider this adult population as part of the breeding population, which can significantly influence the viability of the population.

The Falling Empire

The year 2002 was the beginning of the decline of tigers in Panna. Their population plummeted from a healthy thirty-five to a mere eight or nine by early 2005. These were the most turbulent years for tigers—not only in Panna but in the entire subcontinent. A new market for tiger derivatives (tiger body parts i.e. bones, skins, teeth and claws, penis and whiskers) had developed and demand for tiger skins in Tibet skyrocketed. The resulting spurt in poaching coincided with a change in the management of Panna. A new field director, Sanjay Mukhariya, took charge along with his deputy, Ambade, in 2002.

By the end of 2003, tigers from the breeding population began to disappear, precipitating a grave crisis. Between 2002 and 2005, as a result of a series of mortalities, we saw frequent changeovers of the males which did not help population recovery at all. Changeover of dominant males is a natural phenomenon in tiger society, where a dominant male is replaced by a new male. In a stable population, male tenure as a dominant individual can last for five-six years. Frequent changeovers (due to poaching) can create stress and increase the risk of infanticide (by new males) that can further reduce the reproductive success of the population. F-120 lost her second litter at the beginning of 2001 due to a suspected infanticide by Hairy Foot. But he also did not survive long after his new set of cubs were born. As mentioned earlier, his carcass was found in the early monsoon of 2003 in completely unnatural circumstances. But even before this, F-120 and her cubs had perished. She was found dead, caught in a poacher's snare, in December 2002. We had already lost another breeding female, F-111, who had disappeared in the late monsoon of 2002. Between 2003 and late 2004 more tigers were lost, including the breeding females of the Amdar, Gata and Nararan areas along with F-113.

Such mortalities had an extremely serious impact on the population, which never recovered afterwards. In the subsequent years, the lack of cub survival indicated the dire situation of the Panna tigers. There was, for a moment, one ray of hope. One of the Amdar tigress's female cubs established her territory in her natal area. We had known this young female since March 2002, when she was first photographed with her mother. At that time, she was about 10–12 months old. But then, our research permission was unceremoniously withdrawn in April 2004 and, prohibited from entering the Reserve, our monitoring came to a complete halt. However, we were able to return briefly for a few weeks between February and March 2005, and at this time we found the Amdar daughter raising a litter of two cubs.

By March 2005, there was evidence of only three other females—the now old tigress Baavan, one female cub from her fourth and last surviving litter, and Amdar's daughter with a litter of two cubs (sex unknown). At the same time, there were three males we knew—Madla, Broken Tooth and Baavan's male cub. Their movements overlapped completely. In the brief period during February and March 2005 when we were allowed into the park, we found that over twenty of the tigers that we had known, were missing. Baavan's radio-collar continued to transmit signals up to May 2005. Since her last litter in September 2001, we found no evidence of cubs but our intermittent monitoring of Baavan suggested that she may have given birth twice. We had only been allowed to work for a few weeks before our permissions expired, but we compiled the information we had gathered about the missing tigers into a detailed report titled 'The Missing Tigers of Panna' (2005) and submitted it to the Project Tiger authorities. The report recorded the possible loss of over twenty tigers from our intensive study area in Panna in the past year-and-a-half with photographic evidence to confirm their identity.

Instead of looking into the reasons for the disappearances and taking action to protect the few remaining tigers, the Reserve management set out to prove our information wrong and assured everyone that no such problems existed. They conducted a 'special census' to discredit our report, counting thirty-four tigers once again. They publicly announced a figure before the census had even taken place! The census figure given slightly exceeded the Director's declaration and the previous census number. According to them, nothing had changed and our report was merely an act to malign the authorities. The WII was then asked to conduct another assessment of the tiger population using a camera capture-recapture survey.

The WII survey was conducted in early 2006 and reported a range of fifteen to thirty-five tigers; this was the estimate from their camera trap photographs that captured only the same seven individuals we knew existed. This included the Amdar daughter with one of her two cubs, Baavan the old lady, Baavan's daughter from her fourth litter, Madla (M-125), Broken Tooth and Baavan's male cub. Among these seven tigers, two—Baavan and the dominant male Madla—were past their prime and Baavan's cub had yet to reach breeding age. So our only hope was the young Amdar female and Baavan's female cub from her fourth litter. Broken Tooth and Baavan's male cub (from her third litter) were sighted all over the Reserve.

It seemed as if everything was conspiring against the tigers of Panna. Even before the WII census ('camera trapping') results were compiled, there was another rude shock. The one ray of hope for the future of Panna tigers, the Amdar daughter, along with her two cubs, was found dead in May 2006. Forensic reports confirmed that the deaths were due to poisoning. With this loss, hopes for a recovery dropped to nearly zero. The chances of Baavan's cub surviving long enough to breed in such a situation were extremely slim.

These were very traumatic times for us but we continued to monitor the situation from outside—after being barred from the Reserve—for the next few months. By now, Baavan was ranging over an area that was three to four times as large as her original range; there was no pattern in the males' movements either as they were all frequently sighted in the same area. We continued to gather information by visiting the Reserve regularly as tourists (since we were not allowed in as researchers), and from records and interviews with the other regular visitors. We kept a detailed record of each sighting by other visitors. By early 2008, there had been no confirmed reports of a female tiger in the Reserve for almost a year, and the only sign of tiger presence at all was that of Baavan's male cub—sighted occasionally by the elephant patrol. The authorities kept coming up with unconfirmed accounts of females sighted with cubs in the Reserve and in the surrounding areas as well but presented no evidence of this. Sadly, no one paid attention to our reports and the management's narrative of continued tiger presence in the park remained prevalent.

Actually, the crash of tiger population of Panna had been faster than its recovery. In just a few months during 2003–04, we had lost a significant number of tigers to poaching. The loss of the breeding population gave little chance for recovery, especially when the management failed to take any steps to prevent further decline. I discuss the reasons for this decline and how it happened in the penultimate chapter—why the tigers of the dry forests of Panna were so particularly vulnerable, and how it could have been reversed.

It seemed that the mortalities in 2003–04 were the main trigger that shattered the entire social structure. Instability reigned high, causing other problems and driving this population into a deep vortex of 'small population syndrome' (Soule, 1986). The population was not only vulnerable to poaching but to extinction threats specific to small populations. These threats that operate on small populations, of demographic (biased sex ratios and high mortality rates), stochastic (disease and floods) or genetic (inbreeding) origin, are far more difficult to understand and arrest than human-induced threats. We have yet to develop a complete understanding of how and when they can wipe out a population. Unfortunately, the tiger population of Panna had reached that critical point-of-no-return by the end of 2004. Tigers are a highly resilient species but, at this stage, the odds against their recovery without outside intervention were very high.

The Potential

After the extinction, tigers were re-introduced to Panna from neighbouring tiger Reserves—three females in 2009 and later four more over the year, including one male. Over the last seven years, the population has recovered to the 2002 numbers. Tigers can reproduce very fast, not only in Panna, but across different landscapes. There are several examples to confirm this. Tigers require just a little bit of protection and a suitable environment to show their amazing resilience (Sunquist et al., 1999). Unfortunately, these rapid recoveries are not documented well scientifically. Some of this knowledge comes from hunting records where scores of tigers were hunted repeatedly in the same area, year after year. Some of it comes from two studies—one conducted by Sankhala (1978) and the other by Schaller (1967). More recently, we had seen how the tiger population bounced back in Ranthambhore after the poaching debacle of 1993–94. I remember spending over two months there at the time and seeing a tiger only twice, whereas earlier visitors sometimes spotted 10 tigers in a single drive. But in just a few years, with better protection, the tiger population bounced back very quickly. More recently, there have been similar recoveries in Tadoba and Pench.

During the Panna study, we observed that resident tigresses could either be pregnant or raise a litter at any time of their reproductive age (between 3–14 years). Usually, tigers start breeding at a relatively early age and the gestation period is short for such a large animal (Sankhala, 1977; Sunquist and Sunquist, 2002). All these parameters make it a reproductively successful and resilient species (Sunquist et al., 1999).

In *The Deer and the Tiger,* Schaller provides a very detailed review of these parameters and explains their potential in reviving a local tiger population. However, we have not utilized this resilience in restoring tiger populations across their range. In fact, we have failed tigers by not providing for their basic ecological needs and a secure environment even in many of the protected tiger habitats.

Litter Size and Gestation Period

During our study period, we monitored fourteen litters and a total of thirty-two cubs born of eight breeding tigresses. The average size of litters that we observed in Panna was 2.28 cubs per litter (± 0.125, n=14). This is slightly smaller than those observed in Chitwan—2.98, n=49 for wild tigers (Sunquist, 1981) and 2.9, n=45 for captive tigers (Sankhala, 1978)—and in Kanha (Schaller, 1967). Litter size in Panna ranged from two-three cubs but larger litters of up to seven were also reported from the wild (Schaller, 1967). Sankhala (1978) had witnessed a litter of six in captivity. In fact, litters of four are not uncommon in the wild and have been seen in other tiger populations such as Ranthambhore, Kanha, and recently, Pench.

Our observations are mainly limited to those cubs that have survived more than two or three months. Because it is extremely difficult to make detailed observations on young cubs in the wild without disturbing them, we rarely got the opportunity to see week old cubs. In fact, we did not actively try unless an opportunity presented itself to us without disturbing the tigress. Most of the information on the litter size at birth comes from captivity. We were able to observe litters only a few weeks old on three occasions. We did not see any mortality from the age of 2–12 weeks in them. Our sample was too small to assert anything conclusively, but we did see mother tigresses put a lot of care into raising their cubs.

Based on the twelve matings and subsequent births observed by our research team, the average gestation period estimated for the Panna tigers was 103 days. This is similar to the figure recorded by Sankhala (1978) during his study of captive tigers. There is very little information available from the field on this period. We were very fortunate to be able to meticulously document the mating and subsequent births of the Panna tigers. Determining the actual dates our radio-collared tigresses gave birth was difficult, so we decided to use the second or third day of the tigress's location at the birthing site as the possible date. The time between mating and birth that we observed ranged from ninety-nine to 107 days.

We also observed that it was not uncommon for females to mate with different tigers. However, not all mating resulted in conception. Apart from F-120, we saw all other females mating with different males around the time of their oestrous cycle. In Chitwan, Sunquist (1981) observed that adult males and females meet regularly. We also observed dominant males associating with females regularly and sometimes on kills that they shared with the female and her cubs. However, we noticed that these meetings were not always associated with sexual activities. There is a general perception that male tigers are cub-killers (Forsyth, 1889; Powell, 1957). This conviction is further strengthened by instances of infanticide when a new male takes over another's territory. Contrary to this belief, on a couple of occasions, we saw the male tiger visiting the mother mere days after she had given birth. When the male arrived—we were very lucky to have witnessed this—the mother immediately left the litter and walked towards the male. Both greeted each other and settled down under a thick shade about 50 metres from the litter for a few hours. We could not observe any close contact with the cubs during this time. After that the male made regular visits to the mother every ten to fifteen days, whenever it was in the locality.

Tiger society is generally peaceful. Infanticide only happens when a male takes over a territory; even then not every changeover results in infanticide. If there are cubs from the previous male, destroying them encourages the female to come into oestrus and allows the new dominant male to mate and have its own cubs more quickly. It is not a rare phenomenon but it happens only once or twice in a decade, if everything is normal. Male tenure of dominance is short, usually ranging from 2 to 6 years (Schaller, 1967; McDougal, 1977; Sankhala,

1978; Smith, 1984; Karanth, 2001; Sunquist and Sunquist, 2002). During this time a male maximizes its reproductive potential by mating with as many females as possible, as many times as possible. This is why it will try to expand its area to include several female ranges within its territory. Once it has taken over an area by displacing another tiger, it further maximizes its reproductive success by mating as frequently as possible. In normal circumstances infanticide is only a temporary setback to the reproductive success of the population. If a male can then settle down for the normal four or five years, it can sire more offspring (from multiple females) than a female can produce in her normal reproductive life of 8-10 years.

Females can raise cubs if the conditions are suitable but the cubs' survival will depend on the father's tenure. We monitored the tenures of several males in Panna—M-91, Madla or M-125 and Hairy Foot. The first two maintained dominance for five and six years, and during this time they produced eighteen and ten cubs, respectively. The last couple of years of Madla's and Hairy Foot's reign were marred by high mortality. They did not have the opportunity to pass on their genes and father more cubs.

Mating

Scientific records from the wild show that there is no specific mating season and tigers mate throughout the year (Sanderson, 1912; Brander, 1923; Schaller, 1967; McDougal, 1977; Sankhala, 1978; Sunquist, 1981; Karanth, 2001). However, in Kanha, Schaller observed a peaking of sexual activity during the winter, between November and February, while also noting some mating activity throughout the year. Similarly, Sunquist (1981) and McDougal (1977) observed peaks of mating activity in Chitwan during the winter.

In Panna, we saw tigers mating throughout the year—thrice in December, twice in August and once each in January, February, May, June, July, September and October. Our observations provide an alternate way of looking at the mating phenomenon. We had the unique opportunity of observing three sisters maturing to adulthood, and having their first and then subsequent litters, along with their mother. When we looked at their litters individually, we realized there was no seasonality in the data set. The average gap between two litters (inter-birth interval) was 22 months (± 0.594 n=7) and it worked almost like clockwork for the monitored tigers. As a routine, females in Panna came into oestrus when cubs from the previous litter were around 18 months old, and a new set of cubs was usually born twenty-one or twenty-two months after the first.

Our field observations on the radio-collared tigresses implied that the timing of the oestrous cycle and mating depended on the date of the first litter; as inter-birth interval was around twenty-one to twenty-two months, the subsequent births were three to three-and-a-half months earlier. Thus for example, F-120 first mated in August and gave birth to her first litter in November 1999. The second mating took place in April–May 2001 with cubs born around August–September 2001. F-111 first mated at the age of 36 months in March, her second mating was in January next year and the third around August–September.

The other two radio tele-metry studies also find similar results with a slight peak in winter (Smith and Mcdougal, 1991; Sunquist and Sunquist, 2002; Kerley et al., 2003a). The cycle of mating and littering worked like clockwork throughout the year in Panna, but this may not be true for other populations. Unfortunately, we have no other long-term studies on individual tigers from India to support or contest our findings. There have been estimates of inter-birth period from extensive camera traps (Singh and Majumder, 2013) but these are way off the mark from the findings of this study and other long-term radio-telemetry studies (Smith and McDougal, 1991; Kerley et al., 2003b). However, all long-term studies estimate the inter-birth interval as 21.6 months. There are many different claims in documentary films and literature but most of their information is based only on casual observations and is not always reliable.

Another aspect of mating that fascinated us was the behaviour of females during mating. While with the dominant mating partner, they would occasionally travel beyond their territorial boundaries and spend days in the neighbouring females' territories. It was fascinating to observe these mating females display dominant behaviour in the neighbouring female territories. Their presence would arouse territorial behaviour such as spraying, body-rolling and calling from the resident female. There were no territory takeovers or conflicts during these extraordinary incidents, which took place many times. We have not come across anything like this in the literature on tigers and would hesitate to give an explanation for this behaviour based on just a couple of observations. However, it does raise interesting questions, e.g. could such dominant behaviour in the presence of a male have something to do with establishment of a new hierarchy? We hope future studies may be able to provide more answers.

Mating with Floaters

We also saw radio-collared females mating with various floater males, in addition to the dominant territorial males. We observed females mating with territorial males on fourteen occasions and with floater males on six. A couple of times we saw more than two other males hanging around the mating pair. Three of the four tigresses that we monitored mated with more than one male during an oestrus cycle.

We were very lucky to have witnessed this behaviour when Mike Birkhead and Gordon Buchanan were filming our research project for the BBC film 'Tigers of the Emerald Forest'. Shortly after Gordon filmed a sequence of F-113 mating with M-125, he filmed her mating with Broken Tooth. One could assess who the father was by calculating the days backwards after the birth of a litter. But when mating with a different partner had taken place within days as in F-113's case, it was very difficult to confirm the paternal identity. We observed such promiscuity more often with 123 and 113, and twice with 111. In fact, we saw 111 and 113 mating with their half-brother—a male cub from Bavaan's third litter—on different occasions.

New research on cheetahs in Africa, domestic cats and other carnivores has found from genetic studies that the cubs of a single litter can be fathered by more than one male (Say et al., 1999; Gottelli et al., 2007). Whether this is also true for tiger society is something that would be interesting to explore. Polygynous mating practices are well documented within tigers (Schaller, 1967; Sunquist, 1981; Karanth, 2001; Goodrich et al., 2010) but there are also a few records of polyandry (Schaller, 1967; Karanth, 2001).

The mating period usually lasts three or four days and occasionally longer (Sunquist, 1981; Karanth, 2001; Sunquist and Sunquist, 2002). In Panna, we observed mating lasting up to six days and in one case it went on for over a week. But if we were to include mating with more than one male it lasted longer. When F-113 was filmed mating with M-125 and later Broken Tooth, it lasted for almost two weeks. We noticed a large bald patch on the back of F-113's head as a result of repeated biting of the area by the male. If one looks carefully, it is visible in the BBC film. Information on mating behaviour has been documented extensively in several publications (Karanth, 2001; Sunquist and Sunquist, 2002).

One issue that has been raised repeatedly is whether radio-collaring affects successful mating. Recently, in the case of re-introduction of tigers in Sariska, the issue came up again and the Park's management officials decided to remove the collar to facilitate successful mating. I find it extraordinary that people can continue to believe such speculation and denigrate radio-collaring without looking at the facts.

We radio-collared four females and observed fourteen litters born to them. Ours is not the only research project where radio-collared tigers bred successfully. In Nepal, Siberia and Russia, many tigers were radio-collared for over a decade and they also bred successfully (Sunquist, 1981; Smith, 1993; Goodrich et al., 2010). Other than tigers, there are examples of animals all over the world that confirm that radio-collars have not come in the way of successful mating. However, there are still misgivings about radio-collaring in India. If not failure to breed, the complaint may be that radio frequencies disorient the animal or some other such fanciful damage.

By observing numerous mating interactions, I understood that mating is not always reproductive behaviour. At times it could be associated with dominance play. For instance, we observed that when a new male wants to assert his dominance, he may do so by mating with the female. This also acts as a challenge to the authority of the resident male. Such mating activity usually lasts for only a few hours or at longest maybe for a day. Occasionally it is repeated and sometimes fights between a male and female can happen when the new male is not accepted by the female. Casual observers may mistake such a mating as reproductive interaction. However, one must understand that for successful mating to take place, a female in oestrus must accept the male and copulate many times over a prolonged period of several days to induce ovulation. In ovulation, the release of ova by the rupture of the follicle is induced by repeated stimulation of the vagina and the cervix. A tigress may be in oestrus, but if copulation is not repeated and prolonged, fertilization may not happen and hence mating will fail to produce cubs. Induced ovulation ensures fertilization, but even then conception rates are low—about 20–40 per cent in case of lions and tigers (Wilson, and Mittermeier, 2009).

Conception is dependent on several factors and one of these is female choice. Recent studies observe that the dominant male is not always the best choice to make for reproduction, especially when it does not offer superior mate quality. In such circumstances females may opt for other choices (Qvarnström, and Forsgren, 1998). We still know too little to speculate on the scope of female choice in tiger society.

Growing Up and the Mother-Cub Association

An adult tigress lives a very tiring life. She is always either pregnant or raising a litter. She does get a little break when her cubs are dispersing and when she is pregnant. But even then, a pregnant mother's energy requirement increases many fold and she needs to work harder to make sure her litter is born fit and healthy (Gittleman, 1989).

It is hard to tell whether a female is pregnant until very late in her pregnancy. Despite knowing exactly when our collared animals had mated and when the litter was expected, it was still not possible to identify visible markers of pregnancy. Even among captive tigers, there are not many obvious signs to indicate pregnancy (Sankhala,

Growing up for cubs is not as easy as it might seem from their playful behaviour. After all that play, keeping pace with the mother and her discipline is exhausting.

1978). The Panna landscape is full of escarpments and caves, and we observed that all litters were born in rock crevices and caves at the base of the extensive network of escarpments. Due to the nature of the terrain, we had little opportunity to see new-born cubs, even though we were close enough to hear their cries from top of a cliff on many occasions. We also never made an extra effort to see them, unless we were sure that we could do so without disturbing the family. We knew that our presence might frighten the mother and force her to move the cubs to a new location. Moving the cubs unnecessarily exposes them to mortality factors and we wanted to avoid that.

We did get lucky on a few occasions and were able to observe new-born cubs from the top of an escarpment without being seen at all by the mother. From a well-camouflaged location at the top of a cliff, we made quite extensive and detailed observations of F-120's first and third litters and of F-111's second litter. F-120's third litter gave us the best opportunity. It also came as a big surprise as we had seen her with a litter of around 6-month-old cubs only about ninety days previously.

Although we suspected that the cubs had been victims of infanticide by the new male, Hairy Foot, we were not expecting a new litter quite so quickly.

Birth of F-120's Third Litter

From radio-tracking records we noticed that F-120 visited the birthing site a few days before the litters. Once settled down for birthing, she hardly moved out for the first five or six days at a stretch. This is the first definite sign we got that there was a litter. We were able to observe F-120 from the second week after birth, when the mother spent 70–80 per cent of her time with the cubs, coming out to rest nearby only occasionally, just a few metres away from the cubs. Sankhala (1978) has also observed a similar pattern in captivity. The tigress could not resist the cries of her babies and visited them frequently, even when resting just a few metres away. For the first two weeks, she is like a milk

We were lucky to have extended observations of such young cubs. During the first couple of weeks, the mother is totally devoted to her litter and hygiene is a high priority. Licking her cubs and teats clean after every feeding session was one way to keep her cubs healthy.

bar for the cubs. They suckle, sleep, suckle and sleep—occasionally falling asleep while still attached to her teats. The mother tigress is extremely careful about cleanliness at this time (Sankhala, 1978). We observed that after every instance of feeding, she would not only clean her teats but also clean the cubs thoroughly by licking them frequently.

After almost ten days, F-120 had still not fed herself. Our records indicate that that a tigress will go hunting only eight to ten days after the birth, though the time period may vary. On one occasion, F-111 made a kill on the eighth day after giving birth. We noticed that the tigress was very edgy and nervous during such hunts. Any alarming sound startled her and we often saw her abandon the hunt to return to her cubs. If she made a kill far away from her litter, say two or three kilometres away, she would eat quickly and trot back to her litter straightaway. Sometimes she did not even return to the kill again.

Once F-120 made a kill, but returned to her cubs without feeding at all, never returning to this kill. We witnessed a similar incident with Baavan as well. On another occasion, F-120 killed a large male nilgai on the plateau, not very far from where she birthed her third litter. She dragged the heavy carcass for almost 600 metres and then dropped it from the cliff into the gorge below. It landed about 500 metres away from the cubs. She was so nervous about leaving the cubs that she left the carcass twice midway, to go all the way down to check on the cubs before returning. It is not easy to drag an antelope that weighs over 250 kilograms. She also had the presence of mind to drop it from the cliff, so as to avoid climbing all the way up every time to feed.

The tigress usually moved her cubs to a different location within ten days of birth, not very far from the birthplace. Occasionally, we observed them moving the cubs after two weeks. By the time the cubs were three or four weeks old, the mother began to make longer forays and occasionally, we noted, she did not return for twenty-four hours or more. At this time, she began to patrol different areas of her range again and to spend extended periods of time at her kills. Despite the fact that she was venturing further, over 70 per cent of all our radio-locations (for the first four weeks) were still within 500 metres of the litter.

We also noticed that tigresses never used the same locations for birthing in Panna. The caves at the base of the escarpments provided a highly suitable site for cubs. Climatically, they provide a stable environment for young and vulnerable cubs. We placed temperature data loggers in some of these caves and observed that the maximum and minimum temperatures inside remained within a range of ten degrees over a 24-hour period. Thus, whether a litter is born in winter or summer, the environment in these caves is always moderate. These sites also provide greater security from other predators. In one case, during our 24-hour monitoring of F-120 when her cubs were just three weeks old, our assistants saw an interaction with a sloth bear that had chanced upon the cave. The bear was chased away very aggressively by the mother tiger. On the very same night, she moved her cubs to a new location—another cave about a hundred metres away.

The first movement of any distance that the mother makes with the cubs happens in their ninth or tenth week; only once did we record this happening *after* ten weeks. It is amazing how much distance these young cubs can cover at such a tender age. Mostly, the distance covered is only a couple of kilometres at a stretch, though we have also recorded a trek of four kilometres in one instance. It is also at this time that we began to see the cubs on kills. In Panna, tigers were usually shy and because of extensive grass cover we could only gather limited observations of cubs at this age. We determined the presence of cubs at kills from secondary signs. For instance, one fairly reliable indication was if the killed animal's ears were chewed and eaten before it was consumed or scavenged. Cubs are not strong enough to break open the tough skins, but the ears are an obviously soft part of the body that cubs can get hold of to chew easily. I regularly observed this behaviour in Panna, and it was filmed by Hamir Thapar, son of Valmik Thapar, much later in Ranthambhore. But one has to be careful before coming to the conclusion that chewed ears indicate cub presence: smaller scavengers such as jackals also do the same. Another indication is that the mother will usually open the carcass differently when she has young cubs. We observed that the tigress will eat the skin, in order to expose flesh for easy access. The tigress will use her carnassial teeth (molars) to cut the skin off from a large part of the body, eating it in the process. She will then let the cubs take charge of the carcass. They begin nervously, reaching for their mother frequently for reassurance; after a few rubs and nuzzlings, they will be back to the kill. It is amazing how much these little ones can eat; but seeing their swollen tummies makes one believe it.

Becoming Adult Tigers: Acquiring Skills

Lessons for young tigers start very early. It begins with play at an early age. Play with siblings and the mother is an important activity while growing up as they learn their basic lessons and establish hierarchies. Soon they move from playing with the mother's tail to exploring their immediate surroundings. As they grow, the cubs gain confidence. By the time they are over two-and-a-half months old, they will sometimes, though not always, accompany their mother to only kill. These are exciting times for the cubs. The mother will lead them to the carcass and sit down from where she can watch them.

It is the mother's call when to expose her cubs to observers like us. It varied with different litters. Initially, they were very hard to see, but then one day the mother would feel confident, give a few calls and one saw cubs coming out of nowhere. It can happen at any age, sometimes as early as three months, but in other cases it might not happen until five months.

Some cubs are bold and others very shy, irrespective of their sex. Each cub has an individual temperament that stays with them throughout their life. This diversity of traits is an important element in future survival. In Panna we found that they would slowly get used to our presence until we could watch them play, eat or sleep without any disturbance.

At five or six months the cubs are more confident of their surroundings. If they see prey they may stalk it for a while. In the fawning season—September to November is the peak in Panna—they may get early hunting lessons. Once Joanna saw F-120 catch a sambar fawn alive and leave it for the cubs. The cubs were barely

At nineteen-twenty months, male cubs can be as big as the mother, if not bigger. Interestingly, these two male cubs of Baavan also bear markings very similar to their mother's. Her other litters did not show this similarity.

six months old and seemed to have some vague instinct but no real clue how to kill it. The fawn was like a live toy on which they could practise their hunting skills. One of the cubs took complete possession of the fawn. By this time, hierarchies among the siblings are already established and on this occasion the dominant cub played with the unfortunate fawn until late in the evening and we had to leave as darkness was falling. On several occasions, I saw Baavan, F-120 and F-113 catch a chital fawn and carry it to the cubs, still alive. Once we saw Baavan carrying the fawn over a fairly long distance of one-and-a-half kilometres and by the time she arrived with the fawn it was half-dead. Both the cubs played with it for hours before eating it. Quite often during the fawning season, we observed older cubs (above 12 months) join their mothers to flush out and chase down fawns. This seems like good practice to develop their skills and gain confidence in hunting.

Over time the mother provides them with more difficult prey such as a large wild boar, leaving it for the cubs to handle. On one occasion, two 14-month-old cubs of Baavan struggled for over forty minutes handling a pig. This scene was completely chaotic, creating a lot of commotion, noise and dust as the inexperienced cubs tried their best to bring the pig down. The pig would escape their hold for a while, only to get caught again, and the struggle would continue. All this time, the mother sat at a distance watching the ruckus in an apparently disinterested manner. However, once when it looked as though the pig was escaping out of the cubs' range and they were just standing there in shock, she got up and caught it again in a flash. It was amazing how quick her response was. As soon as she caught the pig, the cubs were at it again. We watched this for over thirty minutes more from the back of an elephant, until it grew dark and we had to leave. We continued to hear the struggle for another fifteen minutes from the road.

On another occasion, a similar thing happened when we were tracking F-111 in the night. She was about forty metres in front of us, when we saw a big wild boar crossing the road towards her. She caught it as soon as it crossed the road, and then gave charge to her two seventeen-month-old cubs. This time it was already dark, so we could only hear what appeared to be the cries of the pig; it sounded similar to the brawl mentioned before. The mother moved several hundred metres away from the site. We left her and came back to where we could hear the commotion. This time, the struggle continued for an even longer time; we sat listening for two-and-a-half hours. When we returned in the morning the pig was half-eaten and we saw one of the cubs at the kill. Another arrived a little later but there was no sign of the mother. We finally located her a couple of kilometres away from the kill site. There were many other such observations showing how the mother created opportunities for the cubs to harness their predatory skills. This process starts at a very early age, though the cubs remain dependent on the mother until they are skilled predators. It is in the mother's interest that the cubs acquire these skills as early as possible because the earlier they become independent, the sooner their mother is ready for her next litter.

We observed an instance of unusual behaviour between mother and cubs in Panna. We saw F-120 teaching her last litter of cubs to climb trees. When her cubs were six or seven months old, she encouraged the cubs to follow her up a tree several times. She did this almost daily for a couple of weeks. She would climb onto the lower branches of a large tree such as a mahua and the cubs would try to follow. They would scramble at the trunk and when they somehow managed to reach her she would move along the branch, jump down and climb another tree. The cubs soon followed and tried again to climb the tree. We noticed this behaviour continue each afternoon for over two weeks. Sometimes, to our amazement, F-120 would climb fairly high branches. However, we observed only F-120 behaving in this way. None of her siblings or her mother were ever seen teaching tree-climbing to their cubs.

From an early age the cubs copy almost everything their mother does—scraping, spraying and claw-raking. They learn these means of communication—to keep in touch with their mother and siblings—fairly quickly. By the time they are over a year old they tend to wander away from the mother and use their skills to navigate or to find a kill site. As they grow more confident, they move further away and keep in touch with the methods mentioned above. These short forays away from the mother, sometimes for several days, are the first steps towards becoming an adult.

Dispersal: Leaving home

Leaving home or 'dispersal' is defined as a movement away from the natal area to another place where an individual can settle for breeding. Such movement is of two kinds: when the adult animal finds a suitable breeding spot near its natal area, this is usually known as philopatry; a long-range movement away from the natal area is known as dispersal. When undertaken by sub-adult animals, both movements are known as dispersal. The distance travelled by the dispersing individual determines the gene flow within the population or with neighbouring populations, and the demography and social organization.

During this study we were very fortunate to have been able to radio-collar Baavan when she had three young female cubs. Since the mother was radio-tagged we could make detailed observations of this litter. Subsequently, we also collared the female cubs when they were over two years old and about to disperse. In addition to this, we kept a detailed record of the movements of other cubs identifiable by their stripe patterns. Since dispersal was not the main focus of our study, information on the subject is limited to our observations of the radio-tagged individuals and their cubs—four females and a couple of male cubs that we were able to monitor for an extended period of time. Additional observations of a few identified but un-collared tigers are also included to create a substantive data set indicating certain patterns.

Three of Baavan's female cubs, F-111, F-120 and F-113 (all radio-collared after two years), were siblings from a litter born in late March–early April 1996. As cubs we noticed that all three siblings had different temperaments and these remained fairly unchanged throughout the period we knew them. Out of the three, F-113 was a runt; she was the smallest and weakest. We wondered how this would affect her adult life. Would she be able to fend for herself, when, even as a large cub, she required her mother to bring her to the kill and stay with her till she had finished feeding? Actually, F-113 grew up to be a very successful tiger—the submissive behaviour of her youth did not persist in her adult life. F-111 was a shy and timid lady but more aggressive when with her siblings. She separated early, around the age of 18–19 months, and extended her range into an area east of her natal range. However, for the first six months, she continued to roam and hunt within her natal area. We were very lucky that she was radio-collared during this transition. We had not been actively targeting her for collaring but on one of her forays, she was caught in a leg-hold snare that had been set up to capture and radio-collar sloth bears. Dr Yoganand was conducting a research project on the sloth bears in Panna, and he resourcefully took the opportunity to collar her before release in March 1998. This provided a great opportunity to document the dispersal process of a young tigress. It helped us track her movements closely and make detailed observations of her interactions with her siblings and mother. We saw her sharing kills made by her mother Baavan and with her other siblings on several occasions. Other than this, she spent most of her time alone in her newly acquired area.

During the monsoon months, she did not stay in her summer range close to her natal area, but extended it further east and never returned. Figures 5.2a and 5.2b show her movements and the area she occupied during the first few months of her independence in the summer as well as the area she later occupied in the monsoon. She settled down permanently in her new area and established her independent territory adjacent to her mother, Baavan. There were no other females in the area that we had noticed prior to her moving in. Therefore, it was relatively easy for her to settle down in this vacant space, which was only patrolled by the dominant male of the area M-91, who was also her father.

During this period, her other two siblings continued to stay mostly within the mother's territory, though we also saw them moving together occasionally in an area some distance away (Figures 5.2a & b). F-113 and F-120 moved in a coalition and they gradually moved into an area to the west that was occupied by an old tigress, whom we called the Bargadi female. After several forays, these siblings established themselves in the area as a coalition by displacing the Bargadi female. Both of these young tigresses were not radio-collared at this time, so we saw them only intermittently during this period. We do not have detailed information as to how this settlement/displacement happened. Was there a fight? Or did the coalition of two tigresses push the Bargadi away without a fight? Since we did not see any injuries on the siblings, we assumed that it was a quiet affair and that the Bargadi female must have moved away without much protest. Bargadi was an old individual past her prime, though she was still raising a male cub who was almost as old as F-113 and F-120. What surprised us was the relationship between the siblings and this male cub. The females were tolerant of his presence in the area and we even saw him feeding on a kill made by the females on a couple of occasions. However, they did maintain some distance from each other and we never saw them actually feeding at the same time. The coalition made kills together. Once when camping at Bargadi, we

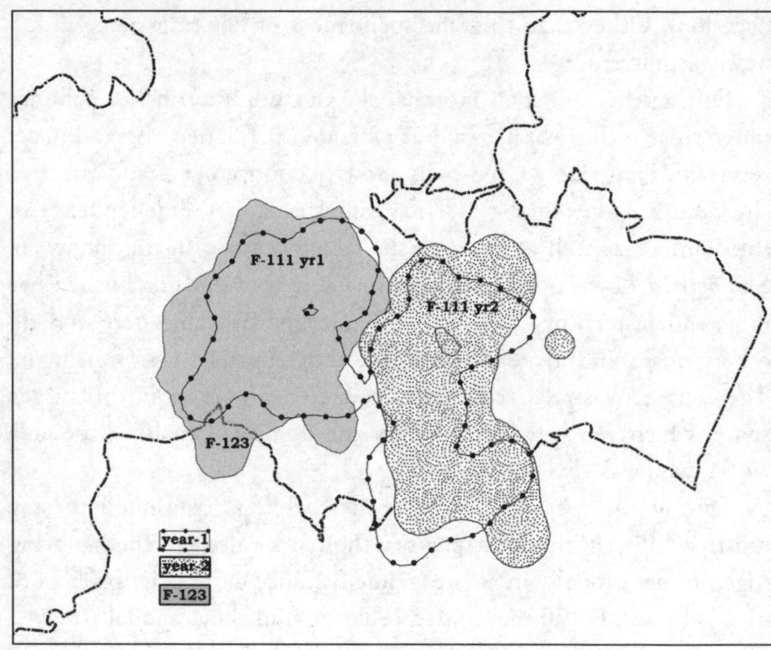

Figure 5.2a

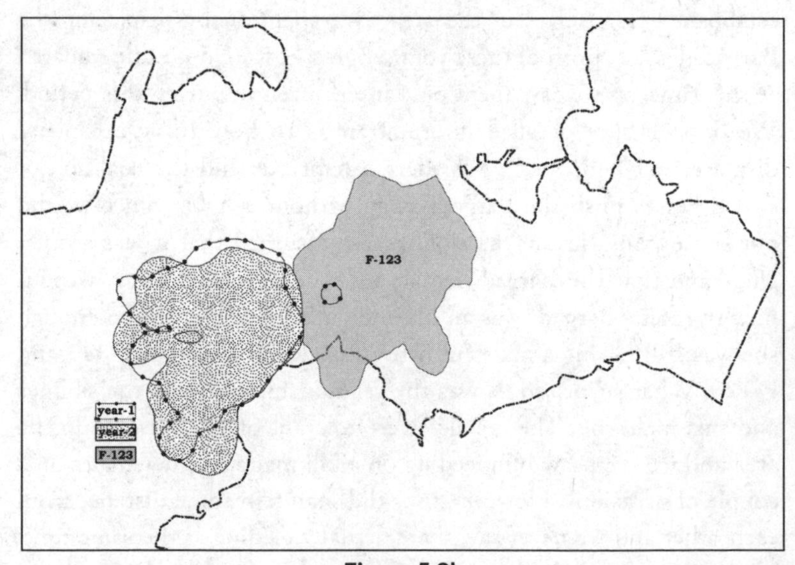

Figure 5.2b

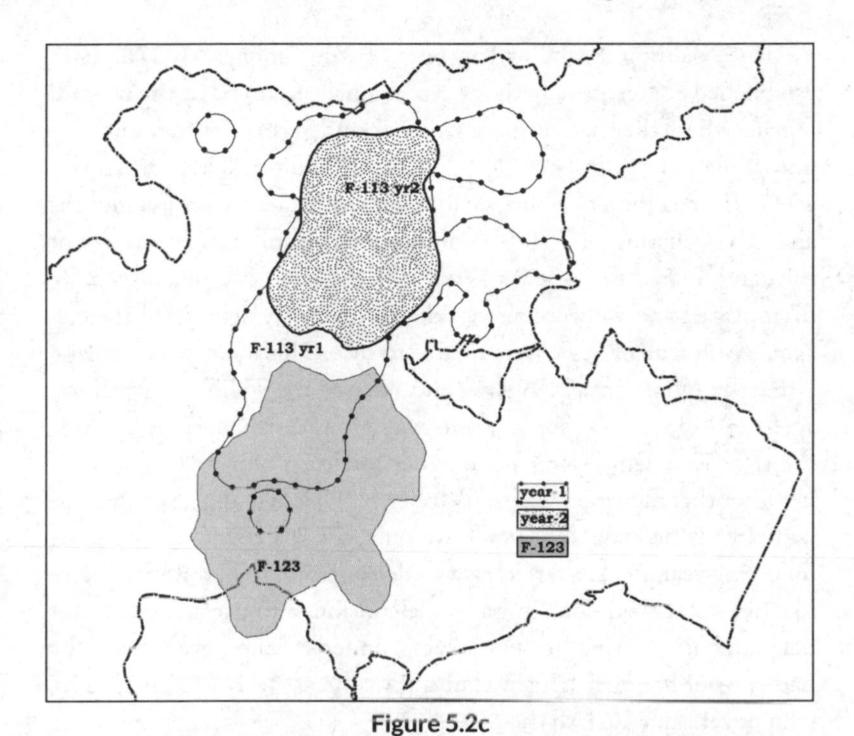

Figure 5.2c

Figures 5.2 a, b & c Dispersal of three siblings F-111 (a), F-120 (b), and F-113 (c), away from the F-123 home range, is shown by 'year 1', when the siblings continued to use the natal area extensively; and 'year 2', after establishing their own territories adjoining the mothers'.

heard the commotion of livestock being chased in the night. Bargadi was an abandoned village but part of the livestock had been left behind and this had grown into several large herds of a hundred or more. These feral herds used this restored area extensively and tigers often preyed on these animals. Early morning, as we came outside, we saw a tigress on the wall of an abandoned house some 120 metres away. After investigation, we realized that both tigers had chased the feral livestock feeding in the area and had killed three cows around the camp. From the rooftop of the camp, we could see both the tigresses, each feeding on a separate carcass. The coalition remained intact for several months and made kills together in this area.

The coalition broke when one of the siblings, F-120, later established her territory in the area previously occupied by the Bargadi female, whom they had displaced. She defended this territory until her unfortunate death in late 2002. F-120 was radio-collared in January 1999. The coalition of siblings had remained intact for several months after the collaring of F-120 and continued until early monsoon of the same year. After a few sightings of the male cub of Bargadi, he disappeared and we were never able to confirm a sighting of the cub again. Unfortunately, we were unable to record his identity on camera. After the monsoon of 1999, we did not see the siblings in coalition again. F-113 was next seen 15 km away in the north, in the area along the river Ken, which later became her territory. Our first sighting of her after that monsoon was in October 1999, and it appeared that she had already had cubs. However, we only saw the cubs in January the following year. F-113's territory was also adjacent to her mother's, and like her sisters had done initially, she continued to use a large part of her natal area during her first year of independence, even when she had cubs of her own. This was in stark contrast to F-111 and F-120, who never came back to their natal area.

Although all three of Baavan's daughters created their territories next to their mother's, we never saw them together again as adults, barring the brief coalition of 113 and 120. In fact, each defended its respective area aggressively, even from their mother. By the end of 2000, we had these four females radio-collared and monitored them regularly. Additionally, we knew three other females who had established territories in Panna. By this time, most of the Reserve was occupied by breeding females. We observed several other litters dispersing but because they were not radio-tagged, we knew little about their movements. Most of them disappeared once they had left their mothers. There were a few exceptions: when Baavan was ageing, the female cub of her fourth litter partially occupied the vacant space created by the death of F-120. Another tigress we called the 'Amdar female' had established a territory next to F-111. The female cub of the Amdar female took over her mother's territory soon after her death. She successfully littered there but sadly, did not survive long.

We had also radio-collared a sub-adult and dispersing female cub of the Bargadi female and she was tracked for approximately four months between April and mid-August 1996. She was about 18–19 months old at the time radio-collaring. Initially, she remained close to Bargadi area (her natal area), then shifted her range to an area 5–6 kilometres away. From this new area, she made numerous 12–14 kilometre-long forays. During these forays she stayed for a couple of days in new areas but always returned to her natal range. There were a couple of occasions during these forays when our tracking team could not locate her for many days. We believe that she had made longer forays on these occasions and this is why she was not found. These forays usually did not last long. Unfortunately, she died in August over a cattle kill.

It is generally believed that dispersal occurs when the mother pushes her grown cubs out of her territory. However, in Panna, we saw that this process begins organically, when the cubs replace their milk canines and other teeth and grow new adult teeth. In carnivores, molars are very specialized teeth known as 'carnassial teeth' (same root as 'carnivore'). Blunt molar teeth such as we humans have, are modified in carnivores into sharp-edged teeth capable of cutting the toughest of skins. This is one reason why carnivores are very successful meat-eaters, not because they have large canines, which many different animals like primates also have. These carnassial teeth are very crucial in opening the carcass. Young cubs cannot do this because it requires fully developed carnassial teeth, strength and skill. By the time they are 16–17 months old, the new canines and molars are well developed and they start catching smaller prey such as the fawns of chital and sambar. By the time they are 18–19 months old, they are capable of catching larger prey. This is when the dispersal process begins.

The belief that the mother pushes her cubs out of her territory does not bear out in our findings. We did not witness such a scene even once. Such misconceptions arise from misinterpretation of isolated incidents. For example, one may see an interaction between a mother and her grown-up cubs where the former is dominating and aggressive. This can happen even when a two-year-old male cub is physically larger. The hierarchy of tiger society prevails in these situations. However, since this may be an isolated incident witnessed without systematic observations of the recent past, it is speculative at best.

When a cub makes a kill he or she is very possessive and usually does not like to share it with the rest of the family—siblings or the mother. However, due to the hierarchy already established with the siblings and the mother, the owner of the kill is not always able to protect it from the rest of the family despite his or her best efforts. A family may feed on the cub's kill for some time, but eventually, they get tired of the cub's antics, and move on. The cub (owner of the kill) then spends a few days with its own kill peacefully and joins the family only after having finished with it. Next time the mother makes a kill, the same cub's behaviour would be very different. Since the cub had not made the kill, its sharing behaviour would change and it would wait its turn to feed. We saw this happen very often.

During this pre-independence period, these young cubs frequently made extensive forays into the forest and if they make a kill, they could remain away from the family for weeks. The more frequently cubs make a kill, the more time they spend away from the rest of the family. This initiates the separation and the start of a new chapter in the young tiger's life. In addition to the food independence, these growing cubs also develop personal spaces that they do not like to share. One also sees more interaction among the cubs. Once he or she is confident enough that they do not need their mother to make kills for them, they find a place to settle down. This happens gradually and the entire process can last for several months, depending on each cub. We don't know how exactly they decide on their choice of residential area, but if there are empty and suitable spaces close to their mother, then they usually settle there (instead of venturing into dangerous unknown territories).

Females learn and show interest in hunting earlier, and more often than males. Males appear lazy at this stage and take longer to achieve independence. Of course the relationship and individual space tolerance between mother and grown-up cubs still with the mother are very different from the time when the cubs were younger. Mother's annoyance with grown-up cubs is observed frequently and this led people to believe that the mother pushes cubs away. This changing relationship may be one of the factors that forces the cubs away but certainly not the only one, as generally believed.

Dave Smith (1984) looked at the process of dispersal in much more detail in Chitwan. He observed that dispersal usually coincided with the arrival of a new litter and the age of dispersing cubs varied between nineteen to twenty-eight months. We also observed very similar trends in Panna: the mothers came into oestrus eighteen to nineteen months after the birth of a litter and a new litter was born around the twenty-second month. Dispersal of cubs from previous litters starts around this time. There is no fixed age for dispersal and it can range from eighteen to thirty months (Karanth, 2001; Sunquist and Sunquist, 2002). Smith (1984) noted that dispersing cubs remain within the natal territory before carving out their own secure place. Associations similar to the coalitions of other carnivores such as lions and cheetahs are seen in some dispersing individuals for short periods of time. We also found male cubs from Baavan's second litter continuing to appear in her territory well after two years of age, and even after Baavan had had her third litter. Though these male cubs remained in their natal area, they lived independently from the mother. More interestingly, they were sighted together occasionally over a kill. Their association continued very loosely until they were almost 30 months old. This male coalition happened before I came to the field full-time and when Neel Gogate was working on the project, so I do not have the detailed information about this association. But it was similar to the coalition of the two female cubs, F-120 and F-113, from Baavan's first litter, which lasted for a few months only and ended with one of the female cubs establishing its territory.

The time during the dispersal is crucial for the cubs—they make several forays to neighbouring areas, learn to become independent by making kills regularly, interacting or avoiding other adult tigers of the area to become a part of the larger tiger society (Smith, 1993). It is also the time during which male cubs experience high mortalities.

Our extended observations also revealed that female cubs generally became independent earlier than males. Male cubs remained in the natal area even after achieving independence. Some of them finally settled in the area as floaters and mated with other females. This, I believe, happened possibly because dispersing male cubs were not able to find other breeding populations in the neighbouring tiger habitats around the Panna Tiger Reserve during their exploratory forays, so they had come back to their original areas. Only a few male cubs are able to undertake longer exploratory journeys, as documented recently by camera traps in Madhav National Park, where a male from the Ranthambhore Tiger Reserve moved several hundred kilometres (Dey, and Naveen, 2013). Another example is from the Bhadra Tiger Reserve (Patil et al., 2011). Very recently, one of the male cubs of the re-introduced population in Panna dispersed successfully to the Bandhavgarh Tiger Reserve. A few cubs, who survive long enough to reach a new breeding population stay there, but others may return to the original population after a long foray, after failing to find a suitable population. In Chitwan (Smith, 1993), only four out of ten male dispersing cubs survived to adulthood, whereas all female dispersing cubs that were monitored there established breeding territories successfully. Forays of a tiger as well-known as the Broken Tail from Ranthambhore and its death during one of these forays is well documented and illustrates this behaviour, highlighting the threats they face during dispersal (Sebastian, 2005). Individuals that survive this risk are the ones that possess better survival instincts in this human-dominated landscape. As adults, these males who have survived through dispersal age have better survival probabilities. In fact, in Panna we found that adult males had better survival probabilities than adult females.

One of the male cubs from Baavan's third litter is an example of a male cub staying on in the natal area. When he was almost four years old, he was seen mating with F-111, his half-sister. A few months later he was seen mating with another half-sister, F-113.

Dispersal is a very gradual process and an individual makes several exploratory journeys from its natal area before settling down. It is not to be confused with weaning away from the mother, which occurs as soon as the mother is ready for a new litter. The timing of dispersal depends on various parameters in addition to individual abilities and choices. It can vary from eighteen to thirty months, when cubs are more or less independent. There is a consensus on this conclusion based on the telemetry studies (Smith, 1984, 1993; Karanth, 2001; Sunquist and Sunquist, 2002).

Becoming Adults: Age of Sexual Maturity

In Panna, we observed that young females gave birth to their first litter, on an average, at the age of 40 ± 2 months (n=4, range=37–44 months). We observed four female cubs dispersing and later breeding. We radio-collared three of them and followed the fourth through intensive monitoring and camera trapping. The youngest female observed during the study gave birth in her thirty-seventh month.

On an average, a new litter was produced after an inter-birth interval of 22 ± 0.59 months (range=20–24 months). Almost all the litters observed were produced in the twenty-first or twenty-second months. One exception was produced in the twenty-fourth month.

We know from research on captive animals that a female is capable of giving birth with just a few months' interval. When F-120's entire second litter—only four months old—was (suspected) killed by the new dominant male, Hairy Foot, her third litter of two cubs was spotted less than two months later, when they were about a week old. Assuming 110 days of gestation period, the tigress had conceived before her previous litter had died. Later, we saw Hairy Foot visiting F-120 at the litter site on several occasions. Once he rested for hours, just a few yards away from the mother and this new litter.

Communication

Adult tigers communicate by means of leaving a trail of scent. They either spray urine, scrape the ground or roll their bodies on the ground or vegetation to imprint a strong and lingering body odour. Tigers use these forms of communication for very particular purposes—these signs are not placed randomly. For example, intensive markings were found where two territories met or overlapped. Over the years, lines of the battleground can shift—as one loses, another one gains new ground. At one such site where M-91 and Madla's territories overlapped, both visited this frontline area regularly. They left signs by rolling over the grass and by scraping the ground along a path. I had never seen such a high density of markings anywhere before. We counted over eighty scrapes along a 150-metre stretch and over thirty-five body rollings, evident from the flattened grass and remains of body hair. This site had not been marked so intensely earlier; but when M-91 and Madla had a fight in October 1997, the former lost a substantial part of its territory. After settling their disputes, they increased their marking activities along this line to a great extent. This high density of marking continued even after M-91 was displaced by a new male, Hairy Foot. After Hairy Foot's death, Madla's reign was left

Spraying urine is one of the most common ways of leaving behind a scent. Both male and female tigers can establish occupation of an area by leaving such scent marks. Female tigers can also communicate their reproductive status. The pheromones in the tiger urine smell very similar to basmati rice.

almost unchallenged and neither my research team nor I came across such intensive markings anywhere else. Generally, males are known to mark within their territories but nowhere with such intensity. We encountered only occasional scats (tiger excrement) on such sites intensively marked by males.

From these experiences, we observed that males mainly scraped the ground and used body rolling to stamp their authority over an area. These signs were left at strategic locations, whereas urine spray and scats were more random. This behaviour was true for females as well. In addition to these, females also used scats extensively. We observed that whenever a female trespassed into a neighbouring territory, the resident female immediately marked the area by scraping and spraying, and asserted her authority by calling (roaring) regularly. I saw this happen between Baavan and F-120, and Baavan and F-111.

We noticed that males started their evening patrol with a few roars. We observed M-91 roaring ten times out of which he started his patrol with roars seven times. M-125 on the other hand, is unpredictable. We rarely heard any roaring from him. These few observations were only of two dominant males—one cannot generalize from these experiences. Occasionally, while monitoring tigers on a 24-hour schedule, we noticed males stop in their tracks to listen. Then suddenly they would change their direction, heading towards a female or another male several kilometres away. We did not hear any calls at these times, and wondered if tigers have a repertoire of calls that humans cannot hear.

Mortality and Survival

A total of forty-one individual tigers were identified and monitored regularly during the study period (1996–2005). This comprised fourteen resident adult tigers—nine females and five males, along with twenty-seven cubs. This cub population does not include the five cubs that we also monitored as adults; the latter are included in the adult population. These five individuals were later monitored as the independent breeding tigresses F-111, F-113 and F-120, and two males.

During our nine years of monitoring, we inferred the death of nine adult tigers, though our research team only saw three carcasses. These mortalities include two males and seven females. Out of thirty-two cubs (including the five counted in the adult population) from the fourteen litters that were monitored by us, only eight mortalities were observed. Five of these were observed in cubs less than twelve months old, which meant that 84 per cent of the cubs survived to the next age class (>12–24 months) and three in the next age class (>24 months). 88 per cent survived till the next age class. No mortalities were observed in the litters that were monitored from a very early age (<10 days–2.5 months). We were able to monitor three litters in this category and all seven of these cubs survived to two and a half months.

The Mortalities

Adults

The nine suspected mortalities in adults included the Bargadi female, who was the original dominant territorial female of the Bargadi region displaced by F-120 and F-113 in 1998. We suspect that she most likely died of old age, after she was displaced from her territory. F-111 went missing over a cattle kill in October 2002, close to the periphery of the Reserve boundary near Talgaon. Her presence could not be confirmed by intensive camera-trapping in the areas she usually visited. After a month of intensive monitoring and looking for other signs, the failure to confirm her presence led our research team to suspect mortality. The third mortality came to light a couple of months later, when F-111's sibling F-120 was found dead in a snare in December 2002. Her body was recovered along with carcasses of sambar deer from the site. Hairy Foot, a new male who had replaced the dominant radio-collared male M-91 and took over its territory, was found dead in a well in June 2003. This was followed by the disappearance of the third sibling of Baavan's first litter, F-113 (radio-collared in 2000) by March 2004. During our investigation, our team was told that she had died due to poaching at a time when she had young cubs. Based on our

All the tigers we knew had a different character. Baavan, or fifty-two, liked to keep a distance and would snarl if she found us too close.

Left: A cub from F-120's first litter stands over its mother, eyes shining in the morning light. In the early years of the Panna study, cub survival was exceptionally good (>80%); their survival was tied more to the parents' survival than anything else.

Top: F-113, the second sibling from Baavan's first litter, was the last to establish her own territory. She was not shy and did not mind tourists around her.

Left: A deathly attack can come unnoticed from this sea of dry grass. Tigers are masters in taking advantage of their colour and stripes in order to get close to prey.

Top: A tiger cub rests in shade at noon; resting is a major activity for tigers of all sexes and ages, especially during hot days.

Left: This beautiful valley of the Ken river is under threat from a proposed dam. The planned 100 km^2 reservoir will fill this gorge and inundate not only the tiger habitat, but also the unique cliff habitat which is important for vultures. This would be the first dam built inside a National Park—areas created to protect our most important natural habitats. If allowed, this would establish a dangerous precedent.

Top: A small group of young Nilgai males. Male-only groups are not uncommon and such play-fights not only settle hierarchy in the group, but also prepare them for more serious battles as adults.

Following page: F-111, one of the siblings from Baavan's first litter, who dispersed and settled close to her mother's territory. She was a shy individual and always moved away when approached. This could be an acquired behaviour, since she occupied an area which encompassed several villages.

findings, the police nabbed a poacher in the Reserve who admitted to having poached over eight tigers from the area. Out of the other tigers monitored less intensively, Amdar and her adult daughter died in May 2006, after our study was over. Two other tigresses from the Nararan and Gata areas complete the list of mortalities.

Cubs

Of the eight mortalities in cubs, two from the first litter of the Bargadi female were more than a year old. The male cub, whose carcass was recovered, died due to an unidentified disease, while the other female cub (our first collared animal) died over a cattle kill. Circumstantial evidence from the recovered carcass suggested death due to poisoning. Two other mortalities were the suspected infanticide of the second litter of F-120 by Hairy Foot, after he replaced the radio-collared M-91. F-120's third litter of two cubs were still young when she was snared and were unlikely to have survived her death. Other mortalities were either due to natural or other unknown causes.

Calculating survival and mortality

Based on the data set outlined above, we calculated the survival/mortality rate of the tiger population of Panna. Probabilities of surviving from one age class to the next were calculated by applying the Kaplan-Meier estimator to our data set of 41 different individual tigers (Kaplan and Paul, 1958; Borga, 2005). Five cubs that grew into adults (>24 months) were included in the next appropriate age and sex groups. This implies that even though we monitored forty-one individual tigers, our sample size was forty-six, with five cubs included again as adults. Mortality and survival rates were calculated for the study period from 1996 to 2005. We have also accounted for the poaching which hit the Panna population from late 2002 onwards.

Due to the limited data set, we classified the subjects into three categories for calculating survival rates: the two adult categories were that of male and female tigers (age >24 months) along with cubs (age <24 months). For all the animals that were radio-collared or identified during our intensive monitoring, we kept a detailed record of ages and dates. Whenever a mortality occurred, we recorded the date. In case we lost contact with an identified tiger, the individual was censored from the age class. Censoring also happened when a known tiger missing but the exact cause was not known or when a tiger was alive at the end of the monitoring.

The probability that an adult female would survive during the study was 76 per cent while for an adult male it was 86 per cent. Cubs' survival was estimated to 89 per cent. The estimate for breeding females was arrived at after fifty-nine months, taking into account the unprecedented poaching that took place from mid-2002 to 2004. For the first fifty-two months, prior to the poaching episode, adult female survival probability was at a reasonable 86 per cent.

Though our data set was limited, it indicated a poor adult female survival rate in Panna. This has serious implications for conservation and population viability. Our findings run contrary to existing knowledge that females survive better in the wild than males (Smith and McDougal, 1991; Kenney et al., 1995; Kerley et al., 2003; Chapron et al., 2008; Goodrich, 2010). Usually, males move over larger areas and it is believed that they are more prone to conflict with people than females, resulting in higher mortality.

This was not the case in Panna, where we lost more adult females than adult males. The key to explaining this superior survival rate of male tigers in Panna might be found in Smith (1984), a study of tigers in Chitwan. In his study Dave Smith found that mortality is higher in males during dispersal. We already know that this is because sub-adult males move over greater distances across a human-dominated landscape, encountering many threats. Each individual tiger responds to these threats according to its unique characteristics, e.g. some are shy while others may be bold in the face of human presence. This diversity in individual responses allows for an evolutionary selection process. Only those individuals that have the knack of avoiding conflict survive to adulthood. As adults, this select group of males is better equipped to survive high-conflict situations.

Moreover, in large and well-managed protected areas, young females usually find a disturbance-free area close to the mother's territory and will not experience the kind of conflict that a male sibling would. But in Panna, that was not the case because most of the breeding territories were exposed to human-related mortalities, especially since they all went up to or beyond the Protected Area boundary. This may be a reason why Panna sees such high mortalities in its female population.

We also observed that an adult tigress is far more possessive of her kill and shows more aggression than the average male. She will growl or charge if anybody ventures near the kill by mistake. If it is a livestock kill, villagers will soon find out about her presence. This knowledge of tigers' presence among the villagers is exploited by the poachers' network. Conversely, the two males we radio-collared were very timid. When M-91 killed cattle, he never returned to the carcass after one meal, resting far away from the site. M-125 on the other hand remained with the kill quietly, without anybody noticing his presence. When disturbed, he would also leave the kill, never to return. These males survived longer, despite higher predation on livestock in Panna than the females. No tiger population can survive the high female mortality rates, such as those we recorded in Panna. As a result, in 2008, we witnessed a complete local extinction of the population.

Summary of Observations

The monitoring of seven radio-collared tigers from 1996 to 2005 generated a substantial amount of information on population characteristics, social organization, survival and mortality. This monitoring amounts to over forty-one radio-collared tiger years. If the observations and monitoring of other tigers and cubs is included, it amounts to an astonishing ninety-five tiger years. Not many studies on the tiger in India have been able to collect the amount of data generated like we have done in our nine-year study. The increase in the tiger population from 1996 to 2002 portrays a steep graph but the fall in 2002–05 was even steeper. The population could not recover from these losses and went extinct in 2009.

- Sex ratios: We positively identified the sex and age of thirty-nine tigers. Their sex-ratio almost conformed to unity (19 females: 20 males), bucking the existing skew towards females among breeding tigers (Sunquist, 1981; Smith, 1984; Karanth, 2001; Sunquist and Sunquist, 2002; Goodrich et al., 2010). In Panna, breeding individuals made up only 31 per cent of the total tiger population in 2002, while 18 per cent belonged to non-territorial adults.
- Sex ratios of floaters: These non-territorial adults are generally known as non-breeding 'transient' or 'floater' individuals. However, we observed that these floaters were resident tigers and mated with territorial females. Therefore, the sex ratio of breeding adult tigers (including floaters) in Panna was also close to unity (1.4:1).
- Age of sexual maturity: Female tigers reached sexual maturity on average after 40 ± 2 months (n=4, range 37-44 months). These observations are in line with other studies (Sunquist and Sunquist, 2002).
- Litter size and gestation period: Average litter size estimated for Panna's tiger population was 2.28 cubs per litter (± 0.125, n=14 litter). Average gestation period observed from twelve mating and subsequent births was 103 days.
- Inter-birth Interval: Average inter-birth interval estimated was 21.9 ± 0.594 months, n=7. Observations from other studies document a range of 18–30 months (Schaller, 1967; Sankhala, 1978; Smith, 1984; Sunquist and Sunquist, 2002).
- Mating: Tigers mated throughout the year in Panna. We observed five mating in winter, three in summer, and five in monsoon months.
- Mortality and survival rates: For the entire study period, including a period of heavy poaching, female survival rates were poor compared to other studies (76 per cent). Male and cub survival rates were 86 per cent and 89 per cent. Prior to poaching, female survival rate in Panna was comparable to other studies at 86 per cent.

6

Tiger Society:

Ecological Responses

Home Range and Movement Pattern

The study of an animal's social characteristics, space-use and ranging pattern provides important information regarding its response to the environment and gives us an understanding of its ecological requirements.

In general conversation, 'home range' and 'territory' are terms often used interchangeably, to refer to the area where an animal such as the tiger lives. However, in biological sciences the two terms have very different meanings. 'Territory' is defined as an exclusive-use area fully defended by the dominant individual. The home range, on the other hand, is an area that may be shared, either partially or completely, with other animals. Whether male tigers have territories or home ranges is a matter up for debate. My study provides an interesting view on this question, which I shall discuss later in this chapter.

Many authors have tried to define the concept of home range (Burt, 1943; Mohr, 1947; Baker, 1978; Dixon and Chapman, 1980; Anderson, 1982; Worton, 1989). Essentially, it is the area wherein each individual resides and operates. In simpler terms, the home range of an animal can be defined as the area that it occupies to carry out its daily activities and which fulfils its energy requirements (Burt, 1943; Jewell, 1966). An animal does not roam at random in this area, as we will see later.

The range size has been found to vary with the body size, energy requirements and sex of the individual, as also with the habitat type, food available and its distribution, and population density (McNab, 1963; Harestad and Bunnell, 1979; Lindstedt et al., 1986; Litvaitis et al., 1986; Zabel et al., 1995; Benson et al., 2006).

The size of the tiger's home range and the resulting density of tigers can be related to habitat quality and the availability and dispersion of key resources (prey, water, cover, shelter, etc.). In prime habitats, which contain a high abundance and variety of ungulate prey base, the home range of a female tiger can be twenty square kilometres, or even less, as can be seen in Chitwan, Kanha and Nagarahole (Sunquist, 1981; Smith, 1993; Karanth and Sunquist, 2000; Sharma et al., 2010). In the Russian Far East, where resources can vary seasonally and prey availability is low, a female requires an area of 250–400 km^2 to fulfil her ecological requirements (Goodrich et al., 2010). It is essential, therefore, for the management to know the ecological requirements of tigers for different habitats.

An animal may not patrol all of its home range regularly. There may be some areas that it visits frequently and others only occasionally. These high-activity centres are of significance for the management of tiger populations, as the reproductive success, abundance and viability of a population is largely dependent on the size and health of these critical habitats. Therefore, for successful conservation of the species, the management must provide the required space for a viable population, to match its ecological needs. Any mismatch between the needs and actual availability of space can lead to serious consequences. In this chapter, we will discuss a tiger's space need in a Tropical Dry Forest.

Beep-Beep, Tigers!

Like most other cats, the tiger is an elusive animal and it is not always possible to see it in the wild. This is because the tiger is a predator—they do not like to advertise their presence. This is one of the primary reasons why tigers are so difficult to study in the wild. How do we then gather crucial information on resource use and home ranges?

Even when an animal is observed, it does not reveal a great deal. Furthermore, a tiger may be sighted at some places more frequently, not because it uses that area more often, but due to better visibility, easy access or important resources like water. Such intermittent glimpses can give rise to faulty interpretations. To truly understand an animal's behaviour one needs to gather information in a systematic and unbiased manner. To achieve this one needs to be able to track an identified tiger over a period of time. This is not possible without the help of technology such as radio telemetry. With a radio-transmitter fitted onto a collar, which is placed on the animal, one can be in regular touch through the beeping radio signals. A radio-tagged tiger can be located as and when required. The idea of a beeping tiger may sound horrendous. Many people find it distasteful—a collar on wild animals looks awkward and inappropriate. I sympathize with this view but also appreciate the need for collars.

One such reaction that touched me the most was from a man I met who had encountered Madla (or M-125) while ferrying his milk produce through the forest on his bicycle. He was shocked to see a collar on the 'Raja'. He could not believe that someone could place a collar on the king he knew. The incident really shook him, perhaps tainting his image of the invincible Raja. I took time off from my monitoring to explain to him at length that our purpose putting the collar on the animal was to study the tiger and to ensure the best living conditions for it. It was not difficult to convince him and he understood and appreciated our work, over just a cup of tea.

However, among the more elite crowd in the cities, there was not always such understanding. Their imaginations quite often ran wild. Once, some people argued that our collar was disorienting the male and affecting his behaviour. This was the time when cell phones had just arrived in the country and the ill-effects of electromagnetic radiation were in the news. I was hard put to convince these acquaintances in Delhi, some of whom were highly influential people. It was very frustrating because no amount of evidence was enough to talk them out of their negative convictions. Eventually, I realized that this was taking too much time. I never did get my permission to put radio-collars on tigers in one go. Permissions came in batches; once I had utilised one permission, I had to start the process again. The 'process' involves applying to the state government for permission to radio-collar; the state government would in turn seek clearance from the federal government. Only after receiving a positive response from the federal government would the state government grant me the permission. The same process had to be gone through for replacing the collar, which was considered a new capture. Therefore, I was wary of any controversy, which could have derailed or delayed the permission. Once I lost an entire year due to such a circumstance.

In most cases, attachment of the collar is temporary. At the most, it is placed on the animal for a few years. It is true that if placed incorrectly, collars can cause minor injuries. When loosely placed, it will move too much and chafe against the fur and skin of the animal, causing lacerations. If placed too tightly, especially on a young, growing individual, it could pose a serious threat when it outgrows the collar. Therefore, one must be very careful when placing the collar. I have witnessed many instances where collars were placed loosely and they came off within a few days. The right technique comes with experience.

When placed correctly, it does not seem to bother the tigers. I have spent many years with radio-collared tigers and have never seen anything to suggest that this foreign object bothered them. This holds true for most carnivores. I would not say the same for ungulates. Their necks are a different shape and require a completely different shape for the collar.

I understand the sentiments against the use of this technology, but one must also look at the benefits it provides. Regular monitoring of radio-collared animals does provide security to free-ranging wild animals that other systems cannot (the example of Panna both before and after the tiger extinction corroborates this). More than this security, the kind of information it generates is important as it can save many more tigers by helping us understand tiger needs better and in a reliable way.

It is argued that collaring is an 'intrusive' approach. I completely disagree with this claim. In fact, when used properly, collaring is the least intrusive way to gather information. How so? If I want to study tigers without a radio-collar, I would need to find the animal on a regular basis. This would require much more movement into its domain on my part. Such intense search operations are bound to cause disturbances. Additionally, large amounts of time would need to be spent with the animal to keep a detailed record.

All this would be far more intrusive to the animal than placing a collar once, before letting it go free and collecting data from a distance. Once a radio-collar is placed, we can follow the animal and collect all the required information remotely or after the animal has moved away from the area. Most of the time, we do not have to physically observe the radio-tagged animal for weeks. He or she is free to carry on its daily life, undisturbed by the observer.

It is the triangulation technique of radio-telemetry that allows us to collect information remotely and reliably (see Figure 6.1). Even our field assistants became experts at it after proper training. There are other telemetry techniques like homing, which rely on locating and sighting the radio-collared animal. It has been employed by many studies in India and requires intensive work in getting close to the radio-tagged animal. In this case, even radio-collaring is intrusive and causes unnecessary disturbance when the same information could be collected reliably, without seeing the animals for weeks. New technology with GPS and satellite telemetry now allow researchers to monitor radio-collared animals more remotely.

Chemical Capture

In Panna we captured tigers twelve times for the purpose of radio-collaring. Seven individual tigers were chemically immobilized, some multiple times. The radio-collaring of tigers was mostly carried out in the winter to avoid the problem of hyperthermia i.e. rise in body temperature that can occur during the hot months.

For capturing and collaring, we tried to locate tigers on a kill. When our field team located the tiger, we approached the area on elephant-back to locate it. Once the tiger was located, our first task was to estimate its body weight and assess the suitability of the area. We considered several aspects before we decided to proceed with tranquillization: is there any precipitous cliff or deep-water pool nearby or the presence of any other tigers in the vicinity? On a few occasions we had to abandon the tranquillization process because these situations can put an individual tiger in danger. Assessing the weight of a tiger is a skill that one learns through experience and it became easier after we had weighed a few tigers. Dr Pradeep K. Malik, a renowned wildlife vet in the country and my colleague from the WII was the lead expert as far as I was concerned. To him every animal is a precious patient and he has an impressive and commendable track record on tranquillizations. I could not have had a better veterinary expert. Whatever the level of expertise, weight assessment is still only an approximation, and gauging body mass is crucial for determining the dosage of the tranquillizer.

The Cocktail

To get the desired sedation, we used a combination of Medetomidine (0.05 mg/kg body weight) with ketamine hydrochloride (3.5 mg/kg body weight).* We knew from existing captive tiger research that the combination of both drugs had worked wonderfully and my expert friends advised me to use it for free-ranging tigers. However, it was only available in Finland and so was expensive and difficult to import. But as the safest and most efficient drug available, it was worth the effort. We were the first to use Medetomidine on wild tigers in India and it really worked beautifully.

For our captures in Panna, I had a team of vets. On several occasions, Dr Malik had also called his veterinary colleagues to assist him. PK Peshin, an anaesthesia specialist for canids and felids from Hisar Agriculture University, took time off from his busy schedule to join the team, and on many occasions Dr Srivastava from the Veterinary College in Jabalpur also assisted us. Dr Malik's team standardized the drug dose and other protocols for the use of Medetomidine, and

* Miller et al., 2003.

thanks to their expertise, the chemical restraining of tigers for radio-collaring purposes went very smoothly in Panna. Details of tigers radio-collared in Panna are given in Table 6.1.

Table 6.1 Details of radio-collared animals at the time of capture and radio-tracking period

Tiger	*Capture Date*	*Age and Sex*	*Weight (kg)*	*Tracking Period*
F-01	09-04-1996	♀ Sub-adult	–	6 months
F-123/118 (Baavan)	27-01-1997 to Nov. 1997 & 2-2000 to 3-2005	♀ 50–55 months	120	71 months Collared thrice
F-111	26-03-1998 to 22-12-2000 & up to 9-2002	♀ 24 months	108	54 months Collared twice
F-120	05-01-1999 to 27-01-2001 & up to12-2002	♀ 32 months	115	46 months Collared twice
M-91	11-04-1996 to 26-10-1998 & up to 5-10-2000	♂ 72 80 months	240+	53 months Collared twice
F-113	21-12-2000 to 10-2002 Collared removed	♀ 56 months	–	22 months
M-125 or Madla	12-01-2002 to 3-2005	♂ 96–100 months	220–230	38 months

Radio Tracking

Radio-collared tigers were tracked with the help of directional H-antenna or Yagi antenna and a portable receiver. With the help of this antenna, the tracking team could ascertain the direction of the source of the signal accurately. The ground-to-ground range for receiving the signals from the radio collars was between 0.9–1.5 km, which went up to two kilometres when standing on top of a four-wheeled vehicle. In case of an elevated vantage point or when on the top of an elephant, the range was even better, up to six kilometres. For this reason we identified many elevated places in the field like hillocks and watch towers, from where the field team could receive the signals efficiently, and marked them as permanent vantage points. We recorded the co-ordinates of these reference points using GPS. GPS machines were rare in those days and even though we had to share ours with several other projects, it made our tracking of radio-collared tigers much easier.

We used trained and domesticated elephants to reach difficult places and approach kill sites when the tiger was still in the vicinity. But most of the tracking was conducted using a four-wheel drive vehicle, a motorcycle or on foot. To reduce our influence on animal behaviour, we estimated the radio-collared animal's location through the triangulation technique. Over 85 per cent of the locations from our tracking were traced using this technique. To obtain accurate estimates and to minimize errors in estimating location of the collared animal, four or five bearings were taken from known reference points using a directional antenna and a handheld compass to decide the direction (Figure 6.1).

To obtain a series of locations ('fixes') of the collared animals we collected data on each animal two-three times a week. The data set recorded by the team in the field included compass bearing pointing towards the source of the signal, x-y coordinates of reference points (geographic location of tracking team), date and time, activity and animal ID. We would take four or five such data sets from different reference points to obtain a single location of a collared tiger. Figure 6.1 explains how triangulation is achieved from these data sets. This field data-set was digitized in a spreadsheet and the animal locations were estimated (triangulation) using a computer program called 'LOAS'. In case of homing, the locations were directly obtained by using the GPS after the animal was physically located and sighted. Home ranges of each tiger were calculated using the Minimum Convex Polygon method to make a comparison with previous studies (Powell, 2000;

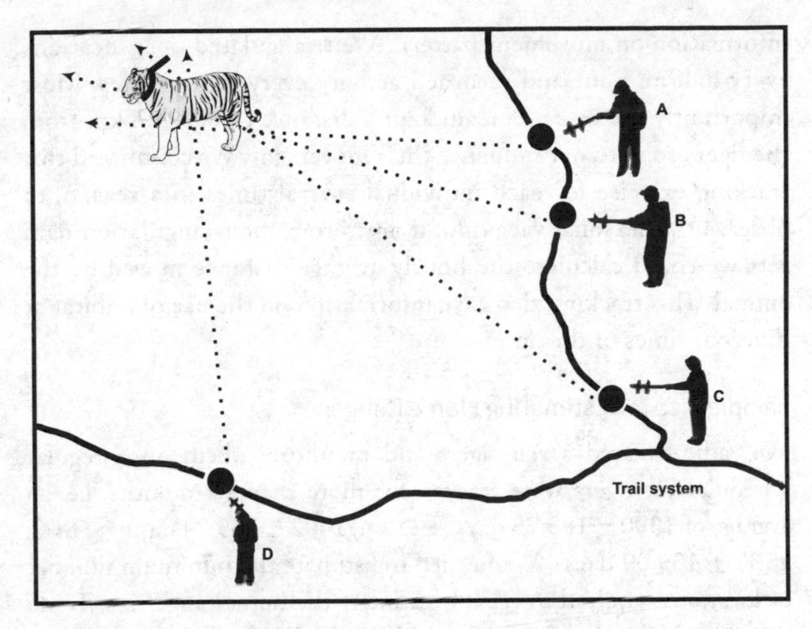

Figure 6.1 How animal locations are obtained by triangulation. Information on x & y coordinates of the reference points A, B, C and D, and the direction of the radio-collared animal from these points is required to estimate animal locations.

White and Garrot, 1990). In this method, the outermost locations are connected to make a polygon and the area of this polygon gives the size of the home range. But we used the fixed kernel estimate for all analyses (Worton, 1989), which is considered a better estimator, using another software called BIOTAS.

Movement Pattern

To find out when the tiger was active, the field team monitored its movement patterns by tracking an individual tiger continuously for twenty-four hours. We were particularly careful at such times to ensure that our presence in no way affected the animal's movement. Any tracking of less than six hours was not included in the analysis. We considered such a sample too small to give appropriate information on movement pattern. We triangulated tiger locations every half an hour and recorded activity every ten minutes. Most importantly the research team kept a distance of 0.8–1.2 km from the tigers so as to not influence their movement. We conducted this tracking exercise for each individual several times in a season, to observe the seasonal variation, if any. From the triangulation data sets we could calculate the hourly average distance moved by the animal. This tracking also gave information on the use of habitat at different times of the day.

Sample Size for Estimating Home Ranges

We radio-collared seven tigers and monitored them on a regular schedule. Six tigers were tracked for more than six months, i.e. an average of 1390 ± 185.75 days (♀: n=4, 1402 ± 265.24 days; ♂: n=2, 1365 ± 159.09 days). We needed to estimate the minimum number of locations required to reliably estimate the home range size. To do this we calculated a series of cumulative home ranges by pooling ten successive locations. We estimated that home ranges of all radio-collared tigers reached asymptotic size after more than fifty locations for females and approximately sixty locations for males. At the rate of two to three locations a week, a minimum of four to five months of monitoring was essential in estimating a reliable home range size. We had enough information to estimate reliable home ranges as we had obtained, on an average, 106 locations (n= 2,553 locations ± 8.23) for radio-collared tigers every year. There was one exception, a sub-adult female F-01, who died within five months of radio-collaring.

Annual Home Ranges

Annual home range is an area that a tiger uses in a year. For the estimation of annual ranges, the year begins on 1 November and ends on 30 October. The annual home ranges of the male tigers were three to four times larger than those of the females (Table 6.2). The average annual range calculated for male tigers was 179.3 ± 11.8 km^2 (95% fixed kernel; n=7). Female ranges were much smaller at 46.6 ± 3.7 km^2 (95% fixed kernel, n=16; not including 2002-03

Table 6.2 Annual home range estimate for individual radio-collared tigers (sq. km) monitored between 1997 and 2005, in Panna Tiger Reserve, India. Figures in parentheses indicate the number of locations.

MCP	*All year Range*	*1997*	*1997–1998*	*1998–1999*	*1999–2000*	*2000–2001*	*2001–2002*	*2002–2003*	*2003–2004*	*Annual mean*	*Std. error*
M-91	260.4	243.8	169.9	113.1	113.6	-	-	-	-	160.1	30.9
	(347)	(97)	(92)	(78)	(80)						
M-125	301.3	-	-	-	-	-	167.4	191.4	136.1	165.0	16.0
	(379)						(102)	(179)	(98)		
F-123	126.0	40.9	-	-	-	31.5	37.3	119.9	53.2	56.6	16.2
	(676)	(161)				(84)	(107)	(212)	(112)		
F-111	79.4		60.7	35.8	40.9	32.4	29.3		-	39.8	5.6
	(426)		(62)	(78)	(118)	(97)	(71)				
F-120	54.8	-	-	30.4	35.5	48.4	32.7	20.9*	-	33.6	4.4
	(494)			(93)	(175)	(99)	(109)	(18)			
F-113	83.6	-	-	-	-	83.6	24.0		-	53.8	29.8
	(231)					(118)	(113)				
Kernel 95%											
M-91	233.2	226.4	148.5	156.2	145.7	-	-	-	-	169.2	19.2
M-125	253.6	-	-	-	-	-	210.7	187.7	180.1	192.8	9.2
F-123	61.5	40.2	-	-	-	44.3	35.6	80.2	58.3	51.7	8.1
F-111	54.6	-	72.5	36.8	42.4	40.4	30.2	-	-	44.4	7.3
F-120	48.6	-	-	36.7	41.1	48.7	41.0	20.6*	-	41.9	2.5
F-113	55.5	-	-	-	-	70.2	26.7	-	-	48.5	21.8

* Not included in average

home range for F-120). These estimates are two to three times larger than previously recorded from other tropical forests like the moist deciduous forests of Kanha, and the terai habitat in Nepal (Schaller, 1967; Sunquist, 1981; Smith, 1984; Karanth and Sunquist, 2000; Sharma et al., 2010).

We also observed that male and female ranges, when estimated from pooling multiple years' data, were significantly larger than the annual ranges estimated (♂ $t = -4.1$, $p=0.01$; ♀ $t= -2.09$, $p= 0.05$). From pooling we estimated that the average home range of male tigers was $\bar{x}= 243.4 \pm 10.2$ km^2, n=2; and that of female tigers was $\bar{x}= 55.0$ km^2 $\pm$ 2.7, n=4.

Similarly, when we estimated the annual home ranges considering the calendar year, i.e. 1 January to 31 December, the home range sizes were usually larger. This happened because a single winter season is split into two separate years. When there is a shift in home ranges, the new area is added in the annual estimates. This not only increases the apparent home range size but also increases the area of overlap between neighbouring home ranges.

To avoid splitting the winter season, we calculated our year from November (beginning of winter in Panna) to 31 October (end of monsoon).

Most importantly, we noticed that tiger ranges are so large that they all either extended up to or beyond the tiger Reserve boundary. Boundaries of Protected Areas create an edge between protected and unprotected habitat (Chundawat et al., 2016). This edge is an area where the tiger is in conflict with humans. To quantify the exposure of radio-collared tigers to the ill effects and anthropogenic edge-effects that prevail at the boundary, we considered a zone of influence of the edge that can potentially occur within the boundary also. Several studies have estimated the zone of impact of human disturbance on wildlife habitat, and some suggest that this indiscernible zone of impact may extend up to four kilometres from the boundary of the protected area (Karanth et al., 2006; Jotikapukkana et al., 2010; Thapa and Chapman, 2010). Typically, it declines with distance from the periphery towards the core of the PA. We created a highly conservative inward buffer of one kilometre from the Reserve boundary. We overlaid home ranges on the protected area boundary with zone of edge effect and calculated the length of the home range boundary that is intersected by this zone of influence. We also estimated the proportion of the tigers' home range perimeter that fell within this zone of influence. With these two indices, we highlight the level of exposure to edge effects both within the tiger Reserve as well as beyond its boundaries.

We found that all the radio-collared tigers were exposed to edge-effects (Figure 6.2). The average length of the PA boundary which intersected the home ranges of radio-collared tigers was 44 ± 6.7 km for males and 6.7 ± 1.64 km for females. On average 42 ± 6.1% of the perimeter of individual home ranges overlapped with the one-kilometre zone of influence of the edge and unprotected habitat outside the boundary.

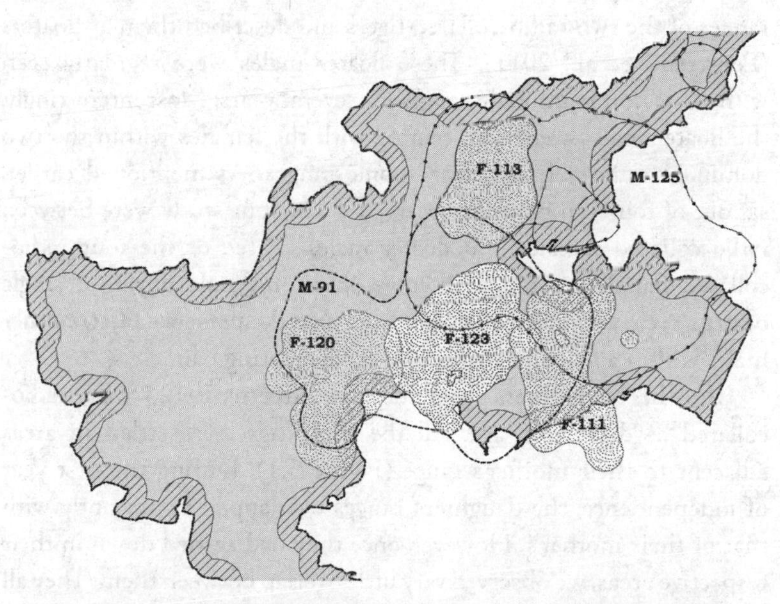

Figure 6.2 The hatched area 1 km inside the Tiger Reserve boundary depicts the zone of high anthropogenic pressure. Home ranges of radio-collared tigers show exposure to this area , a phenomenon known as the 'Edge Effect'.

Home Range Overlaps

Similar to previous studies (Sunquist, 1981; Smith et al., 1987; Goodrich et al., 2010), we found that home ranges of the two radio-collared male tigers overlapped with the ranges of three or four females' ranges (radio-collared as well as non-radio-collared). The average overlap between home ranges of sympatric females and dominant male tigers was small—61.0 ± 5.7%, n=9—when compared with estimates from other studies (Goodrich et al., 2010). We also found that adult female home ranges overlapped very little with the neighbouring female ranges—3.0 ± 1.5%, n=6.

Unlike females, we were unable to radio-collar more than one male at a time. We identified two dominant male territories within the study area but we could never radio-collar both during the same year. We observed the presence of two or three known adult males within the ranges of the two radio-collared tigers and described them as floaters (Penteriani et al., 2011). These floater males were regularly seen within the dominant male ranges for several years. Most interestingly, the floater males were seen mating with the females within the two dominant radio-collared tigers' home ranges. As mentioned earlier, six out of fourteen matings observed during our study were between radio-collared females and floater males. Three of the four radio-collared females mated with more than one male during a single oestrus cycle and on two occasions we saw the presence of two other males within a few hundred metres of the mating pair.

The three daughters from the first litter of F-123 were radio-collared at dispersing age. All the three tigresses settled in areas adjacent to their mother's range (Figure 5.1). During the first year of independence, the daughters' ranges overlapped significantly with that of their mother's. However, once they had settled down in their respective areas, we observed very little overlap between them. They all defended their areas assertively and demonstrated intensive marking and vocalization in the areas abutting the other female ranges.

Within the overlap area, home-range boundaries tended to shift on an annual basis. This was very obvious for male tigers, though not demonstrable, since we were unable to radio-collar two dominant males in the same year. We did confirm a similar trend for several female tigers. During our field monitoring of radio-collared tigers we observed almost no overlaps. However, when we calculated overlap using home ranges plotted over several years, the result was surprisingly large. This was a methodological problem and, realizing the distorted picture it presented, we shifted to estimation of home ranges on an annual basis by defining the year. This way the data set accurately reflected our field observations.

Core Areas

On an average, the core area, i.e. the area with the most activity, remained limited to about 30 per cent of the average annual home range (a 70% kernel estimator was used to define the core area). The core area remained more or less consistent for several years for both sexes, despite considerable variations in the outer boundaries of their annual home ranges. Shifts in the core areas were seen only in cases where an entirely new territory or part of it was taken over by an individual. Consistency in use of the core indicates a strong site fidelity in both male and female territorial tigers. Both radio-collared males showed a similar pattern. After the death of M-91, Hairy Foot took over M-91's range but after Hairy Foot's death, no new male moved into its range immediately. M-125 gradually moved into this area, vacating his old range.

Home-Range Expansions, Shifts and Contractions

Annual home ranges of each individual varied greatly in size, between years (ranging between 8% for M-125 to 63% for F-113). These variations indicate that there were range shifts, expansions and contractions of home ranges. For example, radio-collared M-91 was ranging widely (226 km^2, 95% fixed kernel) and covered most of the Reserve in 1997. In 1998–99 a new male, M-125 (radio-collared in

2001), appeared and challenged the established M-91, defeating and acquiring a large part its range after a series of fights. In one of these fights, both males sustained injuries and M-91's collar was damaged. This collar was replaced and he was treated for his injuries. After this fight, his range reduced to 148 km^2 (Table 6.2 and Figure 6.3). In 2001, M-91 was fully displaced by another new male (Hairy Foot), who acquired his entire remaining territory. This new male died soon after, in the summer of 2003. M-125 moved in to occupy the space created by this male's death, vacating its old range. M-125's old range was soon occupied by one of the floater males.

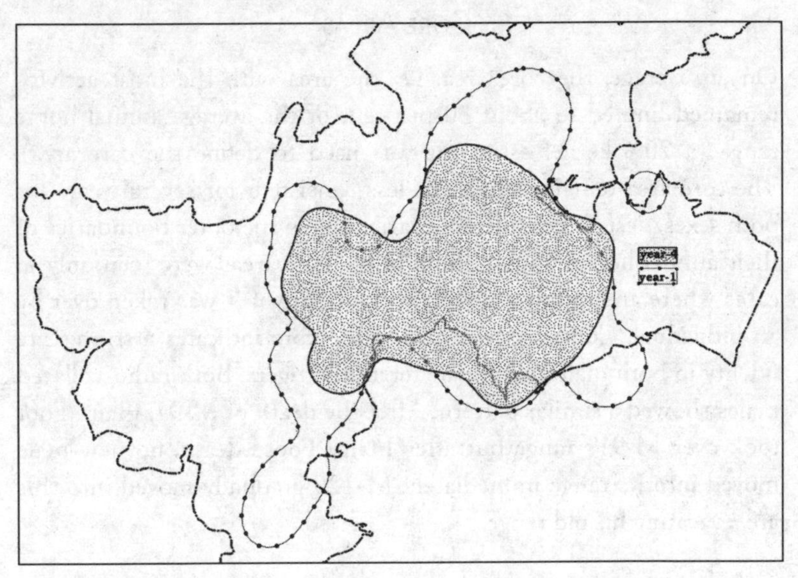

Figure 6.3 Range contraction of M-91 after it had a fight with M-125 in 1997–98.

Three female siblings of the first litter of F-123 established their territories adjacent to their mother after dispersing from their natal area (Figure 5.2). But we witnessed no range contraction in F-123's home-range as a result of her daughters establishing territories (Table 6.2). Two siblings, F-120 and F-113, formed a coalition for the first seven-eight months, together displacing a neighbouring female. In

2003–2004, F-123's range expanded three times, from 35.59 km^2 to 80.15 km^2, into the vacant spaces created due to the poaching of the neighbouring territorial females, i.e. her daughters F-111, F-120 and F-113 (Figure 6.4).

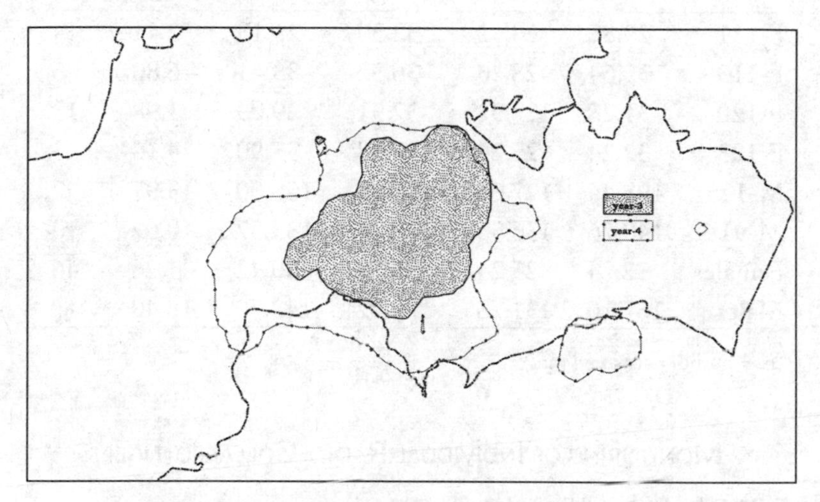

Figure 6.4 Expansion of the range of F-123 in 2002-03 after the deaths of her two neighbours, F-111 and F 120.

Seasonal Home Ranges

Seasonal home range sizes were smaller, representing 65 per cent of the annual home ranges for females and 82 per cent for males (Table 6.3). Summer ranges were the smallest for females whose ranges reduced to almost 55 per cent of the average total area. Male summer ranges were also small but only marginally—no clear trend was apparent in male seasonal ranges like in the females. The seasonal range of female tigers varied considerably and we recorded female ranges dropping down to 30 per cent of the average annual range. Such small seasonal ranges, however, mostly coincided with a litter, when female movement was restricted rather than with any particular season.

Table 6.3 Average seasonal home range (in sq. km) of individual radio-collared tigers and the average for males and females.

Tiger	*Winter*	*Summer*	*Monsoon*	*Average*	*St. Error of Avg.*	*n**
F-111	29.82	24.52	32.50	29.18	2.41	14
F-113	35.64	28.26	36.32	33.41	6.80	6
F-120	31.28	22.92	32.51	29.09	1.98	13
F-123	32.24	25.24	33.78	37.90	4.10	13
M-125	193.44	127.00	138.10	158.00	13.97	7
M-91	140.76	136.55	120.34	133.37	10.62	10
Females	32.24	25.24	33.78	30.42	1.26	46
Males	167.10	131.78	129.22	142.70	18.40	17

* n = number seasonal ranges

Monitoring of Individual Radio-Collared Tigers

F-01 (The Bargadi Female's Daughter)

One of the Bargadi female's sub-adult female cubs was radio-collared in April 1996 and tracked till September 1996. At the time of collaring we estimated her age to be eighteen to twenty months. This dispersing sub-adult female was in the process of leaving the natal area and establishing her territory. Initially, she remained within the Bargadi area where she was radio-collared, but later she moved into a deep gorge near Jhalariya five or six kilometres away. After settling down in the valley she was mostly found in its vicinity. Our team located her here on a couple of livestock kills. After radio-collaring she was never sighted with other individuals. During this period she made a few forays and there were occasions when the research team was unable to locate her. Once, in the last week of June, she was spotted near the Sankaro area along the Ken river, approximately seven or eight kilometres from her usual area. The next day, she was located in the nearby area of Bhorgadh, ahead of the Sakara village. These locations suggested that she was still exploring areas around her temporary home range. Subsequently, she was located in her most frequented area, i.e. around Jhalariya. Twice, despite all our attempts, we lost contact with F-01 for several days. Once, we couldn't locate her for eleven days and, on the twelfth day, we found her again near Jhalaria. Another time during tracking, she was not located for three or four days. In July, our regular tracking was interrupted due to heavy monsoon showers and poor access to the area. This was the most crucial and vulnerable period for a dispersing individual like F-01. We tracked her for thirty-nine days, out of which locations were obtained on twenty-three days. Only the first location of the day was used to estimate the home range. The home range size of F-01 was estimated at 31 km^2. However, 90 per cent of her locations were within an area of 9.8 km^2. This suggests that she was using the area around Jhalariya the most. Her movements, in areas outside the core 9.8 km^2, were not regular and she must have covered these during her occasional forays outside. She was found dead on 16 September 1996 with two livestock kills. There was no conclusive evidence but suspicion pointed towards poisoning.

We were unable to reach the kill site in time for inspection. Getting instant access to tigers' kills is crucial to monitoring any foul play. To ensure this, the Field Director, PK Chawdhary, henceforth gave us full access to elephants for monitoring the radio-collared tigers. This provision was key to the success story that Panna witnessed from 1996 to 2002. In fact, with the elephants, we actually found a few poisoned carcasses, which were removed and burnt. This sent a clear message to the locals that if kills were poisoned, the authorities would find out and the culprits would be caught and punished. From 1997 onwards, we did not record any more suspicious kills. The verification of the kills of breeding tigers at the earliest was a crucial factor in the recovery of the tiger population. This protocol was completely upended in 2002, when our monitoring of kills was disrupted by the new management. As a result, we started losing breeding tigers on a regular basis; once again tiger numbers fell and finally Panna witnessed a local extinction.

F-123

Tigress F-123 (also known as F-90, F-118, and Baavan or 'fifty-two') was radio-collared for the first time in January 1997 (Table 6.1) and was monitored continuously for eleven months with the first radio-collar. Figure 6.5 shows her ranges from 1997 to 2005. Her first collar stopped functioning in November 1997 (Table 6.4). After this malfunctioning, our research team could only monitor her sporadically, in a limited way. After several attempts to replace her old collar, finally, after almost thirty-nine months, her collar was replaced on 26 February 2001. But this second collar too did not last long. She lost it while dragging a sambar kill on 25 December 2001. The collar got hooked to a tree trunk and broke off. This took place while our research team was watching her. This time we promptly replaced her collar within a month, on 12 January 2002. Luckily, this one lasted longer, continuing to work for over three years. Her last radio-location was recorded by us in March 2005 (a total of thirty-eight months' observations for the last collar). She was photographed by the WII research team via camera trap in April 2006.

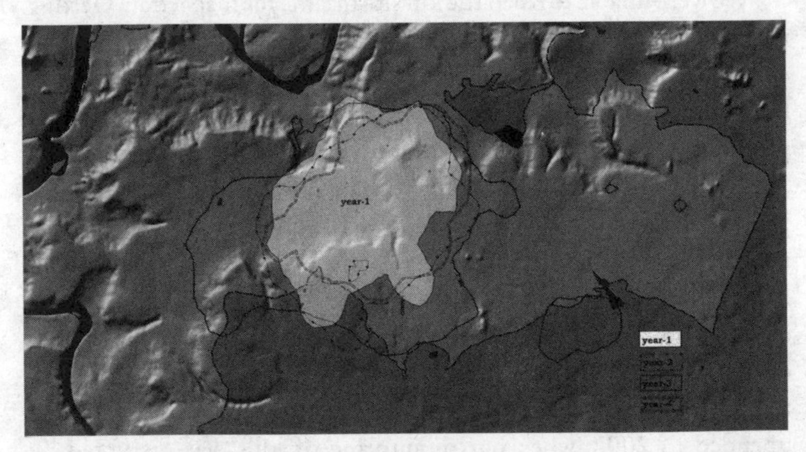

Figure 6.5 Annual Ranges of tiger F-123.

F-123 was raising a litter of three sever- or eight-month-old female cubs (an estimated age assuming that they were born around April–May 1996), when she was collared for the first time. Prior to this, we had seen her courting and mating with the dominant male tiger M-91 in February 1996. In the period between the first and second collaring (spanning over three years), F-123 mated with M-91 in November 1997—just a few days before her first radio-collar stopped working. She later had a second litter—two male cubs—in February 1998. These, like the first one, survived to adulthood and dispersed. We

Table 6.4 Details of significant events observed during the monitoring of F-123

Date	*Month*	*Major events*
Jan-96	0	First sighting
Feb-96	1	Mating with M-91
Apr-96	3	Litter-I (3)
Jan-97	12	First collar
Nov-97	22	Mating with M-91; collar malfunction
Feb-98	25	Litter-II (2)
Aug-99	13	Mating with M-91
Nov-99	47	Litter-III (3)
Feb 01	61	Second collar
May-01	64	Mating with Hairy Foot
Sep-01	68	Litter-IV (3)
Dec-01	71	Collar lost
Jan-02	72	Third collar
Oct-02	81	One cub lost
Feb-03	85	Mating with Hairy Foot
Jun-03	89	Litter-V?
Jul-03	90	Mating with M-125 and floater male
Dec-03	95	Litter-VI?
Mar-04	98	Mating with M-125; +floater male
Apr-04	99	Mating with M-125
May-05	112	No monitoring
Apr-06	124	Photo–WII camera trap

continued to find these grown-up and independent cubs in the natal area, even when F-123 was raising her third litter. We did not observe any conflict within the family. We also did not observe any interaction with the new family. They would disappear for months and reappear for short periods. The last time that I saw one of the cubs was when it was over three years old.

Baavan (F-123) was seen mating with M-91 for the third time in August 1999. By the time we radio-collared her for the second time (2001), she was raising her third litter of three cubs, comprising two males and one female. These cubs were almost fifteen months old at the time of her collaring. Her third litter also survived till adulthood and dispersed successfully. Her fourth mating was with Hairy Foot, the new male who had taken over from M-91. She gave birth to her fourth litter, again two males and one female, in September 2001. In October 2002, one of her male cubs was seen limping, apparently with an injury to one of its legs. We suspect that it may have died due to this injury, as we did not see it again. The cubs were about thirteen months old at this time. Our systematic monitoring of F-123 continued until March–April 2003. But then, the Forest Department imposed certain restrictions that meant we could not monitor her as regularly as we had done previously. Our monitoring was henceforth confined to locating animals only during the daytime and from our vehicle. As a result, we could not collect all the important associated information requiring us to visit locations away from the roads.

Despite this limitation, we witnessed some very unusual happenings. Things were not normal at all by mid-2003—the floater males, who had so far been shy and were spotted rarely, became visible and were sighted regularly. In June 2003, F-123's behaviour suggested that she had given birth to a fifth litter. She remained confined to a cave under a huge escarpment and dried-up waterfall (Dhundwa seha) from 7 June to 10 July 2003. We were able to observe her a few times from the top of the escarpment, when she came out and lay in the open. It was obvious from her teats that she had given birth to a litter. Although we occasionally heard the cubs' cries, we never managed to get visual confirmation. We were also hampered by the movement restrictions imposed on us. We are not sure about what exactly happened to these cubs, but we suspect that this fifth litter did not survive long.

Infanticide was a possibility, because Hairy Foot, the dominant male of the area and the likely father, had been found dead in June 2003. Since his death, a few adult males were regularly seen in the area, but there was no apparent evidence to suggest infanticide. We were pretty sure that it was not M-125, because he was radio-collared and we were still monitoring his movements. But there were other males, any of whom could have been the culprit.

We were more inclined to think that she lost her cubs to another catastrophe. We were concerned about her choice of litter site from the beginning—it was in a gorge next to a huge eighty-metre-high waterfall. This site was very prone to flooding—if there had been a flash flood due to early monsoon, she would not have had time to rescue her litter. We believe that this is most likely what happened. The first shower that year was heavy and was followed by a huge flash flood. I was not there at the time, but our research team believes that Baavan lost her fifth litter in this flood because she was still there when it came.

What followed after this episode was very unusual. The dominant male, M-125, appeared on the scene and proceeded to mate with F-123 within two weeks of her coming out of the gorge. We located her outside the gorge on 10 July 2003. If she were still suckling, it would have been physiologically impossible (under normal circumstances) for her to come into oestrus in less than two weeks and to mate reproductively. The mating association went on for seven days. This was the longest mating episode with one male that we observed in Panna (from 19 July to 24 July 2003). Another interesting observation was that during this mating, the presence of two other adult male tigers was also recorded by the research team. One of these tigers, as soon as M-125 left the female, approached her several times, following her for hours. Unfortunately, the new restrictions on movement within the park hampered our observations. We were unable to identify this male without access to an elephant, and with limited hours in the day for observation, we could not get a clear view or photographic opportunity. Therefore, we could not collect all the details of what occurred after we left the scene, but we did see that Baavan was not very friendly to this new male. As far as we know, she did not mate with him. Our monitoring in the following months became very irregular as we struggled with newer restrictions that were imposed on us every few weeks.

Baavan's movement pattern in December 2003 indicated, once again, that she might have given birth to a sixth litter. However, this could not be confirmed. Whether the cubs survived or not, we don't know, but what followed in March and April 2004 was even more puzzling. We located M-125 and Baavan together again for five days. A day later, she was seen with Broken Tooth, another known floater male. In April, we saw Baavan with M-125 again, for several days. Such associations of female tigers with different adult males were common in Panna (e.g. F-113 and F-111). It was the repeated associations and mating with adult males that were puzzling. However, they happened with enough regularity throughout the study period to impel us to question the concept of the male tigers' exclusive territory and dominance, and view it from a different perspective.

The death of Hairy Foot in a short time period had unsettled the well-established hierarchy. Unfortunately M-125, who had been the dominant male for some time, was by now past his prime, and the two young males we knew well started to assert themselves; the fact that one was F-123's son from her third litter added complexity to the entire situation.

We were never sure whether Baavan gave birth to a sixth litter or not because at this time our research permissions to conduct fieldwork were cancelled and we were banned from entering the Reserve. But the research team from the WII, which was sent to assess the tiger status, did see a female with two cubs in 2005. However, they could not confirm the ID of the mother.

After April 2004, we had no access to the park and our information from this month onward was based on secondary sources. Therefore, we do not have full details about Baavan, despite the fact that her collar was still working. To the best of our knowledge, she gave birth to five litters comprising at least eleven cubs during our nine years of monitoring. We recorded only one mortality, a three-month-old cub, but we believe she lost an entire litter (most probably her last). The regularity of her mating (with gaps of 19, 18, 18 and 17 months) and littering was quite amazing. The cubs were born at regular intervals (of 22, 22, 22 and 21 months) when things were fine and there existed a harmony in the social organization. By 2006, she was approaching her sixteenth year and she could have died a natural death but we will never know. Despite this setback, she was the most productive female in Panna, raising ten tigers to adulthood successfully.

F-123 occupied an undisturbed and high prey-density habitat in the core area of the park. The mean annual home-range for this tigress was 51.72 km^2 (n=5; ±8.06). The mean annual home range of her first three years' annual range estimate provided a comparably better estimate (40.05 km^2) with other tigresses. In 2002–04, she started to range widely after the death of her two neighbours—tigresses F-111 and F-120. Her range went up to 80 km^2 in 2002–03 and 58 km^2 in 2003–04 by encompassing most of their ranges. This was a strong indication of the decline in population. We later observed (from camera trap photographs) that the female cub from her last surviving litter had started to use a part of the adjoining area earlier occupied by F-120. Later, she expanded her range into F-113's area after she too disappeared in 2004. At this time in Panna, there were just a couple of adult females present in the park, but the census conducted by the Reserve authority in 2004 and 2005 reported more than twenty-three tigresses in the same area. One could not get more ridiculous than identifying such a high number within the two known female territories. We used to joke that tigers in Panna lived in multi-storey buildings. I will discuss this controversial census in greater detail in Chapter 11, where I will be analyzing why we lost tigers in Panna.

Baavan's core area of 18.81 km^2, where she spent over 70 per cent of her time, represented only 31 per cent of her entire range. This core never overlapped with neighbouring territories. Her neighbours were her daughters from her first litter. However, we did not see any association between them after they became independent and established their separate territories. There were large overlaps with the daughters' ranges only during the process of dispersal. This is the time when young females explored the neighbouring areas and continued to come back to the natal range regularly. But once her daughters had established territories, the overlap disappeared. Generally, a contraction in the home range of a mother is recorded in such circumstances (Sunquist, 1981; Smith et al., 1987; Goodrich et al., 2010). In Panna, the home range estimate using the MCP estimator shows a similar pattern, though only marginally. However a better estimate, like the kernel, does not show such a contraction.

F-111

F-111 (or F-189, as she was referred to in earlier publications and reports, when she had a different collar) was one of the three siblings of the first litter of F-123. She was first radio-collared in late March 1998, when she was in the process of dispersing (Table 6.5). This happened when, as recounted in the previous chapter, she was accidentally caught in a leg-hold snare set up for sloth bears by K Yoganand. She was the first sibling to become independent and her early collaring enabled our research team to observe her frequently and collect some very crucial information on dispersing individual behaviour. Her annual ranges are shown in Figure 6.6.

Table 6.5 Details of significant events observed during the monitoring of F-111

Date	*Month*	*Major events*
Apr-96	0	Birth
Mar-98	23	First collar
Feb-99	34	Mating with M-91
Jun-99	38	Litter-I (2)
Dec-00	56	Mating with Hairy Foot & second collar
Mar-01	60	Litter-II (3)
Jun-01	62	One cub dead
Aug-02	76	Mating with M-125
Sep-02	77	Mating with floater male
Oct-02	78	Went missing

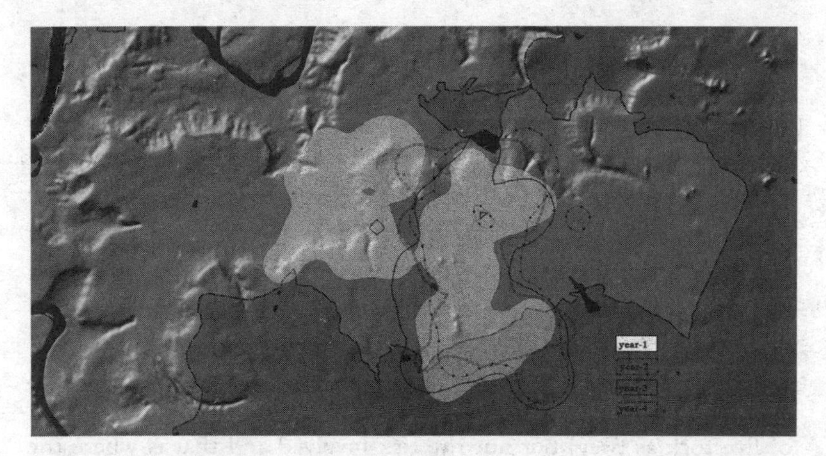

Figure 6.6 Annual ranges of tiger F-111.

The early collaring of F-111 helped us observe some very interesting dispersing behaviour in detail and we were able to witness her first kill when she was about nineteen months old. At this time she was still moving within her mother's range. By the time she was twenty-two months, she had started making forays far away from her natal range. Before this she made several kills within her natal range, and it was interesting to see how differently she behaved when she had made her own kill and when she shared one made by her mother. Over her own kills, she was very possessive and would fight off her siblings and mother aggressively. Even our approach on elephants was not tolerated. On other occasions, we could get much closer to her on elephant-back. Observations on her at this stage of her life and on other dispersing individuals led us to a proper understanding of the dynamics of cub independence and dispersal. We could gain this understanding thanks to observations made possible by radio–telemetry. These behaviour observations indicate that it is not the mother chasing out her offspring so much as the offspring refusing to share their kills and seizing independence. The more kills they made, the more time they spent alone and the more independent they became.

F-111 stayed in her natal area for several months during the summer of 1998, before establishing her own territory on the upper

Talgaon plateau. After six or seven months and several forays in the area, she finally moved into the region immediately southeast of her mother's range during the monsoon months of 1998. By the end of the monsoon, she was permanently settled in the area. Her territory extended for three to four kilometres beyond the Reserve boundary, into the neighbouring non-protected forests of South Panna Forest Division (Figure 5.2). This was not protected tiger habitat but it had good forest-cover and thick undergrowth, mainly created by the invasive exotic bush, lantana. Prey density was the not the best here but there was a high livestock presence. When exploring or using an area, tigers can only assess its quality (good forest cover, plenty of livestock as prey) but not the risk involved and that is where the problem lies in the buffer areas.

Her range fell within her father M-91's territory and she mated with him in February 1999, at an age of almost thirty-six months. Her first litter of two cubs—one male and one female—was born in June 1999, when she was over thirty-eight months. The first sighting of her cubs was when they were over three weeks old. Her second mating was with Hairy Foot (the new male who replaced the father M-91) in December 2001. She gave birth to her second litter three months later, in March 2001. The interval between the two litters was twenty-two months. The second litter comprised three cubs but our research team was not able to identify the sex of these cubs early on. Both times she gave birth in different caves at the base of an escarpment. So we could observe the cubs from a distance but it was too far to ascertain their sex. We put in extra effort to determine the sexes of her second litter but failed. This was because the cubs rarely emerged from the cave during the daytime. When they did come out it was in the weak light of very early morning for a brief time. In a few weeks she moved cubs to a new location and it was difficult for us to see them.

Later, F-111 was seen mating with M-125 in late August 2002, after a gap of approximately twenty-one months. Shortly after this (within a month) she was again seen mating with her half-brother, a floater we called 'Sixty-two'. He was the male cub from F-123's third litter. Sadly, F-111 disappeared before she was able to have her third family.

F-111 occupied an area close to the periphery of the Reserve around several villages situated inside and at its edges. We lost her in October 2002. Her last location was recorded on a buffalo kill, from where she mysteriously disappeared after feeding for a couple days. At first we thought she had left the kill, because tigers occasionally get disturbed by graziers, especially when a buffalo is killed. But we could not track her despite searching in each spot she was likely to be. Our first reaction was to assume that her collar had malfunctioned. It had happened once earlier, in the case of F-123. So we decided to confirm her presence by placing camera traps and monitoring her frequently used areas, along with looking for other indirect evidence. After a month of intensive monitoring, we failed to find any evidence. However, within this month, we found the area occupied by another tigress whom we christened the 'Amdar female' (she had come from the Amdar area). Much later, we saw this tigress mating with M-125 and she continued to include this area in her range (Figure 5.1).

The fact that a new female had moved into the area made us suspect that F-111 may have died. Since she disappeared from a cattle kill, it was reasonable to assume that she may have fallen victim to a human-caused mortality. We deeply regretted not investigating the kill site for any such evidence. At the time, we never imagined that something like this could happen. Panna had been free of poaching for many years. Another reason was the lack of access to an elephant—the only safe way to approach a tiger on a kill in the jungle early on. Earlier, when we could use an elephant on request, we investigated and monitored every kill, and always reached it first. This kind of monitoring provided security for the tiger from human-caused mortalities. In the early years of the study, the park managers recognized the synergy between our actions and their protection efforts. However, subsequent managers restricted the availability of elephants for research monitoring, so we had to adapt a new strategy: visiting the kill site two or three days after the tiger had moved away from it. In this case, we only came back after a week because we were busy trying to establish her location. Unfortunately, this was too late to detect any foul play and I still regret it. After this incident, I tried to explain to the Forest Department how seriously our monitoring and research was hampered by the lack of an elephant and the dangers of this to the tiger. Unfortunately, this elicited a contrary reaction from the park officials and we lost more freedom of movement instead.

When I first investigated F-111's kill site a few days later, we were actually looking for fresh signs of her because we believed that she was still around and only her collar had stopped functioning. I remember seeing the shoe marks of two persons near the kill. By then, the kill site was a week old, so we thought it was likely that some villagers had come across the buffalo kill in between. The possibility of poaching was overlooked. At this time, in 2002, Panna was at the peak of tiger density—the population had been growing steadily since the start of the study. Everyone was feeling positive and poaching was far from our minds. How wrong we were! The success of the population recovery blinded us to the possibility of a poaching crisis. In this positive cocoon around us, we were not overly worried because a new female had occupied the area. However, we had a second setback barely two months later, in December 2002, when we lost her sibling F-120. We did not realize then that this was the beginning of the end of Panna's tigers. I still get goosebumps going down memory lane. It is disturbing to see, in the light of these two incidents, the disappearance of F-111 and the death of F-120, that however well protected, no tiger population is safe from poaching.

F-111 was radio-tracked for fifty-five months (just over 4.5 years). Her average annual range was 42.42 km^2 (n=5; ±=4.7) and most of her activity (70 per cent) was restricted within 33 per cent of her range on the upper Talgaon plateau (Table 6.2). Her seasonal ranges were almost 30 per cent smaller than the average annual range. The area used by her had low wild prey abundance but very high cattle presence. Most of her kills were cattle. During the hot summer months, when there was no undisturbed water available within her territory on the upper plateau inside the Reserve, she had to come either to the Hinauta (lower) plateau to the pools at the base of the escarpment in search of cool resting places and water, or she had to visit a watering hole more than three kilometres outside the Reserve boundary. She regularly killed livestock in the latter area. This brought her into direct conflict with the local human population.

F-120

F-120 or 'Sayani', a sibling of F-111 and F-113, was radio-collared in January 1999, when she was approximately thirty-two months old. However we had been lucky enough to be able to monitor her quite regularly even before this. Her annual home ranges are shown in Figure 6.7. At the time of collaring, she was busy establishing her territory in the area west of her mother's, which she occupied by displacing an old territorial female from the area. The original occupier was the Bargadi female, the mother of F-01. The Bargadi female was a tigress past her prime when we first met her and had already lost one of her canines along with a claw on her front foot. F-120 was able to displace the Bargadi female with the help of her third sibling, F-113. These two siblings formed a coalition for eight or nine months between September 1998 and February 1999. At the time of collaring, F-120 was still accompanied by F-113 and she remained in association with her for a few months. We saw both regularly and since they were not very shy, we had several opportunities to observe their movement on a regular basis. We saw F-120 on a kill with F-113 many times.

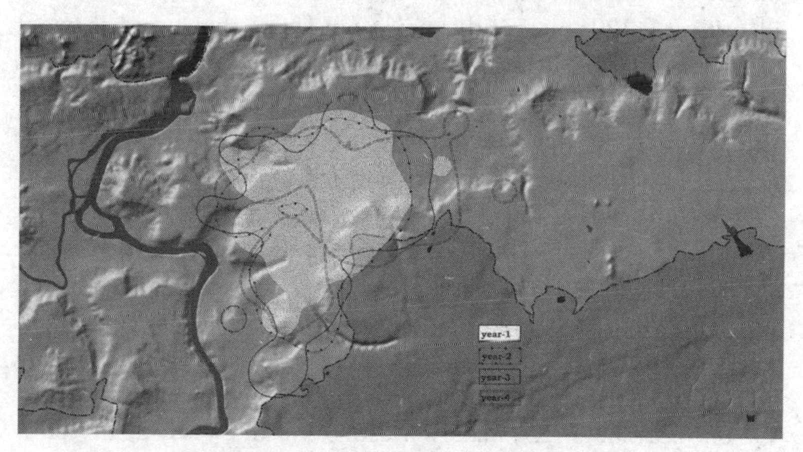

Figure 6.7 Annual ranges of tiger F-120.

Interestingly, she was also occasionally seen with a male cub of the Bargadi female. I saw them sharing a kill on at least two occasions; they did not feed at the same time and kept a respectful distance from each other. We also did not see the siblings actually feeding together; they shared kills separately, too. The siblings preyed on the resident feral livestock population at Bargadi very frequently. Sometimes both tigresses killed an animal each and fed on their respective kills just a few metres apart. After we collared F-120, we saw her moving extensively into this new area—marking intensively and calling. This routine continued until we saw no signs of the Bargadi female in the area. We were never able to ascertain the fate of the Bargadi female or of her male cub. Moreover, we never got a good picture of the male cub, so we could not tell whether he later became one of Panna's unidentified floaters or not.

F-120 first mated with her father, M-91, in August 1999 and gave birth to her first litter, at the age of around forty-three months, in November 1999 (Table 6.6). The litter comprised two cubs—one male and one female. We saw the young cubs within the first few days of birth, observing them until they grew to adulthood and dispersed successfully. F-120 gave birth to her second litter, also two cubs, in August 2001. It was at around this time that Hairy Foot had appeared on the scene and M-91 had moved out. We are not sure about the identity of F-120's mate at this point, but from subsequent behaviour we surmised that it was not Hairy Foot. She seemed to be under a certain amount of stress—her movements were very erratic during this period and not the same as previously observed. She was not using areas as frequently as she used to. She looked nervous and we hardly ever saw the cubs of this litter. They were extremely shy, and never came out in the open. This was odd, as F-120 was the most accessible tigress and neither she nor her earlier cubs had been bothered by our presence. We had enjoyed long observations of her first litter. This time, she was mostly seen alone, always very alert and calling regularly.

We saw evidence of Hairy Foot's frequent movement in the area. On one occasion, F-120 made a livestock kill and was lying in a fairly open space next to the carcass. As we approached, we heard a fast movement through the lantana bushes. I did not see it clearly myself, but one of our team members caught a clear glimpse of the cubs. After this sighting, we heard them once while observing the mother on a kill in early January, but this was the last evidence we had of these cubs. After this we did not even see their pugmarks. She then surprised all of us by giving birth to her third litter at the end of March (or early April) 2002. It became clear that Hairy Foot was the father of this third litter and this substantiated our suspicions that he may have killed the cubs from her second litter. We also surmised that F-120's second litter was thus probably fathered by M-91.

Table 6.6 Details of significant events observed during the monitoring of F-120

Date	*Month*	*Major events*
Apr-96	0	Birth
Jan-99	33	First collar
Aug-99	40	Mating with M-91
Nov-99	43	Litter-I (2)
Feb-01	58	Second collar
May-01	61	Mating ??
Aug-01	64	Litter-II (2)
Dec-01	68	Cubs last seen
Apr-02	72	Litter-III (2)
Dec-02	80	Died

The extraordinary aspect to this whole event, was that F-120 may have come into oestrus and mated successfully when her second litter was *still* alive. If this was accurate, it would be a unique record from the wild of a female tiger coming into oestrus while her previous litter was with her. We know that she did give birth to a new litter well within a hundred days of losing her cubs. Hairy Foot was seen visiting the litter site on several occasions, spending many hours with the female within a few metres of the weeks-old cubs. We made some wonderful observations of her with her cubs. She behaved similarly to when she had had her first litter—relaxed and visible. However after seven or eight months, it all changed once more. We saw her limping and without her cubs over several days, and later she moved her cubs away from her core area. It seemed that another male had moved into the vicinity and was challenging Hairy Foot. Park staff at one of the interior guard posts had heard sounds of a fight and it was after this that F-120 showed signs of stress, moving away from the new male's area of activity, perhaps not wanting to risk an infanticide threat again. The area she moved to was at the periphery of the park, suffering from intense human pressure. Here we saw her with cubs regularly, though we were worried about her using the area for extended periods of time. One tiger had been poached here in the early nineties, well before our project had begun. Unfortunately, F-120 succumbed to the same fate—she was found dead in a snare in December 2002, just two months after we had lost F-111. At the time of death, her two male cubs were almost nine months old.

Like her mother, she had also occupied a prey-rich, undisturbed forest habitat on the middle plateau. But her range extended up to the Park boundary, including areas adjoining the territorial forest and villages at the southern periphery. She was not as successful as her mother and other siblings, as she was exposed to a frequent changeover of males in the area, which coincided with litters fathered by previous males. This affected her reproductive success—she lost two out of three litters as a result.

She was radio-tracked for forty-six months. Her average annual range was 41.86 km^2, ± 2.5. Seventy per cent of her activity was restricted to small areas of 14 km^2, which represents about 26 per cent of her average annual range (Table 6.2). Seasonal ranges were also restricted to 70 per cent of the annual ranges.

F-113

The third sibling, F-113, was radio-collared in December 2000. Like F-111 and F-120, F-113 also established her territory in an area adjoining her mother's, even occupying her range partially. Her territory was to the north of F-123; her mother's range and her ranges are shown in Figure 6.8. At the time of her collaring she was raising a litter of two cubs, one male and one female, fifteen to sixteen months old (Table 6.7). She occupied an area on either side of the river Ken. Most of her range included areas south of the river, in the tourism zone, but it also extended up to the periphery of the Reserve, north of the Ken river. We removed her collar in September 2002 as she was suffering heavily from the pressure of 'tiger shows' that occurred almost every day for several hours during the peak tourist season. 'Tiger show' was the name given to events organized by the Reserve authorities that took tourists on elephant-back to see a tiger they had previously located. Trained elephants made several trips to and from where the tiger was lying and this could sometimes continue for more than two hours. She was last seen by us in December 2003 and she disappeared in 2004. She had raised two litters to adulthood, both of which dispersed successfully.

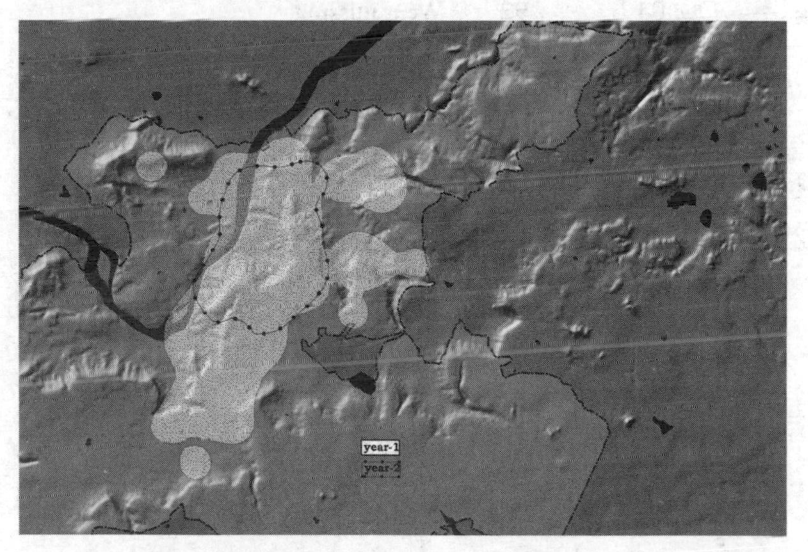

Figure 6.8 Annual home ranges of tiger F-113

Her average annual home range was 48.47 km^2, ±21.77. She covered a large area of 70.24 km^2 during her first year but later settled down to a much smaller area of 26.4 km^2, which was of similar size to that of her other siblings (Table 6.2). She occupied a very narrow belt of tiger habitat along the river Ken. Her seasonal range size changed considerably across the seasons and over the years, too. Like her other siblings, her seasonal ranges were 69 per cent smaller than the average annual range.

Table 6.7 Details of significant events observed during the monitoring of F-113.

Date	*Month*	*Major events*
Apr-96	0	Birth
Nov-99	42	Litter-I seen
Jan-00	45	Cubs seen
Dec-00	56	Collared
Oct-01	66	Litter-II
Apr-03	84	Mating with M-125 and floater
Dec-03	92	Went missing

M-91

M-91 was radio-collared in April 1996 and this first collar was replaced in October 1998 (Table 6.8). The first collar had been damaged during his fight with the new male tiger, M-125. This fight went on for several days in September 1998 and M-91 sustained several injuries. He was treated by the vets and recovered well, but he lost a considerable amount of his territory. After this interaction he never went to the Madla area, because it was taken over by M-125. His second collar continued to transmit signals for the next two years and finally stopped functioning in October 2000, before we could replace it. This incident taught us to replace collars at the earliest—after two years—even though their stated life is three years. At his peak, before his fight with M-125, M-91 ranged extensively and covered almost the entire length and breadth of the Reserve south of the river Ken (Figure 6.9). His home range covered an area of 290 km^2, which was more than 50 per cent of the entire Reserve. At the early stages of monitoring, in 1996 and 1997, this enormous range included only two female territories—F-123 and the Bargadi female—as far as we knew. Later, between 1998 and 2000, his territory included the

Table 6.8 Significant events observed during the monitoring of M-91

Date	*Month*	*Major events*
Jan-96	0	Mating with F-123
Apr-96	4	First collar
Oct-97	22	Mating with F-123
Nov-97	23	Fight with M-125; 2nd collar
Feb-99	38	Mating with F-111
Aug-99	44	Mating with F-123 & F-120
Sep-00	57	Collar stopped

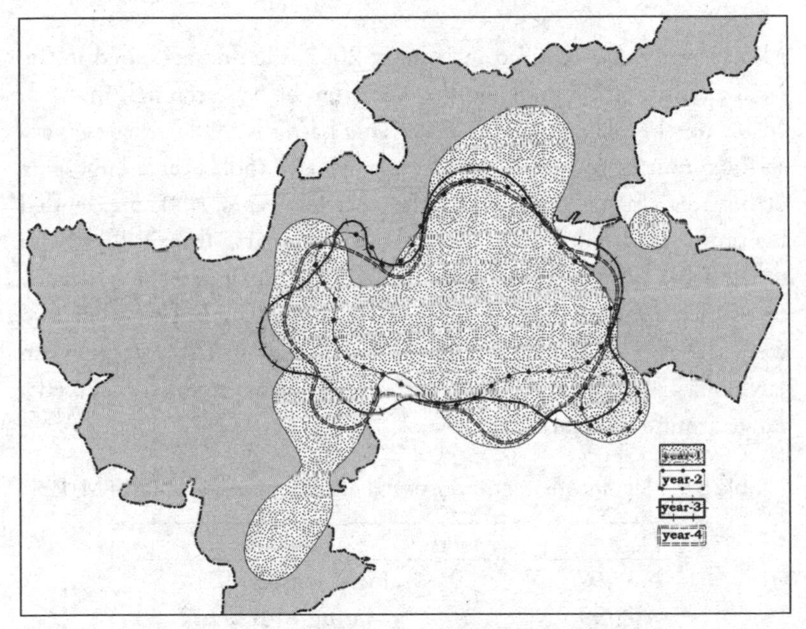

Figure 6.9 Annual home ranges of tiger M-91.

newly established territories of his daughters, F-120 and F-111. The portion of territory he lost after the fight in 1998 was occupied by his third daughter, F-113. He fathered six litters with Baavan (F-123), F-111 and F-120, and two with the Bargadi female. This information is based on mating that we observed. These eight litters amount to seventeen cubs, of which thirteen survived to adulthood in the five-and-a-half years he was the dominant male in the area. Over the years, he lost a considerable part of his territory first to M-125 after a fight and then also to Hairy Foot. After the territorial fights his range was reduced to a mere 91 km^2, and only partially covered the territories of the three females he had once dominated (Figure 6.3). In 2001, Hairy Foot had appeared in his range and replaced him. Hairy Foot was a very shy male; we rarely saw him clearly and could not radio-collar him. After several weeks and many attempts, Joanna was finally able to get a picture of him in a camera trap.

M-125

M-125 was radio-collared in January 2002. He first appeared in the Madla area in 1997 and, about a year later, he was seen fighting with M-91 on the plateau (Table 6.9). This battle resulted in some very serious injuries to M-91. As a result, M-125 took over a large part of his area (Figure 6.10). Over the next few years, M-125 extended his range across all three plateaus, covering an area from Billiya Seha to the areas adjoining Rampura. His territory included three females' territories. One of them, F-113, was radio-collared. The other two were the Amdar female on the upper plateau in the area between Jardhoba and Rampura village, and the Gata female which occupied a range around the Gata area.

Table 6.9 Significant events observed during the monitoring of M-125

Date	*Month*	*Major events*
Nov-97	0	Fight with M-91
Aug-99	21	Mating with F-113
May-01	42	Mating with F-113
Jan-02	50	Collar
Apr-03	65	Mating with F-113
Jul-03	68	Mating with F-123
Mar-04	76	Mating with F-123
May-05	90	Last location

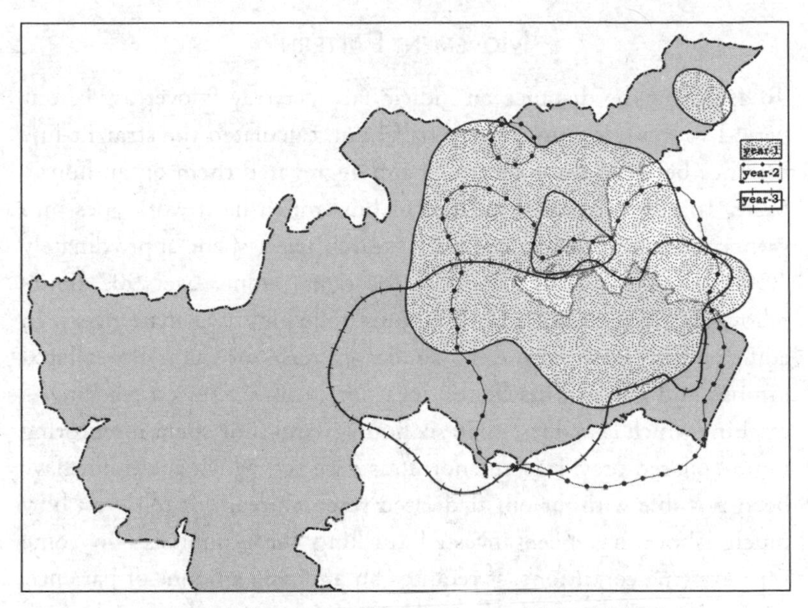

Figure 6.10 Annual home ranges of tiger M-125.

After the death of Hairy Foot, M-125 partially moved into his territory, and after mating with F-113 for the third time in 2003, he left the Madla area and remained exclusively on the upper Talgaon and Hinaura plateaus. Soon after a younger male, Broken Tooth (one of his lower canines was missing when we first saw him) was seen in the area. This young male also mated with F-113 immediately after M-125 had mated with her. In 2003 and 2004, when poaching had killed several tigers, activities of the males became somewhat complicated: M-125 was back patrolling the area in 2004 while Broken Tooth left. Later Broken Tooth was seen patrolling the territory once used by Hairy Foot and lately occupied by M-125. When F-113 disappeared, her mother F-123 extended her range and re-occupied part of this vacant space after six years. This further confirmed the loss of F-113 from the area. After her disappearance, M-125 was frequently seen in association with F-123. This was the first time since we had known them that they were seen together.

Movement Pattern

To ascertain the distance an individual tiger travels over a 24-hour period we took locations every half hour, calculated the straight-line distance between these locations and aggregated them on an hourly basis. To give the reader an idea of how much hard work goes into gathering such information, our research team spent approximately 1,500 hours collecting this data for tigers alone: over 907 hours following four females and 607 hours following two male tigers. In addition to this, we also did a similar exercise for the radio-collared sambar and chital. This figure does not include aborted tracking—tracking which lasted less than six hours—and time spent monitoring radio-collared prey. It is an enormous data set, which could not have been possible without our dedicated research team. It tells you how much labour has been invested tracking these animals—in some very extreme conditions. It requires an amazing amount of patience, endurance and teamwork to spend hours listening to signals and taking locations, while being constantly on the move. Sitting in an open jeep the entire night, when ambient temperatures plummeted below zero in winter and soared above 45^0 C in summer could test anybody's endurance limits. The research team, composed of Kalyan, Suresh, Bansh Gopal, Mahadev, Hargovind, and Joanna and I, undertook this monitoring with great care and sincerity, often working twelve-hour shifts. It was an enriching experience sharing these tracking sessions with them. We learnt more about tigers from these tracking sessions than any other form of field exercises.

We found that tigers in Panna moved more or less similar distances to those that had been estimated from studies conducted in Chitwan (Sunquist, 1981), Nagarahole (Karanth and Sunquist, 2000) and Kanha (Jhala et al., 2010): females on average travelled 4.2 ± 0.031 km per 24 hours and males traversed 10.9 ± 0.052 km per 24-hour period. It is generally expected that the distance covered would show a proportionate increase with home range size. This would mean that the larger the home range, the greater the distances moved; but our results did not confirm this. However we noticed that Panna tigers moved greater distances during the night hours than in the daylight hours. These estimates were obtained after pooling the entire data from male and female movements for daytime (0600 hr–1800 hr) and night-time sub-sets. The average distances travelled by male and female tigers during the daytime hours were estimated to be 4.2 ± 0.055 km and 1.9 ± 0.026 km, and 6.6 ± 0.029 km and 2.3 ± 0.034 km during the night, respectively. These movement rates show that the females travelled more or less at the same rate during the day and night whereas the males travelled greater distances at night.

We further split our data set into three seasons—monsoon, winter and summer—to examine the seasonal pattern of their movements. We looked at the sexes separately. In the case of females, there was little variation in the movement patterns between day and night during winter and summer. However, we found that during the monsoon, reversing the winter and summer trends, tigers travelled more during the day (Table 6.10) and interestingly less overall. We also observed excessive movement by the males during summer nights, which influenced the results of the pooled data. We had expected both sexes to travel more during the relatively cool hours of the summer

Table 6.10 Average distances travelled by radio-collared tigers, estimated by locating tigers every hour, estimating the straight-line distance between two radio-locations and summing the distances for daylight and night hours.*

Seasons	*Male*			*Female*		
	Day	*Night*	*24 hrs*	*Day*	*Night*	*24 hrs*
Winter	4.7 (0.091)	5.4 (0.045)	10.1 (0.053)	2.5 (0.044)	2.5 (.05)	5 (0.032)
Summer	3.9 (0.099)	10.1 (0.10)	14.1 (0.088)	1.8 (0.034)	2.4 (0.046)	4.1 (0.029)
Monsoon	2.6 (0.056)	1.5 (0.047)	4.1 (0.037)	1.6 (0.038)	1.2 (0.031)	2.8 (0.024)
Annual	4.2 (0.057)	6.6 (0.031)	10.9 (0.038)	1.9 (0.028)	2.3 (0.36)	4.2 (0.022)

* Distance and associated standard errors (in brackets) are in kilometres.

nights and the day hours in winter, when temperatures remained at a comfortable level (well below 30° C). But what was new to us was that during the monsoon, tigers were more active during the day than they were in the night. This may be due to their being troubled by insects during the daytime. We observed tigers being harassed by insects and flies, especially horse-flies. They were clearly irritated by these flies: one bite and they'd be off! Plagued by insects, the tigers frequently changed locations. During the monsoon, they escaped from the marauding insects only during the night, so maybe they spent most of their time catching up on lost sleep! Tigers showed the most activity during midday in the monsoons.

We looked at the same data on an hourly basis for a better understanding of the movement pattern. From this, we learned that except during the monsoons, there was a routine dip in activity in the middle of the day, which was preceded and followed by peaks of activity in the morning and in the evening. Both these peaks extended for several hours during the day and night (Figures 6.11, 6.12 & 6.13). Therefore, splitting the data-set into day and night hours blurred the true picture. Our data on movement clearly indicated that tigers are crepuscular for most of the year, i.e. they are most active during the morning and evening hours—except in the monsoon.

The fact that male tigers move much longer distances than the females actually contradicts the general impression of male tigers being lazy and spending most of their time sleeping. This impression has actually come about because most observations are made during the daytime, when they are mostly resting. The large data-set from 24-hour observations gives a more realistic picture about the tiger's behaviour and movement. The male tiger is the busiest individual I have come across and, therefore, always difficult to track in my experience. He is always alert and on the move—one cannot predict his movement as easily as one can for females.

On one occasion, M-91 travelled over thirty-two kilometres in one day, most of it during the night. Males have large ranges and in order to cover them they have to travel long distances. Moreover, in Panna their territories included human settlements, so it made sense for them to

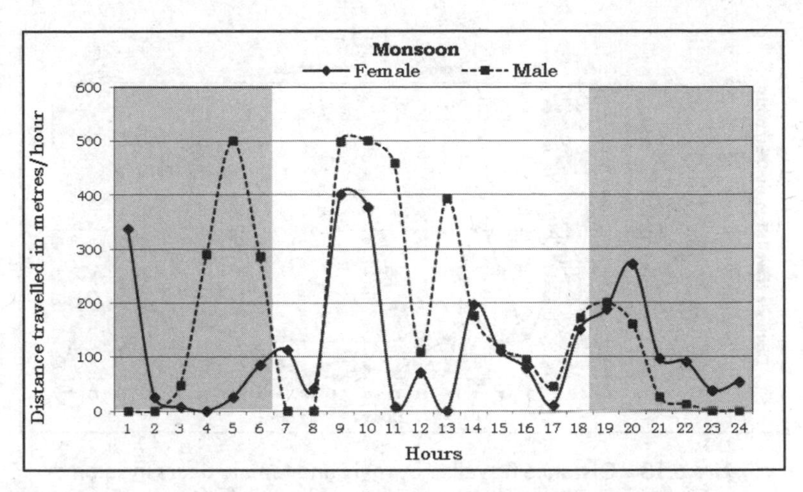

Figure 6.11 Distance travelled by male and female tigers in the monsoon months. Females on average travelled approximately 1.5 km during the day @ 130 m/hr and 1.2 km during night hours @ 102 m/hr. Males on an average travelled 2.5 km @ 214 m/hr during the day and 1.5 km @ 127 m/hr during the night.

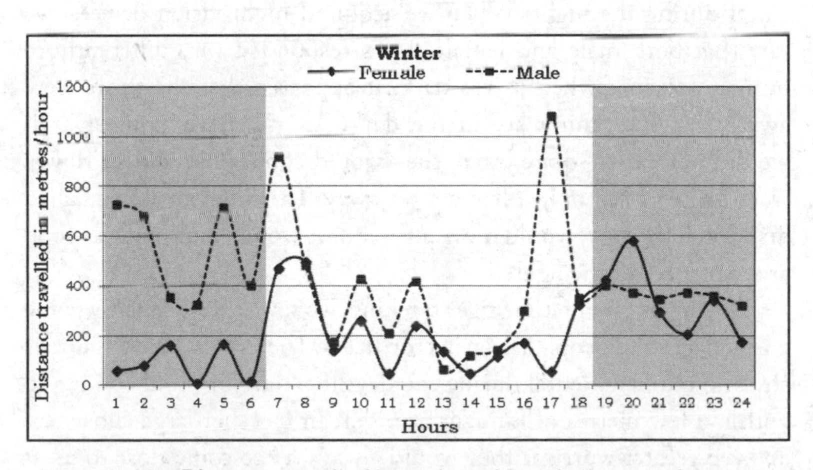

Figure 6.12 Distance travelled by male and female tigers in the winter months. Females on average travelled approximately 2.94 km during the day @ 207 m/hr and 2.5 km during night hours @ 208 m/hr. Males travelled 4.6 km @ 390 m/hr during the day and 5.3 km @ 447 m/hr during the night, on average.

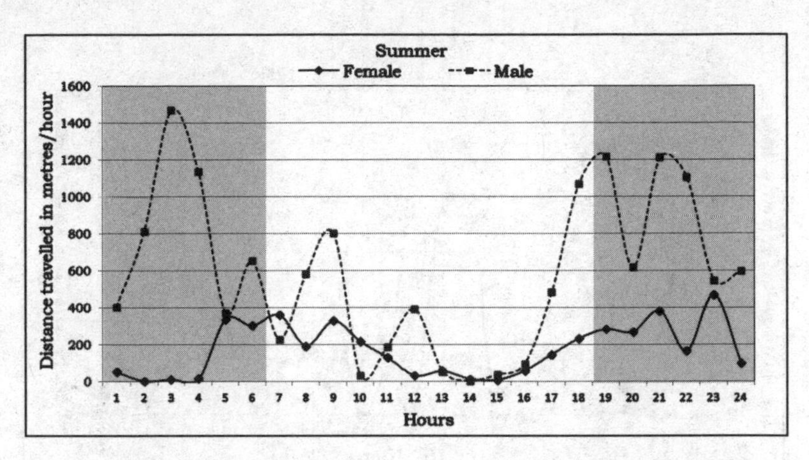

Figure 6.13 Distance travelled by male and female tigers in summer months. Females on average travelled approximately 1.7 km during the day @ 147 m/hr and 2.3 km during night hours @ 197 m/hr. Males on average travelled 3.9 km @ 328 m/hr during the day and 10.1 km @ 843 m/hr during the night.

travel during the night. When we acquired night-vision devices, we saw that both male and female tigers responded very differently to human presence when it was dark. It appeared that the tigers were aware humans cannot see in the dark. They behaved almost as if we did not exist—quite often, they would come close and sit down, watching us from only a few metres away. The moment we switched on a torch the tiger would move away, but it would come back as soon as we turned off the lights.

During our night-time tiger tracking, we saw males regularly going past villages and people asleep in crop fields. The tigress, Baavan, always shy and temperamental during the daytime, did not mind coming to within a few metres of humans at night. In fact, her large cubs were an even greater worry as they would always try to come close to us. It was amazing to see how often these tigers, especially adults, went past humans unbothered and showed no caution in human presence. If they had wanted to, these tigers could have killed men every other day, but they never did. On one memorable morning while in search of tigress

F-111, our team drove past a villager lying drunk and passed out at the edge of the road, still some distance from the village. They had tried unsuccessfully to wake him to encourage him to move on. F-111 was then located several kilometres away; but when she started moving, the tigress got up and headed in the direction where the drunken man had been lying. The team followed the tigress and was somewhat panic-stricken to see him still lying there unconscious. They called out but could do very little, as they were quite far from him. Initially the tigress did not appear to see the man but as she started to move down the slope she was heading straight towards him. She approached the man cautiously and actually sniffed the bicycle next to him, ultimately jumping over him into the long grass. The man had slept through the whole thing. When he was woken up by the team, he did not believe them, despite being shown the tracks of the tiger. He thought that it was a joke they were playing on him. After few more hours of sleep, he bicycled off to his village, a bit more sober but unconcerned. There were also occasions where we saw tigers walking past men sleeping in their fields unperturbed.

During my study in Panna, I never knew tigers as man-eaters and hence, I always wondered what made tigers attack humans. I always saw tigers as very trusting of humans, and generally timid creatures, except for mothers with young cubs. None of the hypotheses put forward for man-eating behaviour totally convinced me but I do not have an explanation for this phenomenon myself.

After some time we could identify some patterns in the movement of the collared tigers, especially the females. Some of the movements were so regular that we used to bet, for example, if we were approaching tigress F-123 at one of her favourite sites before noon, that she would be on left side of the rock and later in the afternoon on the right side of the rock in a particular month. Their preferences for resting sites were amazingly strong. Of course, we were not right all the time, but it was regular enough for us to entertain ourselves by predicting its preference and betting on it. Males visited the same areas repeatedly like a beat patrol, but we could rarely predict their timings. I regarded the male tiger as our expert guide—he repeatedly took us to places where we had never thought a tiger could be, led and introduced us to new females we did not know about and, more importantly, showed us how brilliantly they could avoid humans. In my experience, male tigers were generally timid by nature and usually hid their presence from humans. Contrary to this, females are more aggressive, especially if they have cubs with them. When a female visits the neighbourhood of a village, its inhabitants will eventually come to know of her presence, whereas a male tiger can spend extended periods within the vicinity of humans, completely unnoticed.

M-125 used to go past our research camp at least once in eight to ten days. Since our camp was close to a village, he usually went past during the night. This he did as a routine, but we could never predict his return. However, our team had figured out that if M-125 was in the Judi area, he usually went past our camp after an interval of two or three days. We would sit outside in anticipation of those evenings, listening to alarm calls. We parked our jeep, where we could listen to his footsteps on the gravel path. As he approached the road we switched the headlights on, and he would be right in front of us. His travelled path changed over the years, but what amazed me was the frequency of its use. We noticed that each tiger had its preferred path, which it took regularly when not hunting. We found this routine only in dominant males, less in territorial females and completely absent in other adult tigers that resided in the area. These other adult tigers we have already described as 'transients' or 'floaters'.

'Floater' is a term frequently used by Dr Karanth, which is more appropriate than 'transients' because these non-territorial tigers are not necessarily transient in nature. I describe them as 'leopard-like tigers' as they behave like leopards within a dominant male's territory. They are part of the resident tiger population and stay in the area for several years without owning a territory. They do not challenge dominance but respect the hierarchy and manage to co-exist in an area without conflict, like a sympatric leopard. Unfortunately, we were not able to radio-collar any of these 'leopard-like tigers', so our information on these animals is very limited. We identified a few individual leopard-like tigers. It was very obvious to us that these tigers did not like to expose themselves by following a routine. They also avoided established routes of the dominant males. This may be one reason why we were more successful in catching territorial males and not these leopard-like tigers. We used our knowledge of the routine movements of territorial males to not only catch and radio-tag dominant tigers but also to select our camera-trap sites for the tiger census. Unfortunately, this regularity might also make these animals easier prey for poaching gangs.

Defended vs Undefended and Territoriality

Radio-telemetry-based studies on the land tenure system of tigers inform us that male and female tigers maintain exclusive home ranges (Smith, 1984; Karanth and Sunquist, 2000; Sunquist and Sunquist, 2002; Goodrich et al., 2010; Sharma et al., 2010). In Panna, we found that female tigers did maintain exclusive home ranges, which can be defined as territories. However, this was not the case for male tigers—their ranges were not exclusive of other males. We observed the presence of several adult males within the dominant males' home ranges. Intensive monitoring over a long period allowed us to identify these adult males. More importantly, we saw these tigers in the same area for several years. These tigers also ranged across different dominant male ranges. These individuals are described as transients or floaters and are generally seen as a non-breeding and temporary component of a population (Schaller, 1967; Sunquist and Sunquist, 2002). They are prevented from breeding by territorial or other spacing-related behaviour (Kelly et al., 1998; Logan and Sweanor, 2001; Penteriani et al., 2011). As I mentioned earlier, I found that these floaters behaved like leopards within a dominant tiger's range. These were adult tigers who behaved like leopards socially. These floater males were not temporary components; they were residents for many years and we also saw them mating with the established females.

This is a very important finding with regard to understanding the social organization of tigers and for evaluating the viability of a population because, if these tigers are resident and mating, they are actually part of the breeding population. I believe that the presence of floaters or leopard-like tigers within the dominant males' territories could be an alternate behaviour strategy, where these tigers are enhancing their reproductive potential by co-existing with the dominant males (Kokko and Sutherland, 1998; Pen and Weissing, 2000; Logan and Sweanor, 2001; Penteriani et al., 2011).

Dr Karanth's contention that 'leopards are socially dominated by tigers' is an apt analogy for the relationship between leopard-like tigers and dominant male tigers. As a result of this social hierarchy, we rarely see these leopard-like tigers out in the open, walking on roads the way territorial male tigers or females do, mile after mile. We do not observe any behaviour that suggests dominance. During my entire study period we only had glimpses of these tigers. It was very hard to establish an ID for these individuals because of their shyness; even obtaining photographs was difficult. We rarely captured them in camera traps. However, there were exceptions like Broken Tooth. It was interesting to note that these leopard-like tigers hardly ever made territorial markings, a behaviour similar to that of sub-adult tigers (Sunquist and Sunquist, 2002).

Identifying these tigers from sets of pugmarks always posed a challenge and really tested our ability to identify tigers based on pugmarks. We made mistakes in identifying these individuals so often that we stopped relying on pugmark-based identification and focussed mainly on photographic identification. For our team, pugmarks were not a reliable way of knowing about the tigers. Pugmark identification works selectively, in situations where we encounter pugmarks of known tigers in their known areas or maybe if there is some distinctive and unique aspect to them. But in any challenging situation, pugmark-based identification is likely to fail. And if you are not monitoring the tigers on a regular basis, you will not even know whether you have made a mistake or not.

We saw these floaters mating with known tigresses on many occasions. At times we saw up to three (floater) tigers hanging around when the dominant male was still mating. In fact, we saw some floaters mating with not one tigress but different individuals.

Once the dominant male had mated and moved away, these tigers would then try to mate with the same tigress. Their mating could last a long time. We saw that once the dominant male had mated, he showed little interest in this development. On one occasion, F-123 refused to mate with one of the floaters and was aggressive when he approached her. There were minor clashes between the two, with the male continuing to follow the female's movement for several hours. We could not follow the tigress continuously but the next day when we saw her, she was alone.

We never saw the floaters with the tigresses prior to the arrival of the dominant male. If we had, this would have given rise to different interpretations. If only we had been able to radio-collar these males, we would have had some very interesting observations. They would surely have explained the floater's role in tiger society. Our limited observations, however, are contrary to general perceptions and important because we saw them mating on a regular basis. We had photographic evidence of the male tiger we knew as 62 (one of Baavan's cubs) mating with his sisters from a previous litter, F-111 and F-113. We also photographed Broken Tooth mating with F-113 after the dominant male M-125 had mated with her. This was filmed and is included in the BBC documentary, *Tigers of the Emerald Forest*.

We saw these floaters making kills, mating and living within the territories of several different male ranges. Their presence continued in the same area even when one dominant male was replaced by a new male. This changeover of the dominant males had little impact on these individuals. Based on several such observations, it appears to us that the dominant male or 'territorial tiger' accepted their presence, as long his dominance was not challenged. The dominant males and floaters lived peacefully in the same area. But, when a challenger appeared, he came with definite intention and strongly manifested his presence. He would clearly communicate his assertion and mark so aggressively and obviously that even we could notice the intention. We saw this twice, with the appearance of M-125 and of Hairy Foot.

With these observations in mind, the dominant males' home ranges can hardly be strictly termed territories, as long as that is defined as an exclusive range. But the home ranges were defended vehemently from other rival males, the ones who challenged their dominance. However, within the same ranges floaters or leopard-like tigers lived peacefully with dominant male tigers. The only obvious difference between the dominant male and a floater was that the former had a clearly defined range with a definite movement pattern whereas the movement of floaters was unpredictable, or rather we were unable to track them extensively and therefore knew little about it.

When we review the literature on this subject for other carnivore species, we find several similar observations and a resultant debate on defended and undefended territories and ranges in carnivore communities (Grant et al., 1992). Within a species we see a range of responses to the prevailing ecological conditions, and home-range size and population density are two major examples. Whether a carnivore holds its territory exclusively (or defends it only partially) can depend on its home-range size, the population density, resource availability and the stability of the system. In areas where the male carnivore ranges are small, it may be possible for a dominant male to actively defend its territory but when ranges are large, it will not be possible for a male to keep it exclusive. A large exclusive range would mean an excessive energy cost of patrolling the entire territory. When a tiger's territory extends over hundreds of square kilometres, if it were maintaining an exclusive territory, we would expect that he would be moving longer distances every day and have a greater activity period, with increased communication throughout its range.

Contrary to this expectation, we found that the movement and activity patterns of the male tigers in Panna were similar to other tiger populations with smaller ranges. This indicates that the tigers here were somehow protecting the larger ranges without increasing their daily energetic demand. We observed that the dominant tiger did not mark the entire range but there was intense marking where the territory met that of his dominant neighbours. By limiting intense communication to where it is needed most and tolerating the presence of other adult male tigers within its range, our males could minimize the daily energy cost that would otherwise have been incurred in keeping home ranges exclusive. Importantly, they did not compromise on first access to female, when she was in oestrus. In all mating that we monitored with radio-collared females, the dominant male of the area was always the first to arrive. By ensuring first access to females, the dominant male tigers in Panna were able to achieve reproductive success without expending extra cost and they were able to maintain larger ranges. Although this is new information with respect to tigers, it is not a new finding, as it is known in several other carnivore communities such as leopards and foxes, which also exhibit a variety of social organization setups and responses.

Here in Panna, one reason for the sizeable floater population could be the lack of alternative attractive destinations (suitable tiger habitat with females) for dispersing male tigers. Thus, when young males disperse from an isolated protected population like Panna and can't find a suitable destination during their forays, some of those that survive may return to their original habitat and craft a new existence as a floater. Since all males cannot become dominant males, they opt for an alternate strategy to achieve their reproductive goals. Exclusive ranges for males are considered advantageous for exclusive access to mates but we saw in Panna that dominant males did not have the exclusive right to sympatric females, only first access. Overlap between the dominant males and radio-collared females' ranges was smaller in Panna as compared to other studies. This could be another factor in addition to large home-ranges. In Panna, despite its larger range size, the dominant males' territories included relatively fewer female ranges than known from other studies conducted in the Royal Chitwan National Park (Sunquist, 1981; Smith, 1984). In Panna, home ranges of male radio-collared tigers included two to three female territories only, whereas in Chitwan there were three to six. In both cases the samples are too small to conclusively say much, but since the female ranges in those productive habitats are several times smaller, males could include more females within a smaller home range. Such optimal tiger habitats can support a larger breeding population per unit area than Dry Forest habitats such as Panna, and this information is essential for effective management planning.

In tiger social organization, the polygynous mating system is well studied, where one dominant male's home range encompasses several female territories. Polyandry, where one female mates with more than one male, is rarely reported (Schaller, 1967; Sunquist, 1981; Smith and Mcdougal, 1991; Goodrich et al., 2010). But there are a few references that record the presence of several males around a female in oestrus and females mating with several males (Schaller, 1967; Karanth, 2001). In Panna, we find that once the dominant tiger had mated, he showed little interest in the female mating with other males, after indicating his prior rights and first access to the mate. If these floaters are breeding and contributing their genes to the population, without challenging the hierarchy, this could have an impact on the stability and viability of a population, and this information would be of great importance in conservation and viability assessment.

But this also raises more questions to explore—when there is more than one adult male tiger in her area, does a female still have to prefer the dominant male over other males (Qvarnström and Forsgren, 1998)? Does first access to the female ensure reproductive success for the dominant males? Whose offsprings are they? Since we observed females also regularly mating with males other than the dominant ones, what criteria helps her decide with whom to mate? Do multiple paternities also occur among tigers, as it is known for other cats? Our observations question the established perception that the tigress has no choice but to mate with dominant males. If she is not following that rule, then we need to learn more about mate choice in tigers.

We also noticed that when a new male challenged and fought to acquire fresh territories, the established tigers responded to these challenges by shifting, expanding and contracting their ranges. These responses by dominant males and observations from other studies suggest that tiger social organization can be flexible (Karanth and Sunquist, 2000; Goodrich et al., 2010). The Panna Tiger Reserve supported a small and isolated population, where some of the dispersing males, when unable to find a suitable habitat away from their natal areas, return to reside as floaters. These tigers, which include floaters and other new males based on above observations, may be employing strategies other than a 'land tenure system' of prior rights to maximise reproductive potential (Seidensticker et al., 1973).

Site Fidelity

From our observations of two radio-collared male tiger ranges, it was obvious that their territories were not fixed. They were subject to change and sometimes large-scale shifts occurred. As we know, the male strategy is to include as many females as possible and so, the former will move into an area or extend its range to maximize reproductive success, provided it can overcome the challenge for dominance. On the other hand, we found that female territories remained more or less fixed and tigresses showed a higher degree of site fidelity. We only observed expansion by Baavan into the vacant spaces created by mortalities of neighbouring territorial females. Reading old hunting records and recent observations from Kanha, Bandhavgarh and Ranthambhore supports my impression that female territories are very traditional. The ecological characteristics of an area attract females to a site and as long as these are maintained, a female will stay settled in the space. Individuals may change but the area of use remains more or less similar.

Unfortunately, we were not able to collar two dominant males during the same time period and cannot accurately estimate the overlap of their ranges. Therefore, most of the information is based on intensive field monitoring of these males. We estimate that this overlap is limited to a small proportion (<10%, but could be even smaller) of their home ranges. This is where the battle for dominance begins and communication intensifies with neighbours. We saw a greater degree of marking in these areas if a neighbour had intruded, which they did very often. It was interesting to observe how this triggered territorial behaviour—the amount of vocalization and aggressive marking, like spraying, that is associated with such an intrusion, was considerable. It showed just how possessive these individuals are.

As observed by Sunquist, McDougal and Smith in Chitwan, we noticed such behaviour after an intrusion by neighbours to be very frequent in the case of all females as well. Males did the same but not as often, unless one of them was trying to push its neighbour. Most disputes were settled peacefully through communication, not through violence. Territorial fights are usually associated with males and, to a lesser extent, with females. But the female is likely to be more aggressive in defending her resources for exclusive use than a male. Therefore, the home range size that can be defended effectively becomes an important issue in addition to habitat quality. This response by the females determines the abundance or density in an area.

That is, the male tiger's focus is on a mate, so he requires a larger area so as to include as many females as possible within his territory. But there would be a physical limit for a male to defend. He will have to compromise on several aspects in order to maximize his reproductive success. In Panna, we saw that as long as other males did not challenge his authority for first access to mates, their presence was tolerated. But the presence of these floater males is always a potential threat and the dominant males must work hard to ensure their dominance. The dominant male cannot be complacent as there are several males within his range, nor can he afford to fight and drive away every male who comes into his range, which might extend over 150–250 km^2. He ensures dominance by patrolling the area and occupying different parts of his range, as well as frequently spending time with the female occupants (Karanth, 2001; Sunquist and Sunquist, 2002). A dominant male spending time with a female and her cubs is generally seen as unusual male behaviour. However this is not so: bonding with females, other than during mating, is important for a male. This can help ensure a female accepts him as a mate (female choice is important). Establishing this strong bond can be a rewarding strategy for the male, better than having to physically fight off male threats. We observed that females do not readily accept other males, so this non-mating bonding is an important tactic. Thus, a dominant male and female tiger spending time together is not such unusual behaviour.

The movement pattern of females is not as regular because their movement is governed more by the procurement of food and its dispersion. As already mentioned, the territorial male tiger is a very busy individual and the belief that males are lazy and steal food from females is generally a mistaken one. This misperception has likely arisen due to the fact that the most likely time to see him is when he is resting or sharing a female's kill. A more accurate interpretation of this would be that he is bonding with his female; he does this on a regular basis with all his females, on kills or otherwise. This is one occasion when we can catch up with him, otherwise he is hard to home in on. We know this from tracking his daily movement patterns.

Most of the shifts in home ranges, along with territorial encounters, take place in the areas of overlap. As a result of these exchanges, the shape and size of the annual home range is altered every year. Combined multiple years' home range data can show misleadingly large overlaps. Our data also revealed that if the annual range is calculated based on the calendar year, the analysis is likely to show larger ranges and overlaps. The main reason for this is that one dry season is split into two different years. Secondly, the Kernel estimator is an advanced and reliable estimator for home ranges, but it is not the ideal estimator for calculating overlaps. I say this because the territorial boundary at the overlap site is established almost deterministically, in response to neighbouring males' behaviour, and not probabilistically. Therefore, I believe that the overlap estimated using the Kernel estimator tends to be on the higher side. Despite these dynamics, female territories remained consistent throughout their life-span. This observation reiterates that female tigers show strong site fidelity once they have established a territory. Females will defend and occupy the same area for life until the time they are displaced by a challenger. Male territories can shift during their lifetimes.

Male cubs can disperse long distances as we have seen in Chitwan, but in Panna we observed that some of the young males returned and stayed in their natal area throughout their life. Others disappeared and were never seen again in the natal area. Many of the male cubs radio-collared in Kanha did not leave the area but they did make long-distance forays. Such observations need to be investigated further because if male cubs are increasingly returning to their natal areas and joining the breeding population, it could have an impact on the viability of the tiger population. The 2010 All-India Tiger Assessment by NTCA established that we have lost most of the tigers outside our Protected Area system, so it will be difficult for dispersing young male tigers to find a satellite female population. If he is not able to find a suitable breeding population, he has no choice but to return to his natal area. Breeding with close relations will increase inbreeding and ultimately may reduce the survival chances of the original breeding population.

Space-use and Large Home Ranges

We found no consistent seasonal pattern in the use of ranges in Panna, but we did find that seasonal ranges were on an average 30 per cent smaller than the annual ranges. There could be many reasons for the large inconsistencies that we observed in seasonal range sizes of females, especially with those that had cubs. When females give birth to a litter, their range is limited to a very small area around the denning site, but as soon as the cubs are five to six months old, their ranges expand (Sunquist, 1981; Goodrich et al., 2010). Since there is no particular season for breeding and litters are born throughout the year (Sunquist, 1981), this could account for the inconsistent seasonal variation that we recorded. Moreover, tigers in Panna are likely to exploit the space within their ranges differently in response to prevailing environmental conditions and according to the seasonal availability of resources. Habitat use by tigers is discussed in Chapter 8 in detail.

Home ranges of tigers in Panna were three-four times larger than reported so far from other tropical habitats, except in the case of re-introduced populations. It is a significant finding for tiger conservation in the Tropical Dry Forest habitat. Home range size in mammals are reported to be influenced by a number of factors such as food (prey) availability, population density and body mass (Litvaitis et al., 1986; Powell et al., 1997; Herfindal et al., 2005). The variation in tiger home range sizes (females) from less than 20 km^2 to 390 km^2 in different habitats is mostly explained by the availability of prey biomass (Goodrich et al., 2010). With increased food availability, the home range size will decrease and vice versa. In such a relationship, it is assumed that with high prey availability, individuals can find the required energy from a relatively smaller area and can therefore afford smaller home ranges. The relationship between the home range size and metabolic need has been well established across various carnivore species (Gittleman and Harvey, 1982) and the intra-specific variations in home range sizes in carnivores are well documented. Similarly, a variation in the home range size of tigers is also reported from different habitats.

However, the home ranges of tigers in Panna did not fit this pattern; they were much larger than might be expected. Panna has a high prey biomass that is comparable to, or greater than that of areas where tiger home ranges are two to three times smaller (Sunquist, 1981; Karanth and Sunquist, 2000). In tropical forest areas where we have information on prey availability and home range size, prey availability fails to explain the corresponding home range sizes (Figure 6.14). This could be due to the fact that most of the information available on tiger prey, tiger home range size and population density comes from well-protected high prey-density areas. In these areas, prey availability

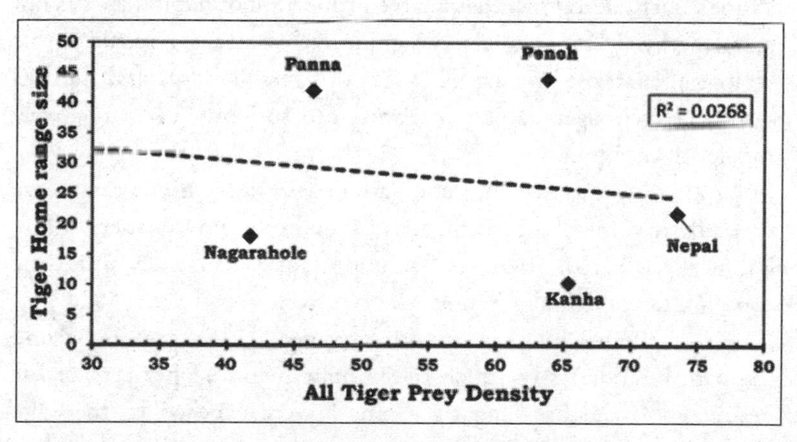

Figure 6.14 Home range size and prey densities obtained at five different tropical habitats show no influence of prey densities on the home range size of tigers.

is more than that required by the tigers' metabolic need. Other prevailing ecological factors may come into play, like the dispersion of key resources such as prey, water and suitable habitat (McDonald, 1983; Hunter, 1998; Broomhall et al., 2003). It is very likely that in Panna, individual home range size is a response to these factors, in addition to prey availability. The above mentioned relationship with prey may be more applicable to areas where prey abundance is lower than the metabolic requirement and an individual has to increase its range to fulfil its metabolic needs.

When we looked at the availability of preferred and less preferred habitats within the home ranges of individual tigers, we observed a strong relationship between the size of the home range and the proportion of preferred habitat. Home range sizes decreased with a proportional increase in preferred habitat within the home ranges. This relationship indicated that availability of preferred habitat can be an important ecological factor in determining the home range size for both the sexes in Panna.

Furthermore, the heterogeneous distribution of resources over time (seasonal) and space (spatial) makes resource availability (especially water and cover) unpredictable. We also found that Panna's tiger habitat includes a large proportion of habitat that is not preferred by tigers. This is very significant because as a result of this ecological characteristic, home ranges of tigers are large and the 543 km^2 protected tiger habitat in Panna can support only a relatively smaller tiger population.

Studies have shown that populations with large home ranges are particularly vulnerable to extinction (Woodroffe and Ginsberg, 1998; Balme et al., 2010). There are two important aspects relevant for the conservation of tigers in Panna.

Firstly, almost all the tiger home ranges either extend beyond the park boundaries or touch the periphery and 42 per cent of the perimeters of all breeding tiger ranges were exposed to the 'edge' (Chundawat et al., 2016). This characteristic exposed the breeding population to external pressures and brought them into direct conflict with humans, resulting in human-caused mortalities. When a population is exposed so heavily to the 'Edge Effect', extinction probabilities can be high (Woodroffe and Ginsberg, 1998; Balme et al., 2010).

Secondly, we find that because of the large space requirement of tigers in Tropical Dry Forests, even the relatively large Panna Tiger Reserve is able to only partially protect a population of just seven or eight breeding females within its boundary. High exposure to human-caused mortalities was responsible for the loss of the tiger population in 2009. The near-continuous presence of researchers, and intensive radio-tracking and monitoring of all the tigers may have provided additional security to the breeding females (Laurance, 2013). When this was curtailed, poaching hit these individuals. Since Panna Tiger Reserve is isolated and lacked connectivity, the small breeding tiger population was not able to withstand this poaching pressure. Tiger populations that suffer from scale mismatch between the size of protected areas and the large space needed by tigers can be highly susceptible to extinction probabilities (Chundawat et al., 2016). Unless this scale mismatch is adequately addressed, security measures provided within the boundary will not be able to protect the breeding population that ranges beyond the protected area (Gopal et al., 2010). We need to consider the role played, or rather not played, by the protected areas in protecting a viable population in these circumstances and find alternative solutions to address the issue.

These were significant findings for the management of tigers, since they are key for an understanding of the space requirements of a viable tiger population in Tropical Dry Forests. They also have important conservation implications and can explain why tigers in Panna are vulnerable to extinction.

7

Counting Tigers and Other Co-Predators

We could generate a fairly accurate figure for the size of Panna's tiger population from radio-telemetry-based monitoring and by identifying individual tigers. But to get a more quantitative assessment of the tiger, leopard and hyena populations and their ecology, we needed a reliable estimate of population densities. As these animals were shy and difficult to observe, direct counts are almost impossible so this could not provide a sufficiently accurate assessment. For tigers, leopards and hyenas we employed a method that used photographs and identified individual tigers from their unique stripe patterns. We placed a series of cameras throughout the tiger Reserve and the photographs were triggered by the animals themselves.

The Old School

In the past, individual tigers and leopards were identified from footprints or pugmark impressions and then counted. This method has been reviewed in detail for nearly three decades along with its deficiencies and lack of scientific rigour (Karanth and Nichols, 1998; Karanth et al., 2003). Pugmark-based counts assume that field staff can find pugmark impressions of all the tigers in an area. After collating the pugmark impressions, it is further assumed that all individual tigers and leopards can be successfully differentiated and identified from these impressions. These impressions of pugmarks on soil were recorded by tracing them over a glass frame or by pouring plaster-of-paris paste on the pugmark to obtain a cast. These casts or 'tracings' were then compared side by side and each individual identity was ascertained. A total count for the population was attained merely by tallying all individual tigers identified through this comparison.

In this approach, individual tigers or leopards are identified from different characteristics such as the shape and size of the pugmark impressions. But this method fails to take into account the differences arising from impressions that are obtained from a variety of substrates or layers of soil. We know for a fact that pugmark impressions collected in the field from different substrates can vary considerably. Such significant variations complicate the identification process. As a result, results from such vastly altered impressions can be misleading. Further complications arise from the subjective nature of pugmark impression assessments. Recently efforts have been made to quantify the characteristics of pugmark impressions to differentiate individual tigers using multivariate statistics, but this method is only effective for a small population (<10–12 tigers), and assumes that impressions are true and come from very similar substrates (Karanth et al., 2003; Sharma et al., 2005).

I remember during our early days in Panna, one of the collared males, M-91, was counted as four different individuals through the pugmark-based assessment. This confusion arose due to the fact that it was moving over a larger area than normally expected. Not expecting a tiger to cover such a large area, the park staff had identified this one individual as four different tigers. It was radio-tracking that allowed us to explain the real situation to the management authorities—that all four were in fact but one tiger—but this still was not convincing enough for them to lower the estimate. This is just one example that highlights the problems associated with pugmark-based population estimates, even when it is sincerely done.

Not all field staff can trace a pugmark impression accurately on a glass frame. Therefore, usually a plaster cast of the pugmark impression is taken from the field, which is then used for assessment.

Each pugmark impression is held in one hand and compared with hundreds of other such casts. Each impression is given a unique identity after a casual comparison. Casts with the same identity are placed in one group, each group referring to an individual tiger or leopard. Identification of individual tigers and leopards from such a subjective assessment leaves much room for errors. If there is a target to be achieved, one can easily assign the required number of IDs to these impressions. This is why population estimates which used this method rarely gave an accurate picture of the status and trend of tiger populations in the country.

In the 1980s and '90s, it was common knowledge that the tiger population was declining, not only in India but around the world. However, the official statistics in the country showed an increasing trend for tigers. This continued for decades. Forty years of tiger conservation failed to achieve its goals. Why? Because these imaginary figures governed our policies and conservation activities. Now, finally, a more reliable scientific methodology has been employed and this has shown that we are left with fewer tigers than when the conservation movement first began in the '70s.

Imagine if we had had a proper assessment on a regular basis as we do now…how many tigers could have been saved? For this, I blame the autocratic system of wildlife management which closed all doors to scientific assessment of tigers for four decades. It persisted with the pugmark assessment blindly and created numbers that mislead the country and the world. Authorities finally did succumb to pressure but only after the extinction of two important tiger populations from the protected habitats of the Sariska and Panna Reserves. These extinctions from two premier tiger Reserves exposed the counting methods as farcical, putting them under the media spotlight. We could have saved many tiger populations from extinction had the pugmark-based estimation not fooled everybody. The loss of tigers in Sariska generated tremendous pressure and, ultimately, a scientific approach was adopted to assess the actual tiger situation. But this came too late for many tiger populations. Too late indeed for the Panna population! The pugmark-based assessment was used very effectively to mask and deny the decline there. Authorities continued to count thirty-five tigers even when the numbers had dropped to single figures; and then they allowed the population to drop to zero by 2009.

Tigers in Multi-Storey Buildings: A Cover-up

Early in 2005, we reported a serious decline in the tiger population of the Panna Tiger Reserve. After reporting over twenty missing tigers, the Reserve authorities conducted a special census to prove the point that, in fact, there was no such loss. Over 2,200 pugmark-impression pads were created to obtain pugmarks from roads, tracks, waterholes and other locations where tiger movement was frequent. In spite of this unusually high number of impression pads, they were only able to collect less than seventy pugmark impressions over a seven-day period. Earlier, when the tiger population was at its peak (30–35 tigers), authorities used to obtain 500–600 pugmark impressions from a handful (200–250) of pugmark impression pads. But in the 2005 census, from a small number of impressions, the wildlife authorities concluded that there was no decline in the tiger population. In fact, they conveniently found one more individual than their previous count. They had a target to achieve, so thirty-four adult tigers were counted precisely, along with one additional cub. At this juncture, our estimate was that only ten or twelve tigers survived in Panna.

The subjectivity involved in identifying individuals using plaster casts taken from pugmarks made this possible. It was shocking to see the charade that was displayed during the census. Around this time, both Baavan's and M-125's radio-collars were working, and we knew their ranges. Mr Asim Srivastava, who was the field director of the Bandhavgarh Tiger Reserve, was called in to conduct the census and show the world that an independent assessment was being carried out under his supervision. Mr Srivastava and his team counted thirteen different adult tigresses in Baavan's home range (an area of approximately 40 km^2) and another nine adult male tigers were found in M-125's range (over 100 km^2). It was our sad joke that the tigers of Panna were living in multi-storey buildings, while the rest of the

Reserve was empty. It was difficult to dispute these figures, because no one was allowed to do an independent assessment. These figures contradicted all the natural history and scientific knowledge of tigers, and in fact made us realize that the situation was even worse than we had thought. From the distribution and paucity of pugmarks found, it became clear to us that the numbers had probably dropped even lower than our feared estimate of ten to twelve tigers.

This was my second experience of seeing first-hand how a pugmark-based estimation can be manipulated to achieve a figure, and how within the wildlife authority there is no space for independent assessments. In this case, the wildlife authorities very successfully achieved their objective of quashing our reported decline in tiger numbers. Here was an opportunity for Mr Srivastava to provide an accurate assessment but sadly he also succumbed to peer pressure. He chose to ignore all the data available to his command and used an outdated technique to cover up the falling numbers. We desperately needed a counting technique that was not open to discrepancies and deceptions—one that could withstand scientific rigour.

Scientific Accounting for Numbers

There are two important points that we need to understand when estimating wildlife populations:

(a) **Counts:** The number of animals that are seen or identified and counted. These numbers are inevitably only a fraction of the total population, because it is impossible to count an entire wildlife population. Counts only provide an estimate, one that is not always very reliable.

(b) **Sampling:** The monitored population usually inhabits a large area, so only a fraction of the area is sampled for estimation (Lancia et al., 1994; Thompson, 2004).

Recognizing the impossibility of counting every single animal in a forest area, we needed a method by which we could estimate the 'unknown fraction' of the count and ensure that the sample is a true representation (or close to the actual number) of the population. Fortunately for us, new technological and theoretical developments over the last few decades have made it possible to apply rigorous scientific methods to achieve such estimates. One of these is the innovative application known as the Capture-Recapture model. This method can be applied to estimate population size.

Capture-Recapture Model

The stripe-and-spot patterns of every tiger and leopard are unique and they help in identifying individuals from photographs very reliably (Nichols and Karanth, 2002). Using remotely triggered cameras, tigers and other animals can be easily photographed with a series of camera traps set up in the forest (Plate 7.1). This method does not expect *all* tigers to be photographed in the sample.

Plate 7.1 A tiger triggering a camera trap and taking its own picture. In the distance another camera takes a picture exposing its stripe pattern from the other side. Since the stripe pattern of a tiger is unique, we can identify individual tigers positively using this method.

This is where statistics come into play; they can help estimate the number of missing tigers (that were not photographed), providing a figure that is much closer to the actual population than a simple count can. In theory, it would be possible to achieve a total count if we continued to photograph the area over a very long time—eventually we could obtain pictures of all the tigers in that fixed space. This is one of the presuppositions of the Capture-Recapture model. However, to reach such a situation would require a lot of time and many camera units, both of which are difficult to get. Another drawback is that over a long period, there is mortality, immigration and emigration, for which one cannot estimate an absolute number. Due to these limitations it is far more feasible to get an estimate that is as close to the actual number as possible within a limited time and using a limited number of cameras.

How does one determine the real population from a sample of the study population? This is actually fairly simple. Imagine you have a box full of toy tigers but don't know exactly how many there are in it. Easiest way would be to count all the tigers. But imagine we cannot do that; in this case we take a handful of toy tigers out of the box and mark each with a unique number. We count this as our first sampling set and refer to the number we picked out as n_1. Return these marked tigers to the box and mix them again with the rest. For a second sampling, again pick up a handful of toy tigers (n_2). This set can have toy tigers already marked from our first sample and some new ones. Let us call the number of already marked tigers in the second sample m_2. Since we had mixed the marked toy tigers very well we can reasonably expect that the ratio of marked toy tigers (m_2) to the total of the second sample (n_2) will be equal to the ratio of marked toy tigers n_1 in first sample to total number of toy tigers in the box (c). Mathematically this can be represented as:

$$c/n_1 = n_2/m_2$$

Thus,

$$c = (n_1 n_2)/m_2$$

This is an ideal scenario but in the real world there can be many daunting possibilities. For instance, when the marked toy tigers are not mixed properly the count can be biased. However, if sampling is repeated several times, the bias arising due to poor mixing will be reduced and the estimate for 'c' would be closer to the real number. The other scenario would be where the toy tigers are mixed properly but when we pick out a small number in the second sampling, we may not get the marked toys in the expected ratio. But if we could pick up a larger number, the chances of getting the expected ratio will also be higher, and once again the resultant estimate would be closer to the actual population. Every time we repeat a sample it provides an estimate for the total number. Once we have obtained several estimates, we can take an average of these estimates to obtain a better overall estimate along with associated error. This is the basic concept from which the Capture-Recapture model is developed. It gets complicated when it is applied to wild animals, but various mathematical models have been developed to overcome such complicated situations (Karanth and Nichols, 2002).

To achieve an accurate population estimate from this method, a record of the capture history of each identified tiger is essential. In field assessment, we compile this history from photographic captures and recaptures of already photographed tigers or marked animals, dating them for each identified individual. This capture history allows us to model detection probabilities to estimate the population size in the sampled area. This methodology and its statistical theory are discussed in detail in several publications.*

Remote Cameras for Counting Tigers

The photographic Capture- Recapture sampling method for the tiger and leopard was developed by Dr Ullas Karanth and Jim Nichols (1998). It has been used successfully in several tropical forest habitats in the Indian subcontinent along with other South Asian tiger habitats (Karanth and Nichols, 1998; Carbone et al., 2001; Kawanishi, 2002;

---

* For my own reference I used *Monitoring Tigers and their Prey* (2002) by Karanth and Nichols.

Karanth et al., 2004; Wegge et al., 2004; Barlow et al., 2009; Sharma et al., 2010; Jhala et al., 2011). Therefore, we sought Dr Karanth's support and expertise, for estimating the tiger, leopard and hyena populations in Panna during our study. Dr Karanth visited our research project on several occasions and, after discussions, developed a detailed survey plan. The first survey were conducted in 2002 and the final results of that survey was published in 2004 (Karanth et al., 2004).

We repeated the same survey in 2003 with a plan for regular annual surveys and to establish a scientific monitoring system for the Reserve. For the 2003 survey, the field exercise was conducted in association with the Centre for Wild Life Studies (CWS), which provided the camera equipment for the census operation. The data used in this section is from the 2003 survey. We used camera traps manufactured by Trailmaster, USA.

Each camera trap unit included an electronic tripping device that used an infrared beam. It is the same technology that is commonly used in automatic doors: a sensor detects our presence in front of the door and sends a signal to the trigger that opens the door. In this case, a similar sensor detects the presence of a tiger or other animal in front of the camera and sends a signal to the trigger. But here, instead of one camera it fires two separate camera units. These two cameras were placed on either side of the road 3.5–4 metres apart, so that both flanks of the passing animal could be photographed (Plate 7.1). These camera trap units were deployed inside a steel shell to protect the camera and the infrared tripping device from theft and damage (Plate 7.2).

We concentrated our efforts in the territories of all the radio-collared tigers. We identified sixty sites for the deployment of our camera traps (Figure 7.1). These sites were identified based on our field experience, knowledge of tiger movements, and other methodological considerations. For example, no two camera sites were within three kilometres of each other. We only had twenty camera units (each unit included two cameras, a sensor and a trigger) but set up sixty trap-sites for sampling. Therefore, we divided the area into three sampling sub-units or zones. Each sub-unit had twenty trap locations. Each sub-unit was sampled for twenty days and, at the end of this period, the camera trap units were moved and deployed to the next sampling sub-unit. These were the pre-digital days, so all the camera sites had to be visited every day to check and sometimes change the film rolls, and record the capture details. This was a very time-consuming and tiring process. It took the research team seven to eight hours every day to complete the task. This daily exercise continued for sixty days, with part of our team devoted exclusively to this work alongside Arjun Gopalaswamy of the CWS.

Plate 7.2 The photograph shows a camera trap setup used by the field team in Panna Tiger Reserve. In the metal box, the camera can be seen at the top and the trigger at the base.

The research team kept a detailed record of all the exposed film rolls. They were marked with identification numbers, the number of frames for each photograph along with site location IDs and dates. This data was essential for creating a capture history after a positive identification. Digital cameras would have reduced the toll of this exercise enormously: it is much easier now with these devices, as the associated metadata and all the information needed for analysis is automatically recorded for every photograph. Most importantly these new cameras can be set up and left in the field for months. We used the CAPTURE software (Rexstad & Burnham 1991) to analyze the data we collected from this survey. A matrix of 0 (denoting 'no capture') and 1 (denoting 'capture') was created from our data-set to develop the capture histories for every photographed tiger (Otis et al., 1978; Nichols, 1992).*

* Table 7.1.

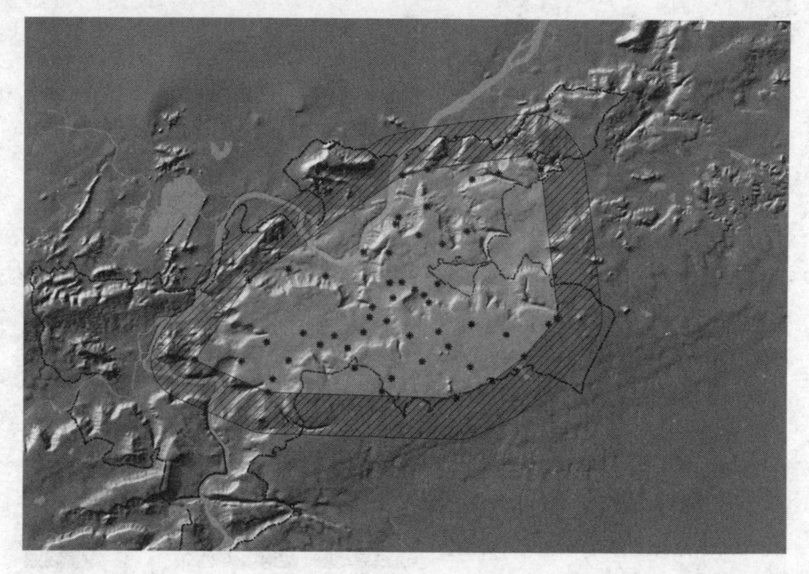

Figure 7.1 The camera trap locations and the trap polygon area in the Panna Tiger Reserve, and the hatched area showing the effectively sampled area.

We assumed that the sampled population was demographically closed (i.e. we assumed that no mortality, birth, emigration and immigration took place during the sampled period), mainly because tigers are relatively long-living animals (Otis et al., 1978; Nichols, 1995; Karanth and Nichols, 1998).

Following are the Capture-Recapture models, which can be considered to estimate tiger numbers:

M_o = Capture probability is the same for all tigers, and is not influenced by behavioural response, time, or individual heterogeneity.

M_h = Capture probabilities are heterogeneous for each individual tiger, but not affected by trap response or time.

M_b = Capture probabilities differ between previously caught and uncaught tigers due to trap-response behaviour, but are not influenced by heterogeneity or time.

Table 7.1 Capture history of tigers created from the camera trap exercise conducted in Panna in 2003.

Individual tigers	*Sampling occasion*																			
	1	2	3	4	5	6	7	8	9	10	11	12	13	14	15	16	17	18	19	20
PAT-101	0	0	0	0	0	0	0	0	0	0	0	1	0	0	0	0	0	0	0	0
PAT-102	0	0	1	0	0	0	0	0	0	0	0	0	0	0	0	0	0	0	0	0
PAT-104	0	0	0	0	0	0	0	0	0	0	0	1	0	0	0	0	0	0	0	0
PAT-106	1	0	0	0	0	0	0	0	0	0	0	0	0	0	0	0	0	0	0	0
PAT-112	0	0	0	0	0	0	0	0	1	0	0	0	0	0	0	0	1	0	0	0
PAT-113	0	0	0	0	0	0	0	0	0	0	0	1	0	0	0	0	0	1	0	0
PAT-114	0	1	0	0	0	0	0	0	0	0	0	0	0	0	0	0	0	0	0	0
PAT-115	0	1	0	0	0	0	0	0	0	0	0	0	0	0	0	0	0	0	0	0
PAT-116	0	1	0	0	0	0	0	0	0	0	0	0	0	0	0	0	0	0	0	0
PAT-117	0	0	0	0	0	1	0	0	0	0	0	0	0	0	0	0	0	0	0	0

M_t = Capture probability is the same for all individual tigers, but varies during the survey only due to time-specific factors.

The model selection criteria also considered more complex models such as M_{bh}, M_{th}, M_{tb} and M_{tbhn} that incorporate effects of heterogeneity, trap response and time in various combinations. The overall model selection test scores potential models between 0.0–1.0, with a higher score indicating a better relative fit of the model to the specific capture history data generated by the survey (Otis et al., 1978). The CAPTURE computer programme generates the number of individual tigers captured (M_{t+1}), estimates the capture probabilities per sample and computes the estimated tiger population size (the number of tigers in the sampled area, inclusive of animals that were not photo-captured at all).

We connected the outermost camera trap locations and created a buffer around this polygon to calculate the effectively sampled area (Figure 7.1). The width of buffer was calculated using MMDM. The MMDM is the mean maximum distance moved by individual animals captured at least two different locations (Wilson and Anderson, 1985; Karanth and Nichols, 1998; Karanth and Nichols, 2002). We used this method so that the 2003 estimates could be compared with previous estimates. This buffer distance was used to generate a buffer around the trap polygon (Figure 7.1) to calculate the effective sampled area (Wilson and Anderson, 1985; Karanth and Nichols, 1998; Karanth and Nichols, 2002).

The Estimation

In 2003, we extended camera-trapping by five days over the previous year. We had a total of sixty days' trapping, i.e. three sets of twenty-day-samplings (in 2002 we had set camera traps for fifteen days each). Other than this, we followed the same protocols as in the 2002 sampling, reusing most of the trap sites. The first day of sampling in each zone was considered as one sample occasion. The sampled area covered by the spread of camera traps was calculated from the minimum convex polygon obtained by joining the outer camera trap locations. The polygon covered an area of 217.7 km^2. The effort was spread over a total of 1,194 trap-nights. From this intensive effort we obtained a total of twenty-eight photographs of ten different tigers (6 females, 2 males and 2 cubs). This implies an average of forty-two trap nights per tiger photograph and almost one picture every second day for the twenty cameras sites. Of these twenty-eight photographs, thirteen were of the left flank and fifteen of the right flank. As generally expected for low density populations of tigers, the sample size or the number of individuals captured (M_{t+1}) in this survey was small. The closure test (z =-0.107, P =0.458) confirmed our assumption that the tiger population sampled during the survey was a closed population (no emigration or immigration) during the sixty days we conducted the camera trapping.

The CAPTURE software scored the various competing models: M_o=0.99, M_h=0.92, M_b=0.78, M_{bh}=1, M_t=0.0, M_{th}=0.31, M_{tb}=0.67, M_{tbh}=0.93. Although the null model M_o and M_{bh} ranked higher, the estimators based on these models are not robust to violations of the underlying assumption that capture probabilities do not vary among individual tigers. In the 2002 estimation, we found the heterogeneity model most appropriate for the tigers in Panna because their social organization consisted of resident breeding populations, which included males, females, and grown-up cubs. An adult population of floaters that roamed across several female and male ranges also existed. We also knew that the dominant breeding male's range overlapped with that of several resident female ranges. Floaters behaved differently from dominant males and usually avoided the paths frequented by them. The movement of other breeding adults remained within their respective territories. As a result of this variable movement pattern, the capture probabilities for different individuals were likely to vary. Considering these factors, we selected M_h as the most appropriate model.

During the survey, eight individual tigers were captured only once and two tigers were caught twice. We used the jack-knife estimator implemented in CAPTURE, which gave reasonably acceptable results in an earlier photographic capture study of tigers in Panna

(Karanth et al., 2004). The estimated capture probability per occasion and individual was 0.06 using the M_h-jack-knife estimator. Based on this, the corresponding population size estimate was thirteen (SE ± 4.23) within 217.7 km^2. Cubs that were excluded from the mark-and-capture analysis were included later in the estimation of total population by multiplying the population estimate with the average group size (1.25). Therefore, the estimated population size, which included the cub population, was sixteen (SE ± 5.29). Capture probability was 0.077. The buffer width was estimated to be 2.52 km (half of MMDM), which resulted in 419 km^2 of effective sampled area. The resulting tiger density was calculated dividing the estimated population size (16 tigers) by the effectively sampled area (419 km^2). The density estimated for the sampled area of the Panna Tiger Reserve was 0.0381 tigers for every square kilometre or four tigers per 100 km^2.

In the previous survey in 2002, we had estimated tiger density at seven tigers per 100 km^2, which was much higher and provided a clear indication that the density of tigers declined by almost half in just one year (Karanth et al., 2004).

Leopards and Hyenas

During the same survey we also obtained photographs of leopards and hyenas. Because of their unique marking patterns, we could identify individual hyenas and leopards, so we used this opportunity to estimate the population sizes of these two large carnivores as well. All the parameters that we described earlier for the tiger remained the same.

Leopards

We identified a total of twelve leopards from the thirty-three photographs obtained from the survey. These included seventeen photographs of left flanks and sixteen of right flanks. The closure test (z=-1.071, P= 0.14) for the leopard confirmed that the sampled leopard population was a closed population during the sampling period. The heterogeneity model M_h was selected over null M_o because the social organization of leopards is similar to that of tigers. The capture probability per occasion and individual was 0.037 and the resultant population estimate was forty-one leopards (±12.67). The effective sampled area estimated for the leopard was smaller: 288 km^2 (buffer width or half MMDM calculated was 1.75 km), which indicated a much higher density of 14.24 leopards per 100 km^2.

Hyena

We obtained twenty-nine photographs of hyenas during the sampling period (16 left flanks and 13 right flanks). From this set of pictures, we could identify eleven different hyenas. The closure test told us that the hyena population was also a closed population during the survey (z =-1.107, P = 0.134). For estimating the density of hyenas, we once again used M_h (0.84) as the most appropriate model based on model selection criteria. Capture probability estimated by the Jack-knife estimator was 0.086 per sampling occasion. The population of hyenas in the sampled area was estimated to be twenty (SE ± 5.96). The buffer width (half of MMDM) calculated for hyenas was 1.9 km and therefore the effective sampled area for density estimation was 305 km^2. This indicated a density of 6.55 or seven hyenas per 100 km^2.

The Future of Panna's Tigers

We spent over eight years watching Baavan (F 123), her family and their neighbours. During this time, we gathered crucial information on known instances of births and deaths of tigers to estimate demographic parameters such as cubs and adult survival, litter size, gestation period, and inter-birth interval. It is now believed that for a small population, demographic problems can be more immediate and deterministic threats than factors like genetics and minimum viable population size that operate over the longer term (Lande, 1988; Hedrick et al., 1996). Despite monitoring a tiger population for nearly a decade, this study only provides a small window into the life-history of tigers, so it cannot answer all our questions. We therefore built several population models for different scenarios using our data, with the aim of understanding population trends over a much longer period and to assess the population's viability. Models such as these are important conservation tools as they help identify threats, define problems, and make reliable predictions. The models we developed were an attempt to explore the consequences of human-caused mortalities (mainly poaching). We expect the predictive models to help us find new directions and approaches that will ensure the viability and stability of the tiger population.

Whether and why we need management of protected areas is an ongoing debate. The old school believes that if we could leave a population alone, nature would take care of itself. However, this is only possible in large landscapes of true wilderness, far away from all human pressures. Unfortunately, such a landscape rarely exists, certainly very infrequently in India. Most of the Reserves here are small and almost all suffer from severe human pressures. In some of these small protected areas, the Reserve management has succeeded in keeping conflict at arm's length. But pressures are mounting and the old approaches may not be sustainable in the long run. We can no longer depend entirely on these smaller protected areas to ensure the long-term future of species such as tigers and elephants, which require larger spaces. In these testing conditions, we need proactive and adaptive management that is equipped to deal with the constantly changing threats to the animals. Unfortunately, when it comes to tigers, the current management systems have so far done little more than fire-fighting. In other words, they have always been struggling to catch up with the problems and rather than preventing them. This has resulted in the decline of several tiger populations.

Population modelling is a tool that can help the reserve managements foresee threats and prepare themselves before these can harm the wildlife populations. These models have their limitations because they work within the framework that we create and rely on the information we provide. Starfield and Beloch (1986) observe that, 'the quality of a model does not depend on how realistic it is, but on how well it performs in relation to the purpose for which it was built'.

Several models have been developed in the past to better understand tiger societies and the factors that can lead to their extinction (Kenney et al., 1995; Karanth and Stith, 1999; Linkie et al., 2006; Chapron et al., 2008; Damania et al., 2008; Horev et al., 2012). The models we used helped us to test specific scenarios like the effect of prey availability and the effect of poaching on specific age and sex classes. This enabled us to propose a minimum population of breeding females that could sustain different levels of poaching pressures.

Method

We used a stage-based population model using the computer programme RAMAS STAGE (Ferson, 1991). We modified our model parameters from those developed by Kenney et al. (1991), Karanth and Stith (1999) and Chapron et al. (2008) by incorporating information obtained from the study in the Panna Tiger Reserve. The ratio of breeding males to breeding females was estimated to be 1:3; mean litter size was 2.28; average time between two litters was twenty-two months; and the average age of tigresses at which the first litter was born was forty months. We classified the tiger population for each sex in four stages as follows:

F1 = young female cubs: 0–12 months old
F2 = juvenile females: 12–24 months old
F3 = females: 24–40 months old
F4 = adult females: above 40 months
M1 = young male cubs: 0–12 months old
M2 = juvenile males: 12–24 months old
M3 = sub-adult males: 24–72 months old
M4 = adult males: above 72 months old

Figure 7.2 shows the network of how these age and sex classes are connected to each other in our models and the equations used to calculate the transitions between the age classes.

The All-India Estimate of 2010 indicated that tiger densities in India varied from less than one individual to 19.8 tigers per 100 km^2 (Jhala et al., 2011). It is known that breeding females hold exclusive territories and as we have seen in dry forests such as Panna, the annual range of females could be as large as 60 km^2. The Panna Tiger Reserve, which is larger than the average protected area, could provide space for only seven to eight breeding female territories.

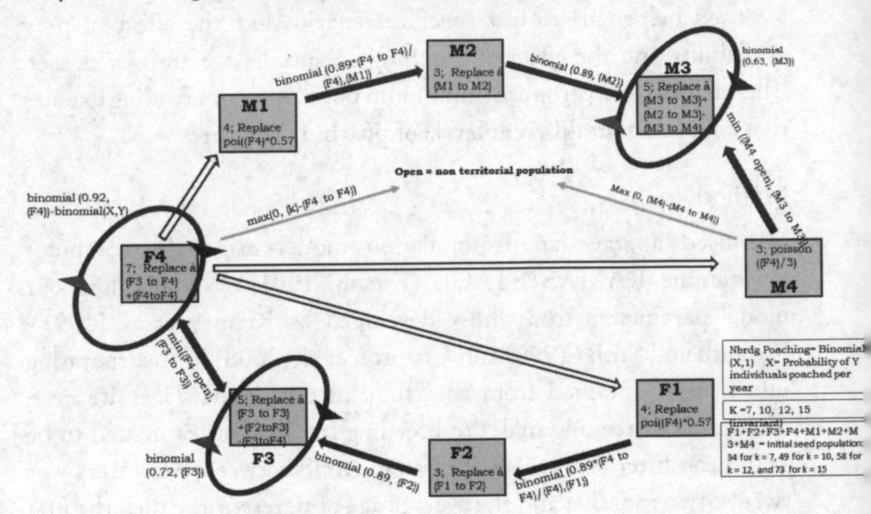

Figure 7.2 Network of various stages identified for the model and arrows showing transition directions between the population stages.

We know that Tropical Dry Forests can support tiger densities of up to eight tigers per 100 km^2 (Jhala et al., 2011). With such densities, one can reasonably assume that the Panna Tiger Reserve could support a maximum of forty to forty-five tigers. This still constitutes a small population but set an achievable goal for tiger conservation. Unfortunately, the reality is much worse, where poaching puts constant pressure on these tiger populations. So we built a model that was as close to reality as possible by simulating different scenarios of poaching pressures for a population that is supported by seven breeding females. We also increased the number of breeding females (carrying capacity or *k*) up to fifteen to predict the probabilities of local extinction in a hundred years.

Our Simulations

The first scenario that we modelled was the one with empirical estimates of the survival probabilities of each age and sex class of the tiger. Our data from Panna estimated an annual female survival probability of 0.76. This survival probability for breeding females represents a population that was exposed to high levels of poaching that subsequently caused its extinction in 2009 (Chundawat and Van Gruisen, 2009; Gopal et al., 2010). In the second scenario, keeping all parameters the same, we changed the survival rate of breeding females, in order to simulate a scenario with no poaching pressures. A survival probability of 0.92 was estimated using the average lifespan of twelve years for adult breeding females in that age class (life after 40 months). We treated this as an ideal situation where we assumed there was no poaching of breeding females. We later built several poaching scenarios by adding different levels of poaching pressures on breeding females that ranged from one breeding female poached per year to one breeding female poached every three years, with the carrying capacity of breeding females kept constant at $k=7$.

In the next set of simulations, we increased the carrying capacity of breeding females from seven (overall tiger seed population=34) to fifteen (overall tiger seed population=73). We modelled the probability of extinction for a population where one breeding tiger was poached annually.

Simulation Results

Over the last few years, poaching has decimated tiger populations from protected areas like Sariska and Panna. These local extinctions indicate that even though prey availability is an important ecological factor, external threats such as poaching can wipe out healthy and viable tiger populations, even from prey-rich areas. There are a few studies that quantify the belief that the tiger is a resilient species. In the past Kenney et al. (1995) suggested that poaching increases the extinction threat, but their conclusion was later questioned by Karanth and Stith (1999) who suggested that tiger populations are more vulnerable to prey depletion than poaching. A recent publication on a similar subject used simulations to demonstrate that more than 15 per cent mortality due to poaching is unsustainable for a tiger population (Chapron et al., 2008). Our models predicted that even a small population of seven breeding females such as Panna shows little extinction risk in an ideal scenario (i.e. complete absence of poaching of breeding females). However, with one breeding female poached annually, the risk of extinction is ineluctably high. It is when only one breeding female is poached every three years that the probability of local extinction of the tiger population reduces below 5 per cent, though it still carries a risk. On the other hand, poaching of one tiger every year belonging to other age- and sex-classes can be sustained without creating high extinction risk (Figure 7.3). Given that poachers usually operate in areas with known movements of tigers, there is a high risk of their poaching breeding females. In the previous chapter,

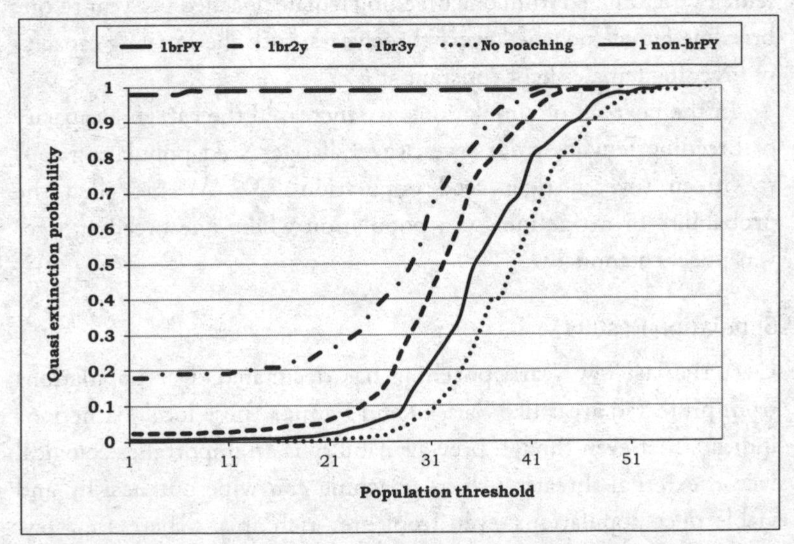

Figure 7.3 Scenario with seven breeding females (k=7) with different poaching levels; no poaching=no poaching of breeding females; 1non-brPY=poaching of one non-breeding ♀ tiger every year; 1brPY=poaching of one breeding ♀ every year; 1br2Y=poaching of one breeding ♀ every two years and 1br3Y=poaching of one breeding ♀ every three years.

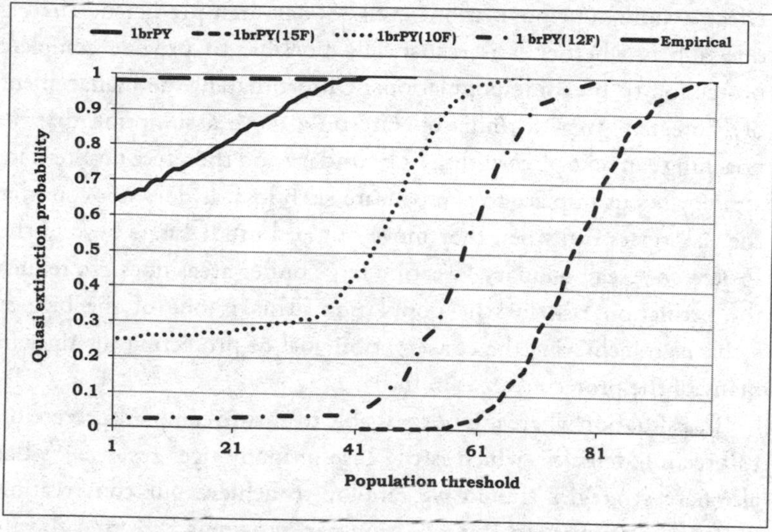

Figure 7.4 Different scenarios modelled for poaching of 1 breeding female every year but with increased carrying capacity/number breeding females (k); 1brPY(7F) = (k=7 breeding females); 1brPY(10F)=(k=10 breeding females); 1brPY(12F)=(k=12 breeding females); 1brPY(15F)=(k=15 breeding females); and empirical where k=7 but breeding female survival was estimated from field study (0.76).

we have discussed why female tigers in Dry Forest habitats such as Panna are more vulnerable to poaching. From our model, it is evident that small populations cannot be viable in habitats where poaching cannot be ruled out. This puts tremendous pressure and responsibility on the tiger Reserve management to keep a tight and effective control on external mortalities due to poaching or disease.

Unfortunately, so far we have not been able to provide such an environment and as a result many of the populations continue to suffer.

How to Ensure Viability for Small Populations?

Complete protection to breeding females is one obvious option to maintain a low extinction risk for tiger populations. However, even a minute increase in their natural mortality rates can have catastrophic effects, wiping out populations even sooner than predicted. The big question is whether it is realistically possible to provide complete protection to breeding populations. Unfortunately, the management of Protected Areas in India operate on a naive assumption that no poaching can take place within its boundary and therefore no alternate strategy is put in place to compensate such loss. It does not consider the risk tigers run when they move out and use habitats beyond the Protected Area boundary. Creating large buffer areas does not reduce the extinction risk for the population. This is one of the biggest setbacks in achieving the conservation goal of protecting the tiger in many of the protected areas in India.

In a situation where it is not possible to ensure complete protection to breeding females (which is the case in many tiger reserves), what alternate strategies should we employ to achieve our conservation goals? The answers to this question can provide a direction to our ongoing conservation efforts. We will discuss these aspects and solutions to this problem in the following chapters.

The solution I propose originates from the next set of simulations (Figure 8.4), where we had fixed the breeding female mortality due to poaching to one every year (high poaching scenario), while changing the carrying capacity and, hence, the overall tiger seed population. We observed from our simulation that increasing the breeding female numbers to ten females also carries high extinction risks. Only when the number of breeding females was increased to thirteen or higher, did the population become sustainable and the extinction probability reduced below 5 per cent, though it still carried some extinction risk. A population with thirteen and more breeding females is viable and can sustain such high poaching pressure. This is a very encouraging observation from our simulations. If we extrapolate the total tiger population from the breeding female population (k=13), we get the figure of roughly sixty-two tigers. This is a fairly large population and very few tiger Reserves in India have the space for it. Even in such a desperate environment, our model provides encouraging possibilities along with a challenge: we must find space for more breeding females. It is evident that one cannot entirely depend on smaller protected areas, as these are unable to play the role expected of them, which is to protect viable populations. Our conservation goal is to find space for a minimum number of breeding females for a viable population and ensure stability. Since increasing the protected area size is not an option in most situations, and providing buffer areas does not reduce the risk, we must explore alternate approaches to strengthen our existing conservation efforts.

Tiger density in Panna Tiger Reserve dropped to four tigers every 100 km^2 in 2003, from a high of seven tigers in 2002. This was the beginning of the decline, which resulted in complete extinction of the population in 2009. Panna's tiger population, when modelled with empirical demographic data, also shows a similar result. Our models re-emphasize that protection of the breeding population from poaching is of paramount importance, especially when dealing with small populations. In Panna, tigers need larger spaces, and since this is not available, the mismatch leads to almost all the breeding tigers having ranges going up to or beyond the park boundary. So even if the wildlife authorities could provide protection to the breeding females within the Reserve, this would not prevent mortalities due to the Edge Effect. Our model suggests that a larger population of over thirteen breeding females could sustain some external threat. However, since many tiger reserves are not large enough to provide space for thirteen or more breeding females, a new strategy must be devised. Instead of looking at a single large population, several small interconnected populations may be an alternative. This means that we must revisit the debate about SLOSS (single large or several small), which was discussed in the 1970s and '80s. We must recognize that even though factors such as prey depletion, habitat loss, and genetics are important, they can be treated as secondary to the direct external threats like poaching, which have a more immediate effect on the population.

8

Finding a Place to Live

Habitat and Food selection

Introduction

The conservation and management of large carnivores needs to be different from other conservation approaches (Ginsberg, 2001). This is an arduous task for managers in India, since the tiger lives in protected areas surrounded by human-dominated landscapes. It often comes into direct conflict with humans, mainly due to its predation on livestock and, occasionally, as a man-eater (Mcdougal, 1987). It is believed that this conflict tends to intensify in areas where the tiger is losing its habitat and the prey population is declining, generally referred to as 'loss of habitat quality' (Dinerstein et al., 2007). Since we have lost most of the tiger population outside the protected areas (Jhala et al., 2011), the conflict is now concentrated around the boundaries of these protected habitats. It has made the conservation and management of tigers an increasingly contentious issue for politicians and the communities who live alongside these large predators. The ideal scenario of peaceful coexistence between tigers and humans is hard to achieve.

Recent studies have documented prey depletion and the loss of habitat and habitat quality as major factors responsible for the tiger's decline throughout its distribution range (Joslin, 1973; Mcdougal, 1987; Seidensticker, 1997; Karanth and Stith, 1999; Dinerstein et al., 2007). Therefore, the key focus of our conservation efforts has been to better manage habitats that are preferred by the tiger and its prey. Our conservation efforts would be more effective if our approach was preventive rather than fire-fighting. The former requires a scientific understanding of tigers' habitat preferences and the relative importance of its prey.

Tropical Dry Forests provide one of the largest tiger habitats in the subcontinent, but it is the least studied ecosystem. Our observations therefore are crucial in filling the existing gap in knowledge on tiger resource use. In this chapter, we look at the tiger's food habits to understand its relationship with the prey community, its response to prevailing wild and domestic prey, and to habitat selection. Finally, based on data collected during the study, we build a predictive model that identifies, characterizes and quantifies the suitable habitat for female breeding tigers in and around the Panna Tiger Reserve. This information can help formulate a detailed conservation plan for tigers for a larger landscape that extends beyond protected area boundaries.

Predation: What Tigers Prefer to Eat

It is very difficult to gather information on predation by large carnivores from direct observations. Therefore, their diet is determined from indirect but reliable sources of information. This includes analysis of faecal (scat) samples and kill records (Flyod et al., 1978; Sunquist, 1981; Tamang, 1982; Johnsingh, 1983; Ackerman et al., 1984; Karanth and Sunquist, 1995; Chundawat et al., 1999). Scat analysis has several advantages over other methods (Reynolds and Aebischer, 1991). Firstly, it is non-invasive, and secondly, scat samples can be collected easily. Most importantly, it is a reliable source of information for identification if predator scats are identified correctly. Great care and experience is required to ascertain the predator species of the scat. In my experience, identification of the predator species is usually very casually done. Genetic studies of scats have found large inconsistencies in correct identifications (Williams and Johnston, 2004). Therefore, we were very careful and looked for supplementary signs like pugmarks to ascertain the species. Most of the time, confusion was between leopard and dhole scats; in cases of reasonable doubt, the scat samples were discarded. Samples were collected regularly on a systematic schedule. A detailed note on date, predator species (if possible, individual ID when the scat sample was collected from an identified animal that was seen defecating), and the location and area from where the scat was collected, were recorded for every sample. The samples were washed thoroughly, and the prey remains in them were separated; these remains were then washed again and later dried. Prey items mostly comprise of undigested parts of hair, bone, hooves, feathers and claws of the prey. There are established techniques by which prey species can be identified positively from the micro-histological structure of hairs (Joslin, 1973; Koppikar and Sabnis, 1976; Mukherjee et al., 1994a, 1994b). In addition to the scat samples that were collected from the field, information on kills found during the field studies and the monitoring of radio-collared tigers also provided information on kill rates and consumption of different prey species.

This method of establishing the diet of the predator from scat samples has its limitations. One of the major constraints that can affect the result is when we interpret data from the presence of prey items and their frequency of occurrence. Studies have shown that in such interpretations, smaller prey items are usually over-represented in the predator's diet (Karanth, 1993; Karanth and Sunquist, 1995). Floyd et al. (1978) found an inverse relationship between the number of field-collectible scats and the prey size, which meant that smaller prey produced more scats per kg of prey biomass eaten than larger prey. Therefore, the frequency of occurrence misrepresents the relative numbers of prey items in the diet estimated from scat samples. Ackerman developed an equation to estimate the biomass consumed per scats for cougars (*Felis concolor*) with a correction factor to overcome this constraint (Ackerman et al., 1984):

$$Y = 1{:}980 + 0{:}035X$$

Here Y is the weight of prey consumed per scat and X is the prey body weight (kg).

This equation is used widely for estimating the biomass consumed by tigers (Joslin, 1973; Koppikar and Sabnis, 1976; Karanth, 1993; Mukherjee et al., 1994a; Karanth and Sunquist, 1995; Biswas and Sankar, 2002). The results of a similar exercise conducted recently in India using prey from tropical Indian forests showed an asymptotic, allometric relationship between the biomass consumed and predator weight (Chakrabarti et al., 2016). Its generalized model used the following equation:

Biomass consumed per collectable scat/predator weight = 0.033–0.025 exp 4.284 (prey weight/predator weight).

We used this formula to estimate the biomass consumed and scat rate from the scat samples.

The SCATMAN software (Hines, 2002) helped us evaluate prey selection by tigers. Prey selection here can be defined as the tiger catching and eating a prey at frequencies which are different from its natural frequency of occurrence in the environment (Chesson, 1978). When the tiger is not selecting a prey, it would be expected that the prey is taken at a frequency which is similar to its availability. Any significant deviation (statistically) suggests either a preference or avoidance for the prey type in question by the tiger. In the software, input data included the frequency of occurrence of prey items, density of prey groups and the associated standard deviation (calculated from line transacts), live weight of the prey species, and the scat production rate calculated from the above equation. The software estimated the expected proportions of prey species in the scats by using likelihood-ratio tests (G tests) to compare it with observed proportions (Zar, 1984).

Kill Records

Over a six-year period, we recorded 416 kills made by tigers: 266 kills between 1996 and 1999, and 150 kills between 2000 and 2002. Tigers usually took several days to finish larger prey like sambar, nilgai and livestock. However, prey such as chital and wild pigs were finished within a few hours, especially when full-grown cubs accompanied a mother. Although we were monitoring the radio-collared tigers intensively, we physically observed them mostly on larger prey kills. We were dependent on clues from the radio monitoring to determine whether the tiger had made a kill. One important indication was their restricted activity in the vicinity of the kill site. When our signals showed lack of movement for longer than usual or indicated repeat locations from one locality, the research team would suspect a kill and investigate the area, thereby finding the carcass.

In the early years of the study, vultures would often provide the first sign of a kill, but by 2001 the vulture population had declined to such low numbers that we rarely found kills from observing them. During the late '90s, I remember how frequently we looked at the sky for vultures. If we saw a line of them gliding in one direction we would follow them, which would invariably lead us to a kill. We never recorded the number of times we found kills from watching vultures, but it was fairly high. This was even true for the kills made by radio-collared tigers. But by 2002, this was no longer possible and we had to depend on radio signal information—repeated radio locations from an area. Later we spotted the occasional vulture, mostly the king vulture or red-headed vulture (*Aegypius calvus*). Earlier the white-backed (*Gyps bengalensis*) and long-billed (*Gyps indicus*) vultures were numerous. After arriving at the site, crows and vultures provided us with the exact kill location and other crucial information. Their presence on the trees indicated a predator presence nearby, so we would use an elephant if we wanted to investigate the kill immediately, especially when it was outside or near the Reserve boundary. Otherwise, we waited for the predator to finish feeding and leave the area. This could take a few hours or several days. Vultures or crows on the ground meant that the predator had left the kill and we could comfortably investigate the kill site. As mentioned before, if radio locations came from one area continuously for more than eight hours, it was likely that the tiger had made a kill, although, in the summer months, restricted movement also occurred when tigers spent a long time in cool spaces during the daylight hours. Even then, we would investigate the area as a policy if a tiger had spent eight to ten hours in one spot. Since smaller prey could be consumed more quickly than this, our data set of kill records may be slightly biased towards large prey. The information needs to be appraised with this limitation in mind.

In addition to this monitoring, we also conducted several one-week-long continuous monitoring sessions of the radio-collared female tigers to determine how often they made a kill. From this monitoring, we estimated that female tigers in Panna were killing one large prey weighing more than 40 kg every 7-8 days on average. They would spend 3-4 days over a large kill of an adult sambar or nilgai but they would spend less than a day on a chital kill, if there was more than one tiger (or if it was a female chital).

Using all the kill data alone, the average kill rate of female radio-collared tigers ranged between 2.7–3.6 large kills every month, which is a slightly lower figure than the one obtained by the intensive one-week monitoring. The latter produced a figure of 3.5–3.8 kills per month or 42–45 large prey every year. During our regular monitoring, we also noticed that over the years, from late September to early November there were fewer large kills. We investigated this periodic lack of large kills through continuous radio monitoring with little result. However, when we followed the tigers on elephant-back, we realized that they were predating very heavily on fawns, especially those of the sambar, during this time.

Since the prey were small, they were being killed and eaten largely undetected by our regular monitoring. On one occasion we saw F-123 kill three fawns in one day. Tigresses would often catch a fawn alive and put it in front of her young cubs to give them predation experience. We have seen this with tiger cubs as young as seven months old. We witnessed a tigress carrying a live fawn over many kilometres to her cubs on several occasions. We also observed tigresses employing different strategies to catch fawns. From elephant-back, we saw a tigress walking in a zig-zag pattern to flush fawns from cover so she could catch them. A fawn's protection instinct is to lie motionless, and this is very effective: much of the time a tiger can walk past these fawns without noticing them. Only when the fawns are almost stepped on, would they would run for a short distance—ten metres or so—before stopping. But this would give the tiger enough time to pounce on them.

Once, while following F-123 on elephant-back, we saw the tigress sitting down. It was only after a minute that we realized that between our elephant and the tiger was a sambar fawn lying hidden in the grass motionless, barely 8 metres from the tiger. She had no clue about the fawn's presence and we were concerned that our presence might disturb the fawn. We retreated and watched her from a distance and after a while, the tigress moved away and the fawn survived. In a similar incident, we were watching a tiger family resting. One of the tiger cubs appeared some distance away from where its mother was lying. It accidently flushed a fawn on its way to the mother but this time, the fawn was caught by the tigress in a flash.

We did not gather quantitative information on predation on fawns, so we can only make an estimate based on our observations from elephant-back. From this monitoring, we concluded that one tiger killed 4-5 fawns every week during these months. The demographic data from our monitoring of prey population also indicated a similarly high predation on the fawn population. This predation on fawns could put serious pressure on prey populations, especially those of sambar. The chital population—which can achieve very high abundance—can better sustain the cumulative predation pressure of tigers and other predators on its fawns. But prey populations of the sambar and four-horned antelope may not. As we have seen in the earlier chapter on prey, the sambar population in Panna gradually declined from 1997 onwards, whereas, the chital population grew substantially. Sambar and four-horned antelopes can never achieve the densities that the chital can. Many tiger Reserves have an abundance of chital, and this can encourage high predator densities. From fawns (of a few kg) to adult males (70–80 kg), chital provide the ideal prey size for tigers, leopards, dholes and jackals. But excessive predation by these predators can be severe on other prey populations. Ungulate species sympatric to chital not only compete directly for resources but also suffer from this increased predation pressure. I can think of swamp deer in Kanha as an example: very high abundance of chital has not only modified the grassland, but has supported high predator densities, creating a dangerous and difficult environment for the swamp deer. Chital may be one of the many reasons why a recovery of this endangered species has not taken off as expected, despite the management's best efforts. In the enclosure, where these deer were protected from excessive predation, the swamp deer population responded well and grew. This is only my hypothesis. But certainly, information on the cropping rate of major prey species by various large predators, especially tigers, leopards, and dholes are important for the Reserve management.

Table 8.1 Comparison of kills made during 1997–99 and 2000–02 by the radio-collared tigers in Panna Tiger Reserve

Species	*1997–99 (n=266)*	*2000–02 (n=150)*
Sambar	22.9	25.3
Chital	2.3	9.3
Nilgai	22.2	26.0
Cattle	51.1	30
Wild Pig	1.5	7.3
Others	0	2.0

We compared kill records from 1996-99—when there were fewer tigers and the wild prey population was low—to those from 2000–03, when tiger numbers were at their peak and prey abundance had increased considerably (especially that of the chital). It is noteworthy that the tiger predated at a higher frequency on livestock in the '90s. The predation by tigers shifted more towards wild prey during 2000–03, which was accompanied by an increase in wild prey density (Table 8.1). Predation on livestock came down to 30 per cent from a high 51 per cent. However, this figure was still high in comparison to other studied populations and at a level that added to the tiger's vulnerability. Interestingly, predation on nilgai and sambar remained more or less the same, but increased on the chital and wild pig. For an increasing tiger population, the shift to wild prey was a positive sign.

~

Although data from kills do not give a totally accurate picture of predation, they do provide reliable information on the predation pattern that exists in the region. The kill records of individual tigers reveal variability in predation patterns. Male tigers predated almost exclusively on larger prey, including livestock (Table 8.2). We did not record kills of smaller ungulates like chital or wild pig, but it appeared that the males predated on larger prey like sambar and nilgai on a regular basis, along with cows and buffaloes. But males were timid in nature at the kill locations as compared to females—each male's behaviour was different at livestock kills. M-91 only fed once on livestock, rarely returning to the same kill, whether disturbed or not. He would always settle far away from the kill site. In fact, it was very difficult for us to find his livestock kills. He was a naturally shy and timid individual and when a human approached his kill, he would quietly escape, never exposing himself. Rarely would he return. Most of the time he would rest a couple of kilometres away from the livestock carcass. We located M-91 on a livestock kill less than 15 times out of the total 45 livestock kills of his that we found.

F-120 on a Nilgai Kill

Table 8.2 Kill composition (in %) of individual radio-collared tigers in Panna National Park 1997–2003, (n=416).

Species	*F-123*	*F-111*	*F-120*	*F-113*	*M-91*	*M-125*	*unknown*
Buffalo	1.3	11.5	1.2	16.7	17.9	25.0	12.1
Cattle	10.0	46.2	30.6	8.3	52.2	37.5	43.9
Sambar	45.0	17.9	14.1	45.8	17.9	12.5	18.2
Nilgai	25.0	23.1	32.9	20.8	11.9	25.0	22.7
Chital	7.5	0.0	14.1	4.2	0.0	0.0	1.5
Wild boar	11.3	1.3	4.7	0.0	0.0	0.0	1.5
Small prey	0.0	0.0	2.4	4.2	0.0	0.0	0.0

We estimated that on a regular basis he could eat over 25-30 kg in one sitting, lasting 4-6 hours. This estimate was calculated from an average of what each field-team member thought the amount in kilos was, that had been eaten. When we tranquillized M-91 for radio-collaring, we had located him over a kill with a full belly. During recovery, he vomited and emptied out his belly. I'm loathe to say this, but the volume was so large that we weighed the meat he regurgitated. It was 19 kg. Contrary to his otherwise timid behaviour, we regularly located M-91 on sambar and nilgai kills (if within the park) and found that he was not disturbed by our approach. Unlike with livestock or wild prey kills outside or on the periphery of the park, he would only leave the wild prey carcass once he was finished with it, after feeding for 2-3 days.

M-125 behaved very differently. He would stay put and never showed aggression; we could even approach the kill on foot when he was lying only a few metres away. He could stay unnoticed for days. I remember one occasion when he had killed a cow right on a footpath and dragged it just 20 metres inside, where he remained for a couple of days. This was his usual behaviour, but on this occasion there was a weekly bazaar at the nearby village and hundreds of villagers crossed the path that day. Apparently, the noise and crowd did not bother him. He kept such a low profile that none of the passers-by noticed his presence. Curious and concerned, we stayed at the site with our monitoring device for the rest of the day. M-125 remained at one location the whole day, about 120 metres from the carcass. Some villagers did notice the carcass and hurried away. But such an event could never happen with our four collared females, certainly not with F-123, 111 and 113. F-120 could tolerate an approach if she was some distance away but the other three would make their presence known by growling, raising themselves or their tail in the air and occasionally even charging. We would never approach a kill made by a female on foot, if she was within even a 300-400 metre radius. Even if she was further away we would be cautious and approach very carefully, always alert, with the receiver switched on the whole time. If the radio signal indicated activity, we would wait and watch before moving further. Approaching a female kill was a very different story from that of the males.

Similar to the males, tigress F-111 also predated extensively on livestock (Table 8.2). There were a couple of villages in her range whose livestock were grazed within it, so she had easy access to cattle. Moreover, there were less wild prey around her. The kill records for F-120 and F-113 also show fairly high livestock predation. In the case of F-120, it was mainly due to the large feral cattle population within her range, which had been left behind after a couple of villages were relocated outside the park. F-113's range was close to the river and included a village with a high buffalo population, so her predation on buffaloes was high. This was a matter of great concern for us, because the loss of a buffalo causes more serious economic loss to the owner than that of a cow and is more likely to raise the possibility of retaliation.

A notable anomaly in the livestock predation pattern was Baavan, or F-123. The livestock component in her diet was low—only around 11% (see Table 8.2)—and she survived the longest. The survival of the other tigresses was low—F-111 had the highest livestock predation numbers and she was the first poaching casualty from Panna, disappearing from a livestock kill in 2002. F-120 and F-113 were also poached not long after. This illustrates how dependence on a livestock diet makes a tiger vulnerable to poaching. This is one reason why all tiger biologists, especially Dr Karanth, have stressed the importance of wild prey availability for tiger. There can be no other alternatives.

Scat Analysis

As we have seen, monitoring the kills of radio-collared tigers gives us a good measure of tiger predation on the larger prey, but smaller prey are under-represented by this method. However, by identifying the prey remains in the tigers' scat, we get a much better representation of what the tiger has been eating, including even smaller prey like hares. To establish a fair representation of the tiger's diet, one requires a minimum number of scats. To build an accurate picture, one cannot just sample 10 or 20 scats because the results would be biased. To establish that we have the minimum number of scats, we plotted the cumulative percentage occurrence of all the major prey items recorded in the randomly selected scat samples. The point where occurrence of prey in the tiger diet reached an asymptote, or a plateau, for most of the prey, would be the minimum sample size (see Figure 8.1). In our samples from Panna, we observed that the minimum number of scats required was 45–55. This means that if we have more than 55 scat samples, we can be reasonably sure about the tiger's diet for that

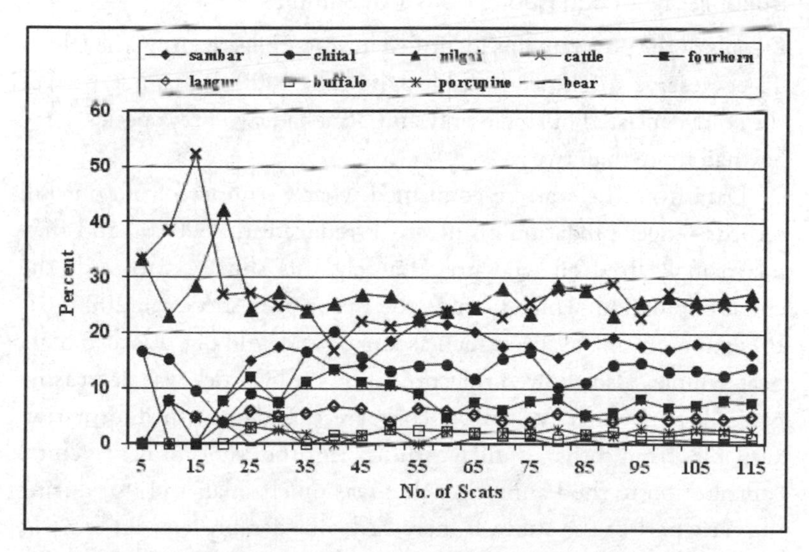

Figure 8.1 Cumulative percentage occurrence of tiger prey items in every five scat samples.

period. Considering this, our samples sizes were fairly large in most cases, except when we were looking at samples from individual tigers. These are very difficult to obtain and have not been attempted before, but they provide an interesting perspective and, for that reason only, we have included these results (Table 8.3).

Table 8.3 Food habits of individual tigers as determined from scat samples collected for individual radio-collared tigers between 1999 and 2003.

Prey Species	*F-113* (*n*=35)	*F-111* (*n*=43)	*F-120* (*n*=71)	*F-123* (*n*=52)	*Average*
Chital	28.2	17.8	27.5	25.0	24.6
Sambar	23.1	13.3	22.5	23.3	20.6
Nilgai	12.8	20.0	16.3	25.0	18.5
Wild Boar	7.7	8.9	6.3	11.7	8.6
Langur	17.9	22.2	10.0	6.7	14.2
Cattle	5.2	15.6	17.5	3.3	10.4
Others	5.2	2.2	0.0	5.0	3.1

Building Tiger Food Habits from Scat Samples

Details of the prey remains identified in scats collected from the Panna Tiger Reserve are shown in Table 8.4. In the 2000–03 sample, 61% of the scats consisted of single prey and 36% had two prey species. Very few had more than two.

Data from the scats re-confirmed what we noticed from our kill records—tiger predation on livestock reduced in 2000–03 and they increasingly lived on wild prey. Largely, this shift was towards the chital population, which became the major prey species in 2000–03. Predation on smaller prey, such as langur and wild pig, was also high. Scat samples also showed that predation on livestock was decreasing but still fairly high. When we compare this data with information available from other similar studies in the subcontinent, chital contribution to the Panna tiger diet was much smaller (13%) during the early part of the study. It increased considerably later on but was still much lower than in other tiger habitats (Schaller, 1967; Sunquist, 1981; Karanth, 1993; Biswas and Sankar, 2002; Bagchi et al., 2003).

Table 8.4 Comparison of food habits of tigers from two different scat samples collected between 1996–2003 in Panna Tiger Reserve (n=total number of scats).

Prey species	*1996–99 (n=315)*		*2000–03 (n=226)*	
	No. of prey items	*Occurrence (%)*	*No. of prey items*	*Occurrence (%)*
Sambar	84	19.7	55	22.4
Chital	58	13.6	59	24
Nilgai	100	23.4	43	17.5
Livestock	107	25.1	31	12.6
Langur	33	7.7	20	8.1
Wild Pig	22	5.2	32	13
Bear	3	0.7	2	0.8
Others	20	4.7	4	1.6
Total	427	100	246	100

Tiger predation on sambar is more or less the same as in other tiger habitats of the subcontinent (22%). Smaller mammals (<40 kg) including wild boars, langurs, chinkaras, four-horned antelopes and porcupines, together accounted for over 14% of the diet. The sloth bear appeared regularly in the scat sample, indicating a possible conflict between these two large carnivores. During monitoring, our team saw radio-collared tigers feeding on a bear carcass on two separate occasions. We also saw a tiger feeding on a leopard carcass twice. One very unusual observation was that several radio-collared tigers, including M-91, were seen feeding on bear droppings full of termites, ants and mud. We witnessed this on several occasions and wondered about the rationale behind this.

The most surprising contribution in the diet of the Panna tigers was the nilgai (17% of the scat data). This is remarkable because the nilgai is usually missing from the list of tiger prey in most protected areas of the subcontinent, or its contribution is minimal. In terms of size and abundance, the nilgai form a suitable prey base, but the habitat these antelopes occupy is not used much by tigers. However, the nilgai distribution in Panna is widespread—spanning across habitats, some of which are also preferred by tigers. So in Panna, nilgai is likely to be predated more often in the areas that are also frequented by tigers. The nilgai-preferred habitat in Panna can be characterized as open, savannah-like forest, patches that are not used as often by tigers as the other habitats. In the summer months this habitat is particularly unsuitable for them due to the lack of water and high temperatures. But these nilgai-preferred habitat patches are large and widely distributed throughout Panna. This could be one of the important factors that influences the tigers' use of space and possibly its range size, particularly when such habitats are abundant and widely distributed.

The frequency of prey remains in a predator's scats provides information on the relative importance of prey. We used the equation developed for cats from the Indian subcontinent to calculate biomass consumed to produce a scat (Chakrabarti et al., 2016). The scat rate refers to the number of field-collectible scats produced from eating a prey (Table 8.5).

Table 8.5 Calculation of scat rate using {x= (prey wt./tiger wt.)/(0.033-0.025*exponential(-4.284*(prey wt./tiger wt.)))}; (Chakrabarti et al., 2016)

2000–03 sample	*Prey wt.*	*Biomass consumed*	*scat rate*
Sambar	175	44.25	3.95
Chital	47	13.82	3.40
Nilgai	125	31.84	3.93
Other Prey	20	8.029	2.49
Langur	8	4.69	1.71
Cattle	200	50.53	3.96
Buffalo	400	101.01	3.96
Wild Pig	34	11.07	3.07

Our estimates reveal that in terms of biomass, sambar (34%) and nilgai (19%) were the major wild prey species for tigers in Panna (Table 8.6). Chital contributed much less to the tiger's diet in Panna than has been recorded in other studies (Schaller, 1967; Sunquist,

Table 8.6 Estimation of biomass consumed by tigers in Panna Tiger Reserve (without langur estimates; 2000-03 sample; n=226).

2000–03 sample	*Estimated wt.*	*Biomass per scat*	*No. of scats*	*Biomass consumed*	*Prey killed*	*No. prey per tiger per year*	*@7tigers/ 100 km²*
Sambar	175	44.25	55	2434.1	13.91	10.0	69.72
Chital	47	13.82	59	815.7	17.35	12.4	86.98
Nilgai	125	31.84	43	1369.3	10.95	7.8	54.91
Cattle	200	50.53	22	1111.8	5.56	4.0	27.86
Buffalo	400	101.01	9	909.1	2.27	1.6	11.39
Langur	8	4.69	20	93.8	-	-	-
Wild Pig	34	11.07	32	354.5	10.43	7.5	52.26
Bear	60	16.63	2	33.3	0.55	0.4	2.78
Others	15	6.80	4.0	27.2	1.81	1.3	9.10
Total			246	7148.8	62.85	45.0	315.00

1981; Karanth, 1993; Biswas and Sankar, 2002; Bagchi et al., 2003). Based on kill records and monitoring of radio-collared tigers, it was estimated that tigers made a kill (average size of over 40 kg) every 7–8 days. This meant that tigers annually killed approximately 40–50 prey, excluding langur, the occasional four-horned antelope, chinkara, porcupine and even sloth bear. This estimate is very similar to those from the long-term studies in Chitwan and Nagarhole (Karanth, 1993; Sunquist, 1981). According to my calculation, if a tiger in Panna was killing 40–45 prey in a year, the make-up of the various prey would be approximately ten sambar, eight nilgai, six livestock (including buffaloes), twelve chital and seven wild pigs (Table 8.6).

In 2002, we had estimated a tiger density of 7 tigers per 100 km^2 in Panna (Karanth et. al., 2004). During this time our estimated predation rate indicated that tigers cropped 6% of the wild ungulate prey population (excluding langurs). This figure is broken down into 6.7% cropping of the sambar population, 5.2% of chital, 4.2% of nilgai and almost 3% of other, smaller prey (Table 8.7). The cropping of wild pigs was very high but I believe this did not give the correct picture because our distance sampling probably underestimated the density of their population. Other than wild prey, the predation on livestock was very high: at the estimated tiger density of 7 tigers per 100 km^2, there were over 42 livestock kills every year. Panna still supports a high feral livestock population left behind by the villages relocated outside the tiger Reserve. However, high predation on livestock, especially buffaloes, is a serious cause for concern and needs to be examined carefully.

When tiger predation pressure is assessed with the cumulative predation of two other major co-predators, i.e. leopards (population density of 14 per 100 km^2) and the dhole, the combined predation on prey populations was quite high. From the leopard and dhole scat samples we find that approximately 15% of the prey population was harvested annually by the three predators, which was fairly high predation on the prey population. Panna's tiger and prey population was growing at the time of this study (up to 2003). The high cropping rate of the prey population can affect the growth that we have seen so far. It would have been very interesting to know what kind of equilibrium would have been reached between prey abundance and predator numbers, had the study continued and the tiger population survived.

Table 8.7 Estimation of prey harvested by tigers in Panna Tiger Reserve annually (2000–03 sample). Tiger density of 7 tigers/100 km² was estimated using camera traps in 2002 and prey density/km² using distance sampling from 2003 data.

Prey species	*Prey density*	*Prey in 100 km²*	*7 tigers/100 km²*	*% cropped*
Sambar	10.35	1035	69.72	6.74
Chital	16.67	1667	86.98	5.22
Nilgai	13.12	1312	54.91	4.18
Wild Pig	1.5	150	52.26	34.84
Other	3.5	350	9.097	2.59
Total	45.14	4514	272.97	6.047

In Panna, the highest density of tigers recorded by us was only 7 tigers/100 km², which was much lower than in many tiger habitats that support comparable prey numbers and biomass density. Considering the prey cropping rates that we estimated, if the tiger population was to grow, would that be at the cost of leopard and dhole abundance or its prey? Or would its growth be limited by ecological factors other than prey numbers? Tiger, leopard and dhole are sympatric co-predators and compete for the same space and prey base (Karanth and Sunquist, 2000; Harihar et al., 2009; Odden, 2010). We know that the cumulative effect of predation of all predators on shared prey can regulate prey abundances (Sinclair et al., 2003). When prey numbers are a limiting factor, the coexistence of predators will be adversely influenced, and this is described as exploitative competition. In the social hierarchy, the tiger is the dominant predator and the leopard carves a niche within tiger dominance by discrete use of the habitat and different predator behaviour (Karanth and Sunquist, 1995). Leopards can achieve this co-existence by paying a cost in terms of the kind of prey it selects, the space that it uses and when, and the densities it can achieve (Karanth and Sunquist, 2000; Wegge et al., 2009; Odden, 2010). A camera trapping study in Sariska has indicated a discrete temporal use of the area as one such behavioural mechanism to exploit the same habitat, thereby effectively avoiding interference competition with tigers (Mondol et al., 2012). But such a discrete existence will become increasingly difficult as tiger densities multiply, which can limit leopard and dhole numbers in the area. Prey abundance will be an additional and important influence in determining the equilibrium. In Chilla, in the Himalayan foothills, researchers observed a decline in leopard densities from 9 to almost 2 leopards per 100km^2, following an increase in tiger densities (Harihar et al., 2011). They speculate that leopards moved to peripheral areas and subsisted on small prey and livestock because of high dietary overlaps and competition. Similar spatial exclusion is reported from the Nepal Terai habitats (Seidensticker et al., 1990; Odden et al., 2010). In Sariska, a decline in leopard densities was noticed after the reintroduction of tigers. Like in Nagarahole (Karanth and Sunquist, 2000), we did not observe spatial exclusion of leopards in Panna. During our monitoring of radio-collared tigers we saw leopards and encountered evidence of them on a regular basis within known tiger territories. Leopard densities estimated by us using camera traps also document high leopard densities in the same area. In Panna, leopards could perhaps achieve high densities because tiger ranges are large and therefore leopards were likely to experience low interference competition from them while using the same space, despite high prey cropping rates.

An increase in tiger numbers in an area can increase conflict levels between tigers and leopards or dholes. I remember Dr John Seidensticker's visit to Panna clearly because we observed unique behaviour from one of the radio-collared tigers. We had been picking up the F-123's signal from early morning in a locality where our field team had seen her fighting off wild dogs. By the time we reached the spot there were no signs of the wild dog pack, though the tigress was sitting close to the road. Then we spotted three wild dog pups who had taken refuge among the crevices of a rocky escarpment not very far

Figure 8.2 Comparison of prey selection by tigers in Panna Tiger Reserve between the 1996-99 and 2000-03 samples.

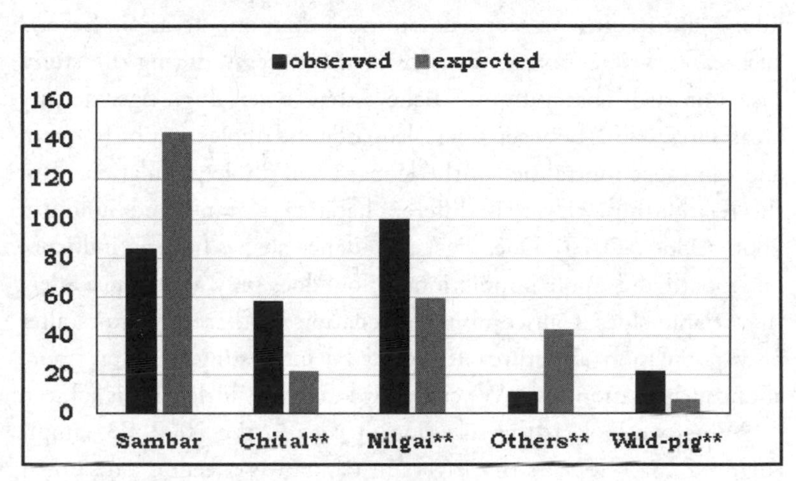

A. 1996-99

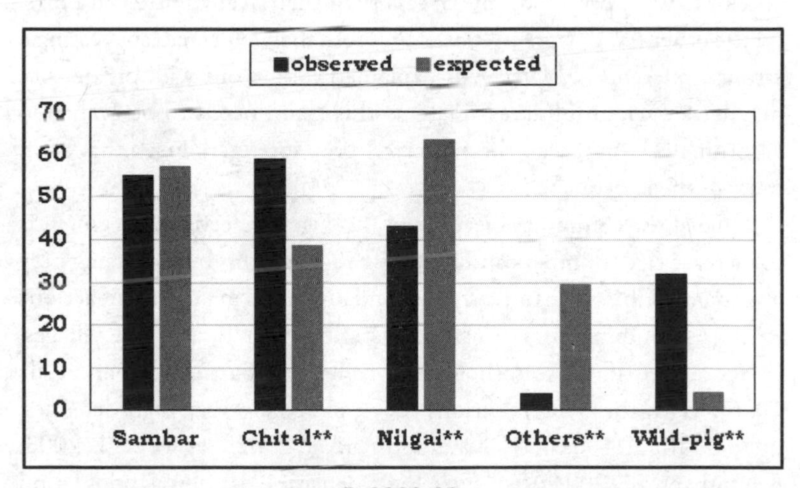

B. 2000-03

** significant selection or avoidance

from the tiger. The tigress remained there for the whole day and even the next day until she had killed all the pups. We also observed tigers killing and feeding on leopards on more than one occasion. Several such cases were reported to us from the Reserve during the study. Based on such observations, I believe that in very high tiger density areas, interactions between tigers, leopards and dholes may be frequent and can cause mortalities in the leopard and dhole populations. But this relationship will vary in different habitats (Karanth and Sunquist, 2000; Odden, 2010). Does tiger abundance always have an influence on leopard and dhole populations? How does prey abundance affect this relationship? Can combined predation by these predators alter prey population structure? It would be interesting to know more about such relationships. We currently know very little on this subject.

When we look at the selection of prey in the 2000–03 sample (Figure 8.2), it appears that tigers in Panna were feeding on sambar as expected from its availability while nilgai were much less preyed upon. Similarly, smaller prey such as chinkara and four-horned antelopes were preyed on much less than their availability. Wild pigs, on the other hand, were predated on more than expected, suggesting a strong preference. However, as explained earlier, our wild pig density may have been an underestimate so this claim needs to be evaluated accordingly. Chital was the preferred prey for tigers in Panna, as in most of the subcontinent.

One of the common objectives of the Tiger Reserve management is to increase tiger numbers and they try to achieve this by increasing prey abundance. Chital, particularly, respond rapidly to management actions such as maintaining large grasslands after the relocation of villages, creation of artificial waterholes and controlled burning (Khan et al., 1996). With these interventions they can achieve very high densities, up to 80 chital/100km^2 (Biswas and Sankar, 2002; Bagchi et al., 2003; Karanth et al., 2004). At such high densities the chital population is capable of sustaining the combined high predation pressure (tiger and its co-predators) while other prey may not. Low-density prey such as sambar, four-horned antelope, barking deer and swamp deer may struggle against the resulting rise in predator density and suffer the consequences. This is an important ecological perspective that Protected Area management must not ignore, i.e. they must provide a suitable environment for a diverse prey base. Focusing too much on tigers and chital can have a negative effect on other species.

This is why prey and predator populations must be monitored intensively, but most importantly, management actions should be reviewed periodically based on the monitoring results. It may be time consuming and costly, but it actually helps them to establish a system memory and prepare for a crisis before it hits the protected populations. This way we can avoid crisis management (Halvorson and Eastin, 1999). In protected areas that are small, it is particularly important for management to know the suitable habitats for both tigers and their prey, and how these can be characterized; they need to be identified and quantified so their availability is known within the conservation landscape.

Identifying and Characterizing Suitable Habitats for Tigers

Habitat Selection

When we visit a tiger reserve looking for a tiger, we tend to spend more time in areas where tigers are seen often. We do this because we all know that tigers use some areas within their home range more often than others. When an animal uses an area more than others, rather than wandering randomly, it is considered to be 'selective' in its use of space. The preferential use of space is mainly a behavioural response to availability and distribution of important resources such as water, prey, cover density, forest type, human habitation and disturbance. Animals do this for a good reason—to maximise their fitness (Rosenzweig and Abramsky, 1986). Fitness here means a smart use of resources which will help an individual animal to achieve greater reproductive success. A generalist predator like the tiger occupies a range of habitats by responding to the availability, quality and quantity of resources in a way that minimizes its energy expenditure and maximises its reproductive potential (Sunquist and Sunquist, 1989). Criteria for selection of areas within the home range are likely to be different from the larger landscape-level selection of finding a suitable home range. Similarly, resource selection can be broken down into various scales and viewed as a multi-level, hierarchical response by the animal (Johnson, 1980; Rettie and Messier, 2000; Rolstad et al., 2000; Chamberlain et al., 2002; McLoughlin et al., 2004).

Utilization Distribution (UD) is a tool frequently used to assess the space use pattern to understand home range behaviour (Worton, 1989). In this study, we quantified the differential use of space within a home range by predicting the probability of animal occurrence and generated a UD surface (White and Garrot, 1990). A UD surface is created by dividing the home range as a grid and estimating a probability of animal occurrence for each cell. UD is commonly used to identify 'core areas' or areas of frequent use. The resource use is determined by developing individual and population-level multivariate Resource Utilization Functions (RUF) (Marzluff et al., 2004). The RUF method assumes that the probabilistic UD is the result of a response to the available resources or environmental 'covariates'. The RUF relates UD values with resource availability by using multiple regression, as opposed to logistic regression used in Resource Selection Functions (RSF) (Manly et al., 1993). The results from the RUF technique enhance our understanding of tiger responses to the prevailing ecological conditions and habitat requirements (Marzluff et al., 2004).

Utilization Density Estimation for Space Use

We used fixed kernel estimator (same as that used for estimating home ranges in Panna) for generating a utilization density surface with cell size of a hundred square metres or one hectare. We considered a one hectare cell size to be appropriate for a long-ranging species like the tiger. We fixed the h value at 1000m and used the bivariate method in Hawth's Tool in ArcGIS 9.2 to generate the UD surface for individual tigers. We used smoothing factor (h) of 1000m based on the information we had on the distance a tiger can travel in a few hours. These UD surfaces were converted into x,y,z layer in ArcGIS using the centre of each cell as the point and denoted by x and y coordinates, with z denoting the UD value for each sampling unit (raster cell). The z values were then transformed into 0-99 for further analysis.

Predictor Variables for Habitat Use

We created seventeen different predictor variables as geographical layers of resources that we identified as important for the tiger. These layers were: availability of tiger's major prey (sambar, chital and nilgai); an index of livestock grazing intensity (disturbance index); eight different habitat classes; distance from the nearest perennial water source; three temperature isotherms (one each for winter, summer and monsoon seasons). Each prey species' distribution layer was generated based on post-hoc estimation of density across each strata in Distance Sampling using the 2003 dataset. The eleven transects were grouped into three different strata and density surfaces generated for chital, sambar, nilgai, other ungulate prey and langur. We used the LISS-III dataset for preparing habitat classes using supervised classification with the help of ground-truthing habitat evaluation plots. A thermal isotherm for the entire study area was generated using thermal spectral band (Band-7) of the Landsat data and converting its spectral radiance to temperature. We used Landsat data from January for winter, April for summer and October for monsoon. The water availability map was prepared by visiting each water hole in different seasons and recording its geographic location. We generated concentric buffers at 100m intervals to create a surface denoting each point's distance from the nearest water source. Combining three factors—grazing, human presence and MFP collection—a disturbance intensity map was prepared by quantifying the grazing pressure within a compartment (smallest administrative unit of forestry management) and overlaying it with the remote-sensed habitat layers. To allow a direct comparison between covariates and to stabilize the models, we z-transformed all spatial data-sets with continuous values (mean = 0 and a standard deviation = 1)

Resource Utilization Functions (RUFs)

We extracted the predictor variables using the UD surface by overlaying them over each other. We estimated the standardized coefficients and associated standard errors for the predictor variables for each tiger using the function ruf.fit in R.

The RUF function (Marzluff et al., 2004) takes the following form:

$$Y = \beta 0 + \beta 1x1 + \beta 2x2 + \beta 3x3 + \beta nxn \ldots\ldots$$

where,
$\beta 0$ = intercept
β = coefficient
x = resources

Predictor variables or co-efficient values, whose confidence intervals did not overlap with zero, were considered to be significant predictors for a selection or avoidance by an individual tiger. We then averaged the standardized coefficients for males, females and all tigers together, and estimated their standard errors to understand the resource use pattern at the population level. Figure 8.3 shows RUF co-efficient values that were obtained from multiple regression between seventeen ecological parameters that we identified and UD values for each individual tiger. The confidence interval is shown by a bar. A positive coefficient value indicates selection for that resource and a negative value, avoidance. Distance from zero indicates the strength but the error bar shows whether the selection or avoidance is significant or not. When the error bar is touching the zero line, it shows no significance and when it remains entirely above or below the zero line without touching the line, this indicates a significant selection or avoidance for that resource parameter.

Results of Analysis

Male and female tiger strategies are to achieve fitness are different. A female's strategy is resource-oriented because females spend a considerable amount of energy raising litters. We would therefore expect females to select resource-rich areas that can provide food, cover and water to successfully raise her cubs. A male tiger's strategy is mate-oriented, and they will try to incorporate as many females within their range as possible. Thus, use of an area by males will be governed by the females' use of space and more.

When information from all tigers on resource use are pooled together, the results distort the differential-use pattern. Males avoided human habitation, open and mixed thorn forest, open scrub, and forest with dense understory, mainly dominated by lantana. Though the distance from water source shows a negative relationship, it actually means that as the distance from it increases there is a higher probability that the tiger will be avoiding such habitats. Therefore, this relationship suggests that tigers prefer areas close to water sources.

Combining data of all the females together shows that out of seventeen parameters, only one was significant—distance from water (Figure 8.3). Whereas, on an individual level, a female's resource-use shows strong selection or avoidance and variations. On average, eleven parameters were either selected or avoided by individual females. For example, F-123, out of the seventeen parameters, showed preference or avoidance of fifteen parameters. In fact, her data shows avoidance for fourteen parameters. Figure 8.3 shows the resource use by female tigers, and the variation in individual resource use that we see here is in complete contrast to our result obtained from combining all female data, except a few parameters that were common to most. One of the parameters that almost all the tigers were partial to was water source, the only exception being tigress F-111. Her use was different from the other females because of the presence of two villages within her territory. A large livestock population from these villages used the same water sources and this was the main reason she did not use the habitat close to these water sources. Another common parameter that was avoided by all the females was anthropogenic pressure. That is, tigers avoided areas that were under heavy grazing or other human activities. All females were partial to areas with high prey densities but their preferences for a particular prey species were different. F-123 and F-113 preferred sambar areas while F-120 preferred chital areas.

Most of the individual variation was seen in the use of forest habitats. F-120 did not show preference for any of the forest habitats we identified and in complete contrast to this, F-123 and F-111 showed preferential avoidance and selection, respectively, for most of

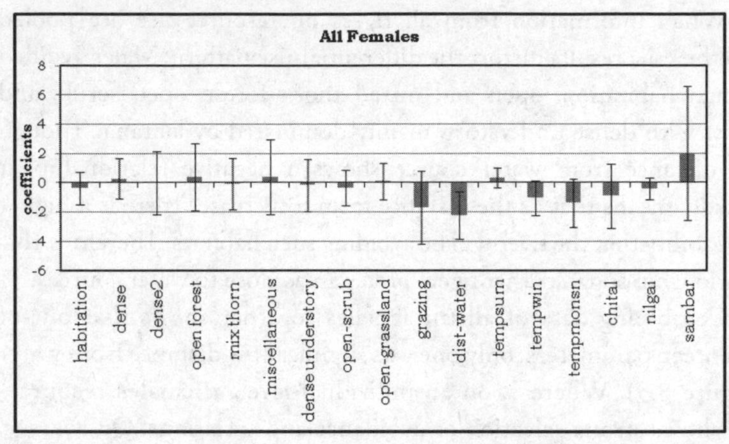
All Females
coefficients
8
6
4
2
0
-2
-4
-6
habitation
dense
dense2
open forest
mix thorn
miscellaneous
dense understory
open-scrub
open-grassland
grazing
dist-water
tempsum
tempwin
tempmonsn
chital
nilgai
sambar

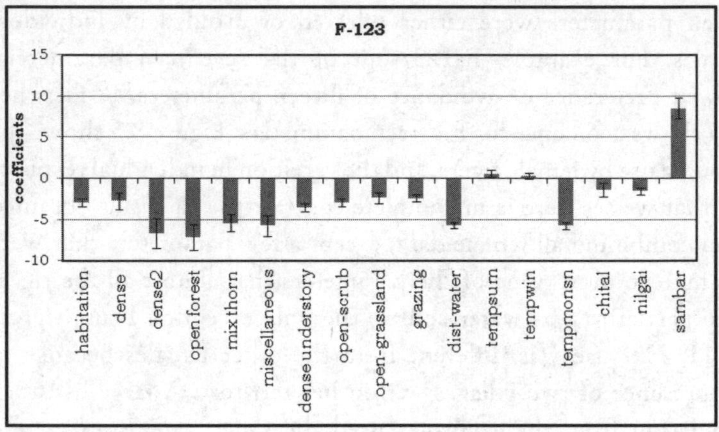
F-123
coefficients
15
10
5
0
-5
-10
habitation
dense
dense2
open forest
mix thorn
miscellaneous
dense understory
open-scrub
open-grassland
grazing
dist-water
tempsum
tempwin
tempmonsn
chital
nilgai
sambar

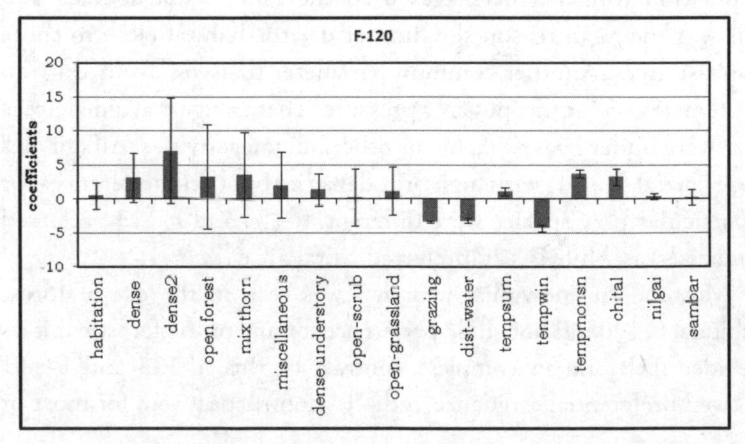
F-120
coefficients
20
15
10
5
0
-5
-10
habitation
dense
dense2
open forest
mix thorn
miscellaneous
dense understory
open-scrub
open-grassland
grazing
dist-water
tempsum
tempwin
tempmonsn
chital
nilgai
sambar

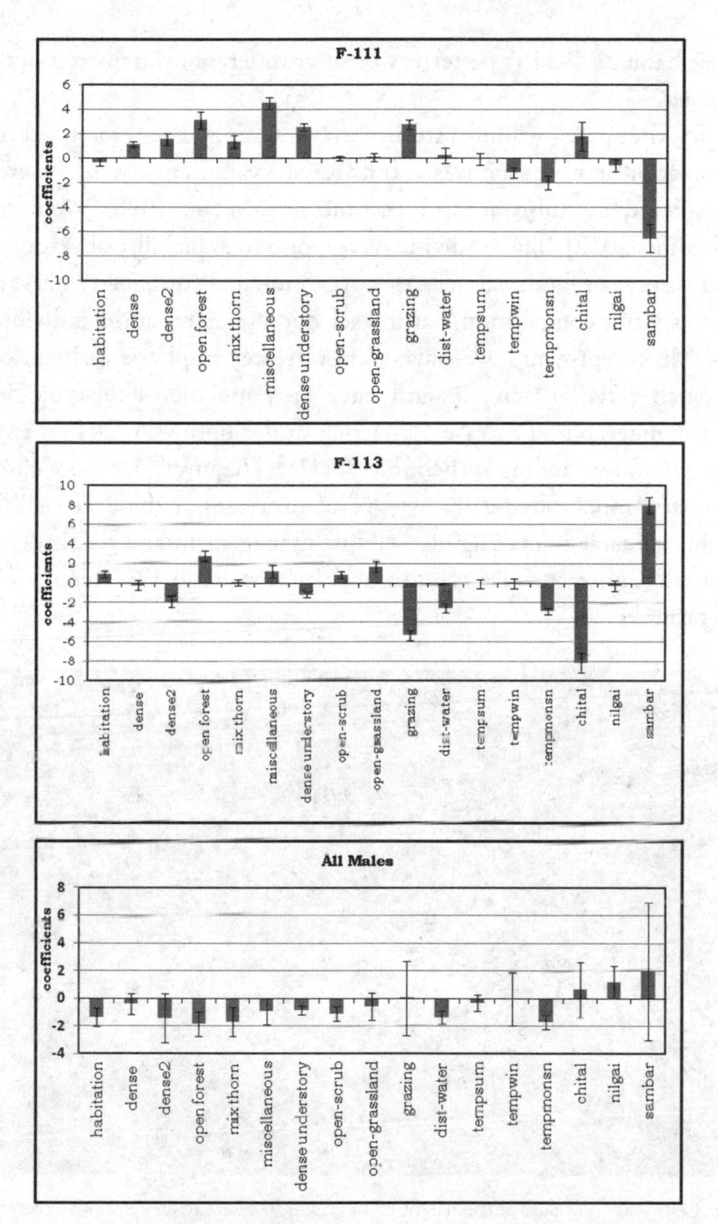

Figure 8.3 Resource Utilization Function (RUF) coefficients for tigers in Panna Tiger Reserve. Positive coefficients are above the zero line and indicate that use increases with increasing value. Error bars (SE), which do not overlap with zero indicate significant relationship.

these habitats. F-113's patterns were very different from the rest of the females.

In the past, wildlife studies have mainly been focussed on population-level responses. Individual variations were merely considered as noise around the mean (Martin, 1998; Wolf and Weissing, 2012). Since individuals respond to availability of resources such as prey or food, water, forest cover, human disturbance, inter- and intra-specific competition, natural selection operates at the individual level. In recent times, we have seen a greater emphasis in literature on such variations and its influence on population-level ecological and demographic processes (Merrick and Koprowski, 2017). Even though understanding at the individual level requires a lot more effort, time and money, better knowledge of processes at this level will be highly valuable in making our wildlife management and conservation planning more effective (Smith and Blumstein, 2013; Merrick and Koprowski, 2017).

The belly and underside of the thighs is for a tiger like ears to an elephant—they are used to dissipate heat. After a hot day the tiger will move into open spaces, away from canopy cover to cool down their body temperature by exposing the belly and thighs. Soaking only these body parts in water during hot days also helps them cool down.

When a larger part of the population is successful in achieving fitness by using the space effectively, it creates a viable or growing population. However, there is a lack of published scientific information on the habitat use of tigers available to managers. A better understanding of such responses is critical for the management to identify spaces that can support a viable tiger population. Such knowledge is important in developing conservation strategies, especially when we are looking at the increased presence of tigers beyond the Protected Area boundaries.

Identifying and Characterizing Suitable Habitats for Tigers

Understanding what constitutes a suitable habitat for a species and where these habitats are is essential in conservation planning. Therefore, the building of predictive species distribution models is a very important exercise.

To develop our predictive model, we used RUF estimates for associated ecological factors which are likely to influence the distribution of tigers. Our formula for predicting the suitable areas for tigers in Panna was:

Y = 72.08 + (Sambar × 0.13) + (chital × -0.08) + (nilgai × -0.04) + (grazing × -1.44) + (water × -0.01) + (temp-monsoon × -0.9) + (temp-summer × 0.64) + (temp-winter × -1.9) + (dense-forest × -3.33) + (open-forest × -4.45) + (mix-thorn-forest × -6.89) + other habitats...(Marzluff et al., 2004)

The resulting predictive maps for females, males and all individual tigers show the differences that we discussed earlier (Figure 8.4 a-c). Since there is such great variation across individuals, it is difficult to prepare one conclusive map of suitable tiger habitat in Panna. This predictive map gives an average picture of the probabilities of tiger-preferred areas in the Panna Tiger Reserve. Even though this masks all the individual requirements, it still provides important information that can assist the management in preparing an appropriate conservation plan.

Figure 8.4 Predictive map of relative resource use by tigers in Panna Tiger Reserve. Values used for this predictive map were derived from averaged RUF standardized coefficients of all female tigers (a); average for males (b); all tigers (c). Darker areas show increased probability of use of the space.

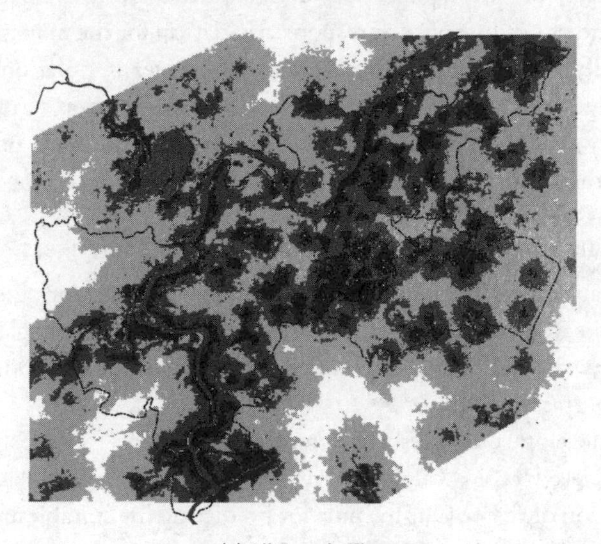

(a) All Female Tigers

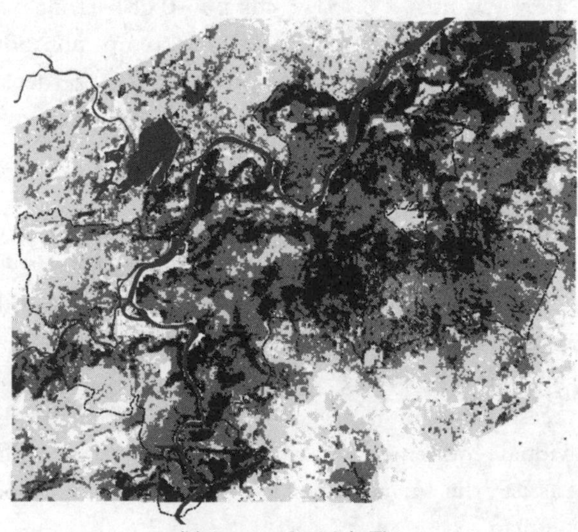

(b) Average for Male Tigers

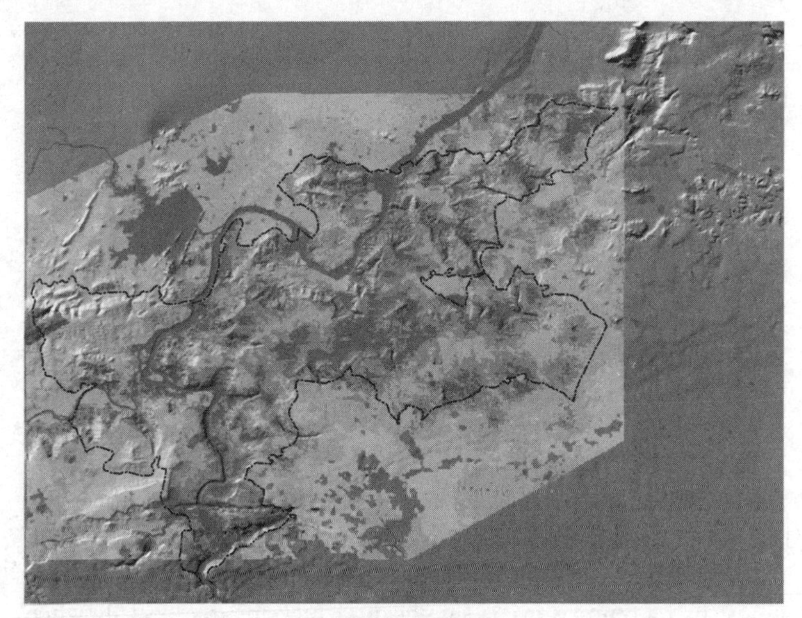

(c) All Tigers

To manage spaces for tigers within the Reserve, the management must be able to identify key resources and determine their availability as well as their relative importance. An understanding of these will mean that one will be better prepared to look after the ecological requirements of a tiger population; studies on resource selection provide a cornerstone for the management of any wild animal population. Information on resource selection by tigers not only establishes the inter-relationship between the animal and its environment, but it helps us create a predictive resource map that provides quantitative information on the availability and distribution of these resources. For truly effective management, it would be very useful to have information at the scale of an individual's breeding territory. Knowing what is available and the requirement of breeding individuals, would allow management to intervene if necessary and ensure reproductive success. This could be crucial for a small population like Panna.

9

The Science of Saving Tigers

Good Conservation Should be Based on Good Science

The recent all-India assessment (2014) estimated 2,226 tigers in India. The journey from 2,500 tigers in the early 1970s to over 2,200 was treacherous and India has done well to keep the number intact for almost half a century. It is a significant achievement, especially when compared with other Asian countries. India managed to stabilize the number but the tiger lost much of its range and now most of the population (>80%) survives only in Protected Areas (Jhala et al., 2011). The prospects of a couple of thousand tigers may look promising but a closer look raises deep concerns. Many are satisfied with 2,226 tigers after a difficult 40 years of intensive conservation, but I am not—for reasons I will explain below. I would have been happy if India had more than double that number. In fact, the status of the tiger in most parts of the country is worrying, barring a few landscapes such as Corbett, Nagarahole-Bandipur, and the central Indian highlands neighbouring Kanha. In the early 1990s, it was more or less accepted among conservationists that the tiger population in India was declining in large parts of its range; we saw a serious crisis due to poaching for tiger bones for use in Traditional Chinese Medicine in China and South-east Asia, as well as other human disturbances and development activities (Seidensticker, 1986; Johnsingh et al., 1991; Kumar and Wright, 1999; Thapar, 1999). Unfortunately, official figures did not agree with the experts' opinion. For over 30 years, we had been dependent on figures that only grew, even when it was very obvious that the tiger population had declined to a precarious level.

Criticized very heavily, the NTCA eventually modified its approach and began conducting a more acceptable, science-based 'All-India Assessment of Tiger and Prey' every four years (Karanth et al., 2003; Jhala, 2008 Jhala et al., 2011, 2015). This brought the official figure down from over 3,500 tigers to 1,411 in 2008. The 2011 census gave a figure of 1,706 and in 2014, 2,226 tigers. This increase from 2008 to 2014 was not entirely due to an increase in tiger numbers but the fact that a larger area of tiger habitat was assessed. But for some of us, range loss is still a huge worry, because range contraction is the first sign of extinction. Tigers now survive in only 7% of their former range (Sanderson et al., 2006). The 2008 number shocked the country as we realized how few wild tigers survived in India. The reaction was widespread and heartfelt: in 2010, I overheard a discussion between taxi drivers in Khajuraho where one of the drivers, shocked by the Aircel and WWF media campaign on television and advertisement hoardings announcing JUST 1,411 LEFT, exclaimed to his colleagues that his village had more cows than the number of tigers in the entire country. He declared that it was a shame for all of us.

The pre-2008 census figures for 30 years were of very little use in answering even the basic questions: the figures did not even tell us where these 3,500 tigers were. Sometime back in the early '90s, before I started my research project in Panna, I wanted a list of all the protected areas where tigers were present: I was shocked to find that such basic data was not available. Also, I found that the authorities did not even have a map to show details of the distribution of tigers in India. I shunted between the MOEF and Project Tiger (now NTCA) for months but failed to get the information I needed.

It took 37 years of conservation efforts and the extinction of two populations to finally put in place a scientific protocol to monitor tigers. But a decade later we are still waiting to see how this information from the new all-India assessment will be used in policy development and its effectiveness for tiger conservation plans. Unfortunately, in the meantime, we have lost tigers in many places. All this has gone either unnoticed or worse, ignored by officialdom. If we had a reliable and honest monitoring system, this would not have been possible and the total losses from Sariska and Panna could have been avoided.

In addition to the problems that are often documented in literature, there are two important characteristics of the tiger population in India which, if not taken into consideration, could lead to a serious crisis for the sub-species. One of them is the small and isolated nature of the tiger habitats. The population of over 2,200 tigers is actually divided into many small populations. The second is that the average size of the area protecting the tiger habitat is small (366 ± 25.5 km^2) and 66 % of these areas are smaller than 400 km^2 (Rodgers and Panwar, 1988). We know that small populations of large carnivores are extremely vulnerable to extinction due to the demographic (sex-biased mortality, poor survival, etc.) and environmental stochasticity (unpredictable events such as disease, or poaching related to spike in demand) that can impact small populations (Gilpin and Soule, 1986; Caughley, 1994). But recent studies on wide-ranging carnivores suggest that protected area size is a more immediate and critical threat due to their exposure to the Edge Effect (Woodroffe and Ginsberg, 2000).

The results of any viability analysis using the figure of 2,226 tigers as a single population will predict a reasonable survival prospect. But in reality, the extinction processes are acting on each of the isolated and small populations simultaneously and independently. As a result, these tiger populations will be lost sooner than one large population. For decades, tiger managers, biologists and conservationists have recognized this vulnerability and the importance of connected corridor forests between two tiger habitats to increase the survival probability. But very little has been done to ensure this connectivity. Despite this lack of effort, results of recent genetic studies do show some encouraging signs—some of the corridors may still be functioning and maintaining historical gene flow (Sharma et al., 2013).

We also know that the tiger is not a habitat specialist, and it occupies a diverse range of environments (Sunquist et al., 1999). This ranges from the hot arid regions of western India, and the mangroves and humid rainforests of tropical Asia, to the arctic climate of Siberia.

In these diverse habitat types and environments, one would expect tiger responses to vary according to ecological need. In productive ecosystems, such as the terai flood plains and tropical moist deciduous forests where a tiger's ecological needs can be fulfilled in a relatively smaller area, tigers can achieve high densities (> 15 tigers/100 km^2) (Sunquist, 1981; Karanth et al., 2004; Jhala et al., 2015). We have seen that their space requirements also vary widely in various habitat types, from less than 15 km^2 to more than 40 km^2 in tropical habitats, and more than 250 km^2 in temperate boreal forests (Sunquist, 1981; Smith, 1984; Karanth and Sunquist, 2000; Goodrich et al., 2010; Sharma et al., 2010; Majumder et al., 2012). The managers of each protected area need to know the ecological requirements of tigers in their area to ensure their availability for a viable population.

For this, we need a better understanding of the tiger's ecology in specific habitats. This understanding will mainly come from long-term ecological research. Our track record in understanding tigers' ecological needs for the various habitats it occupies is extremely poor. It is sad, and somewhat shocking, that throughout the first thirty years of the tiger conservation movement, Project Tiger and the recently formulated NTCA, have failed to support long-term ecological studies on the tiger. This is in spite of being created with a strong mandate for research. We still only have Schaller's *The Deer and the Tiger* from 1967 to consult for reliable scientific information. A couple of efforts made in the past by a few individuals came to an abrupt end due to the management's rather harsh and autocratic actions: Dr Ullas Karanth's project in the 1990s and our study in 2005. The MOEF does recognize the importance of science in tiger conservation in its policy but only on paper—the reality in the field is very different. Management of wildlife populations is a highly specialized field, and in the present scenario we cannot afford ad-hoc management decisions; rather we require informed judgments and good monitoring to assess the effectiveness of past management decisions. There is presently no such review system and management plans for most of the tiger Reserves in the country suffer due to deficient scientific information on wildlife populations. In the absence of such crucial information, and due to whimsical and ad-hoc intervention of the authorities, habitat and wildlife populations are destroyed rather than benefitted. Conflicting signals from the scientists and managers also affects the morale of the protection staff.

Currently, management of the country's tiger Reserves is based entirely on Annual Plans of Operation (APOs). These APOs are heavily weighted on administrative and infrastructure needs rather than ecological understanding. I once had an opportunity to view APOs from five tiger Reserves and was shocked to find that they were proposing to spend almost 70% of the tiger conservation funds on civil construction and purchases. Almost 40 years since the start of our intensive tiger protection, we still continue to propose the building of new chowkies (guard posts), roads, check dams and watchtowers. Reading the APOs feels like going through a civil construction department's annual plan or a PWD (Public Works Department) annual plan. There is very little input from science. This gives us an idea of where management priorities lie and why it can fail tigers. How can long-term planning work when we are so dependent on such year-to-year vision?

Reliance on APOs means that there is no science involvement and no 'system memory'. That is, every time a new officer is appointed, they start with a clean slate and no critical baseline information. For example, prior to 2003 we recorded very high four-horned antelope densities and used to see 10-12 of them on a single drive (Chundawat and Sharma, 2008). Later, between 2010 and 2016, we saw only 2-5 four-horned antelopes in almost 100 drives per year. We tried to alert the management authority to this alarming decline, but every time, without fail, they would refute this by saying that they saw one a month ago. They were not aware of what it was like in the past. I gave up in frustration. The same thing happened in 2004-05 when we noticed the tiger population decline: the management continued to rely on an outdated, non-scientific assessment that suited them, as it allowed them to mask the decline. My point here is that an outsider should not have to point these things out to the management; there should be a system in place that immediately sounds the alert for remedial measures. After decades of managing these reserves, we have yet to establish such a system that would identify a problem and react to it effectively. This would require robust scientific monitoring of the wildlife population, understanding of its ecology and a team dedicated to this job. Most importantly, a system is required where management actions are based on information generated from such monitoring. Unfortunately, in the current ad-hoc system, science has very little role to play. We tend to confuse science with the use of technology, i.e. camera traps and more recently, drones.

Here is another example to describe the problem: every year the Panna Tiger Reserve management spends huge amounts of money on water management and its conservation. But instead of a better natural hydrological system for the park, there are many ugly hand pumps, failed ponds and anicuts dotting the landscape, many of them non-functional. Dams have been constructed everywhere. A more sensible, logical way would be to conduct a hydrological study to identify priority areas and continually assess the potential impact of different interventions. The study could suggest strategies, uncover new technologies and chart out ten annual plans to achieve the objectives. Then it would have made no difference even if we had ten different directors during that time. At the end of a ten-year water conservation plan, we could have achieved something substantial. Instead, every year an annual plan is formulated, without scientific assessment, in an ad-hoc manner. Thus, the end result is negligible and the water regime in the Reserve remains more or less the same as it was 20 years ago. A large amount of money is spent every year on civil construction projects. All these problems could be corrected by funding a hydrological study of the area and employing an expert on the subject to come up with a plan.

I cannot agree more with Ullas Karanth when he stresses that good conservation is always based on good science. Unfortunately, this is where the wildlife management of this country has lagged behind and much work is needed. In addition to a general lack of information, most of the information on tiger ecology that does exist comes from studies conducted in Nepal (Sunquist, 1981; Smith, 1984), Kanha

(Schaller, 1967), Nagarahole (Karanth, 1993) and in the Russian Far East (Goodrich et al., 2008, 2010), where tiger populations are now doing fairly well, not from habitats where the tiger desperately needs help. That is why our study on the tiger in Panna Tiger Reserve is important. Until this study, almost nothing was known about this habitat in spite of it being home to a majority of the tiger populations in India; it is also the one where tigers are most vulnerable.

To understand the tiger's ecological requirements, we require reliable and unbiased information on its ecology. To achieve this, we need to be able to observe tigers almost at will or on a systematic schedule. This requires permissions from the authorities to conduct such a study and its success is entirely dependent on the management's goodwill. This goodwill is hard to obtain and one reason why wildlife science in India is far behind the rest of the world.

Radio-telemetry is an important research tool, used for gathering information in an unbiased manner and in sufficient detail. It is commonly used in the rest of the world, but in India it is very controversial. In Panna however, running counter to its contentious past, this intensive and constant monitoring of radio-collared tigers had an unexpected benefit: it provided security to individual tigers in a way that no other surveillance could. Intensive monitoring helped significantly reduce human-caused mortality of radio-collared tigers and increased the survival potential of some of the breeding individuals. It was exciting for us to witness such a success, but little did we realize that this was only temporary relief. As long as the monitoring was allowed, tigers flourished; as soon as the goodwill vanished, and our radio-tracking was curtailed to a bare minimum, the tigers started disappearing fast.

We now know that protected areas like the Panna Tiger Reserve need a permanent solution to ensure the long-term survival of tigers. The re-introduction of tigers there in 2009, after their extinction, was a 'recovery' that is a repetition of the increase we noticed during our radio-tracking. I worry what will happen to this recovered population if and when this intensive tracking of reintroduced tigers is stopped. The management has learnt little from past events as it lacks 'system memory' and does not appreciate outside knowledge. Sitting at the periphery is frustrating, knowing that they have not found a permanent solution to the underlying problems that caused the extinction in the first place. We still see high mortalities in adult females. Behind the veil of the successful reintroduction, the threat is obscured for now. It can, however, strike back with a vengeance. The authorities and managers of the park continue to believe that biased sex ratios and poaching were the reasons for the loss. But in fact, the biased sex ratio was a result of the decline and not the cause. Poaching is of course an issue, but it is not happening only in Panna or Sariska. It occurs everywhere and maybe, in places like Corbett or Kanha even more tigers were poached, but their populations did not go extinct. It is important for the management to understand what it is that makes populations like those in Sariska and Panna vulnerable to poaching. The end result can be devastating as we have seen; especially so when real problems are denied, allowing time for the poaching to take its toll.

Past Trends of Tiger Survival in India

Before we discuss Panna specifically, let us look at the past trends of tiger survival in Tropical Dry Forests in India. Since the inception of Project Tiger, more than four decades ago, we have not been able to halt the decline of the tiger population in most of its distribution range in the subcontinent; we have only managed to successfully stabilize the population in a few pockets within our Protected Area network (Seidensticker, 1997; Thapar, 1999; Karanth and Gopal, 2005; Walston et al., 2010; Jhala et al., 2011). The early years of Project Tiger saw some success with population recovery in a handful of tiger Reserves (Mountfort, 1981; Panwar, 1982; Karanth, 1987; Panwar, 1987). These successes were mainly due to the creation of inviolate spaces essential for a large carnivore and long-ranging species like the tiger. Project Tiger (now NTCA) managed to keep the human-animal conflict at arm's length in these highly protected tiger habitats (Seidensticker, 1997; Karanth et al., 2003). But pressure in the peripheral areas has been building, as very little has been done for the communities outside protected areas to minimize the conflict (Kothari et al., 1995; Karanth and Gopal, 2005). This neglect is increasingly affecting the protected areas themselves. Over the long run, we are now realizing that keeping conflict at arm's length will not be sustainable and protected populations are being affected by factors that exist outside the protected areas.

Old stratagems that worked in the 1970s and early '80s are not working as well as they used to (Thapar, 1989; Seidensticker, 1997). The situation is very different now and I believe that we have not put enough effort into trying new approaches and creating new models for conservation to address these pressures. In India we were lucky earlier, when there were plenty of tigers in the forests outside the protected areas. I remember we would be told very proudly that there were as many tigers outside our protected areas as there were inside them. But the situation after 40 years of tiger conservation is very different—we have lost most of the tigers that lived in forests outside our protected areas. As mentioned, the All-India Tiger Estimate showed that 80% of the tiger habitat currently occupied by tigers falls within the protected areas. One of the biggest failures of the system was that it did not recognize the importance of the supporting population residing outside these areas in maintaining the viability of the protected populations. Since most tigers now live within these reserves, many of these populations can only survive with inputs from neighbouring populations. In the absence of such inputs, many of the recent losses were in these isolated populations and poaching was the major issue (Jackson and Kempf, 1994; Kenney et al., 1995; Hemley and Mills, 1999; Kumar and Wright, 1999; Chapron et al., 2008). We have recently seen two local extinctions as a result of this. More recently, tiger conservation has had to contend with the negative effect of 'development projects', such as linear projects, dams, roads and mining leases. These are major threats to connectivity between many of the tiger populations. The battle on these issues is harder because it has to be fought away from the field in the corridors of power in Delhi and the state capitals.

Tigress F-120, sibling of F-111 and F-113, was a favourite because of her cool temperament. She allowed us to observe her extensively and spend some very intimate moments with her. Her death by poaching hit us hard.

Left: Fires in Panna are common and because of extensive grass cover, they can spread extremely fast when there are winds. The effects can be devastating

Top: Management and Science—A Partnership That Worked Wonders: Raghu Chundawat and Deputy Park Director, Shashi Malik, interacting with the Panna Tiger Reserve staff. Things became very different after a change in leadership and this symbiosis fell apart drastically.

Left: Male M-91 was our first and the biggest radio-collared male. Before M-125 arrived, his range extended over half the Tiger Reserve.

Top: Wild-dogs or Dhole are not as abundant in Panna as they are in other central Indian forests, though occasionally we saw large packs of up to sixteen dogs.

Top: The Amdar female, an un-collared tigress whom we knew and monitored, occupied a territory near F-111. She extended her range after F-111's death and mated there with M-125.

Right: M-125, or Madla, had a cool temperament—a gentle giant who lost one eye and later, one of his canines too. He also survived a leg-hold trap by leaving behind one of his toes. He managed to evade all threats, and was one of the last two surviving males of Panna.

Leopards are the most abundant large predators, twice as common as tigers. During our study, they were not sighted as frequently as they were after the extinction of the tigers. How leopards survive and live with tigers is a fascinating subject that we know very little about.

Historical Perspective

For three decades prior to 2006, overall tiger numbers declined but we had little idea where this was happening (Seidensticker, 1997; Thapar, 2001; Dinerstein et al., 2007). I wanted to identify the areas where tigers had disappeared and where they had survived, so we collated all the available information using maps from various sources. For historical distribution we referred to Gopal et al. (2014), which documents tiger presence over the past 100 years in the Indian subcontinent. Information on current tiger distribution was obtained from the All-India Tiger Survey (Jhala et al., 2011) and a map of all the protected areas collated from sources such as the Ministry of Environment, Forest and Climate Change website* and the World Database on Protected Areas (WDPA). First, we created a list of 203 Protected Areas which protect tiger habitat (>50 km^2) and assigned the PA size and corresponding habitat type following the classification in Wikramanayake et al., (1998). This protected area layer, with corresponding habitat types and PA size, was overlaid with the historical layer to identify locations that held tigers 100 years ago. We then overlaid the protected area layer with the current tiger distribution layer to identify locations that still had tigers in 2010. From this analysis for each protected area, we obtained associated PA size, forest types, tiger presence 100 years ago and tiger presence in 2010. To avoid biases from smaller protected areas we included only those which were larger than a conservative 50 km^2. We ran a generalized linear model with a logistic link (logistic regression) to assess the effect of the size of the protected area and its corresponding predominant forest type on the probability of tigers going locally extinct, along with exploring the singular and additive effects of forest type and area on the local extinction of tigers (Table 9.1).

The objective of this simple exercise was to identify habitats where most of the decline in tiger population was taking place and determine whether PA size was also relevant to it. There are studies that have

---

* http://www.moef.nic.in/downloads/public-information/protected-area-network.pdf

documented the positive role played by PAs in reducing the extinction risk in India (Karanth et al., 2010) and that PA size is indeed important for wide-ranging carnivores (Woodroffe and Ginsberg, 2000). We were especially interested in Tropical Dry Forests, because it is the largest (> 46%) tiger habitat in India and recent losses indicated a vulnerability that exists in its tiger populations (Wikramanayake et al., 2004, 1999).

Table 9.1 Models used to estimate probability of local extinction of tigers in Protected Areas using size and predominant forest type as variables.

AIC	*ΔAIC*	*Model*	*Likelihood*	*AIC Weight*
235.71	0	Area + Forest	1.00	0.92
241.09	5.37	Forest	0.07	0.06
244.57	8.85	Area + TDF	0.01	0.01
246.52	10.80	Area x TDF	0.00	0.00
247.82	12.11	TDF	0.00	0.00
274.73	39.01	Area	0.00	0.00

AIC = Akaike Information Criteria, ΔAIC = difference between the AIC values of the corresponding model and the top model (with minimum AIC), Area = Protected Area size, Forest = predominant habitat type (Alluvial Grassland and Subtropical Deciduous Forest, Mangrove, Tropical Dry Forest, Tropical Moist Deciduous Forest and Tropical Moist Forest), and TDF = Tropical Dry Forest, and all other forest types pooled together. (*Source*: Biological Conservation, Chundawat et al., 2016)

Results from our logistic regression were noteworthy; as they showed that PA size was not able to explain the extinction risk on its own. However, when it was considered across different habitats, it becomes very clear that it is an important factor for some tiger habitats. The combined effect of small PA size and Tropical Dry Forest type is a lethal combination for tiger populations. In fact, PA size and forest types together explain most of the local extinction of tigers across the country in the past 100 years. Though PA size and forest types were not able to explain the extinction on their own (Figure 9.1). Our model was able to predict 70% of the 89 extinction events correctly even at a conservative threshold of probability—0.5 or greater. Figure 9.1, shows the probabilities of extinction of tigers in the PAs and it is very clear that tigers in India have survived better in larger PAs across all habitat types and not so well in smaller ones. For a specific PA size, Tropical Deciduous Forests have the greatest probability of extinction. For example, a 100 km^2 protected area in alluvial grassland and sub-tropical deciduous forest (AGD) has a tiger survival rate as impressive as that of a 800-900 km^2 area in other habitats. On the other hand, a 100 km^2-sized PA in Tropical Dry Forest has a very high extinction risk but its survival rate improves greatly with an increase in area in the same habitat types (Figure 9.1). This analysis supports our preliminary estimates that over the last 100 years tigers have disappeared from TDFs at a much higher rate (64%) than other habitats in India (Table 9.2). The most worrying fact is that PAs in TDFs are relatively small (366.92 km^2); the average PA size where tigers have disappeared in this habitat in the last 100 years is even smaller (304.6 km^2; t = -2.37, p = 0.01; Table 9.2).

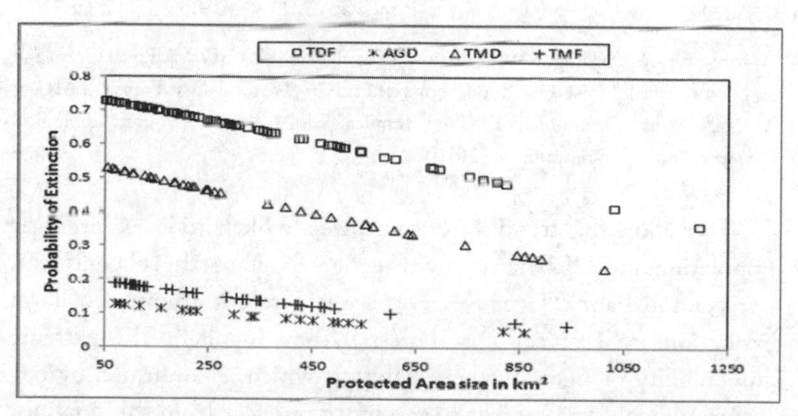

Figure 9.1 Probability of local extinction of tigers in 203 protected areas using logistic regression model: $p = \frac{e^{(-1.852-0.496*Area+2.42*TDF-0.47*AGD+1.55*TMD)}}{1+e^{(-1.852-0.496*Area+2.42*TDF-0.47*AGD+1.55*TMD)}}$ (where, Area= z-score of PA size, TDF= Tropical Dry Forest, AGD= Alluvial Grassland and Subtropical Deciduous Forest, and TMD= Tropical Moist Deciduous Forest)

Table 9.2 Areas that harboured tigers approximately 100 years ago and presence of tigers in the same area in 2010 in India. (All = all point locations; Current = tiger presence in 2010; Extinct = in the last 100 years; percentages and Standard Deviation values are given in parentheses).

*Forest type**	*Tiger habitats*		*Average Protected Area size (km2)*		
	All	*Current*	*Overall*	*Current*	*Extinct*
AGD	21	19 (90%)	344.19 (229.25)	372.55 (222.44)	74.80 (6.58)
Man	2	1 (50%)	846.25 (684.27)	1330.1 (NA)	362.40 (NA)
TDF	97	35 (36%)	366.92 (422.12)	477.30 (617.14)	304.60 (239.16)
TMD	44	26 (59%)	438.20 (363.54)	487.13 (392.74)	367.53 (313.84)
TMF	39	33 (85%)	278.43 (207.55)	293.80 (218.65)	193.91 (106.13)
Total	203	114	367.74 (365.22)	416.45 (429.59)	305.35 (249.40)

*= forest types according to Wikramanayake et al. (1998); AGD = Alluvial Grassland and Subtropical Moist Deciduous Forest; TDF = Tropical Dry Forest; TMD = Tropical Moist Deciduous; TMF = Tropical Moist Forest. (Source: Biological Conservation, Chundawat et al., 2016)

If we allow this trend to continue, we are likely to lose more tiger populations in TDFs than in any other tiger habitat of the subcontinent. Sariska and Panna Tiger Reserves are two recent examples of local extinction in Tropical Dry Forests. They highlight the extreme vulnerability of tigers in these habitats, which is confirmed by our historical analysis. One has to recognize one fact from this analysis: the local extinctions from Panna and Sariska are not exceptions or unique events, but rather part of a larger pan-India trend in Tropical Dry Forests.

The other pertinent trend revealed by the analysis is that we are losing tigers from relatively larger PAs in TDF areas, indicating that tigers require larger areas to survive in this habitat. Since Tropical Dry Forests provide the largest tiger habitat in India, it is important that we find solutions to these problems. The challenge is that Protected Areas in TDF are, on an average, small (366.9 km^2), and increasing their size is not always possible. We must, therefore, find new ways to achieve our conservation goal of making these tiger populations viable within the available spaces. This is a crucial point to consider while drawing up future conservation plans, as demanded by the 2006 amendment to the Wild Life (Protection) Act, 1972. The managers have access to all this information, but they need to invest time and effort to use it constructively.

This challenge provides an opportunity for us to develop new and innovative ideas to ensure the long-term survival of tiger populations within the PAs of Tropical Dry Forests. Science alone cannot protect the tiger, but it can definitely provide a roadmap to achieve conservation goals.

What Makes the Panna Tiger Population Vulnerable?

Let us now discuss Panna specifically and understand the basic ecological needs of tigers that occupy Tropical Dry Forest areas. We found that survival rates of females were extremely poor (0.76) compared to other tiger populations (Smith and McDougal, 1991; Kenney et al., 1995; Chapron et al., 2008; Goodrich et al., 2008). This was a major observation from our study and has serious conservation implications. Previous tiger studies have recorded a higher adult female survival rate than that of adult males, much better than we observed in the Panna population. Even in the re-introduced population, there is high mortality among the females of the population. Therefore, understanding the reasons for this low female survival is crucial.

Because resources are not infinite, individual animals optimize space, resource use and energy expenditure to maximize reproductive success, achieving greater fitness (Stearns, 1992). But there must be a threshold beyond which reproductive success can be impacted. In Panna, we have seen how variable individual tiger responses were and we also noticed that reproductive success of tigresses differed with the variable ecological conditions that existed within their respective territories. Tigress F-123 occupied the best of all territories, with high prey abundance, distribution of resources such as water and prey, a high proportion of suitable habitat and almost no human disturbance. The result was a high reproductive success rate and she was able to raise most of her cubs successfully (almost 90% survival of the 11 cubs in her four litters of 3, 2, 3 and 3), surviving throughout the study period. We estimate that she lived for more than sixteen years.

However, neighbouring territories had a higher proportion of unsuitable habitat, poor availability of water, and highly variable prey densities along with a high livestock population. Tigresses here had limited reproductive success in raising cubs to adulthood (<40% on an average). Moreover, none of the breeding females survived the entire study period. F-111, F-120, F113 and the Amdar female survived only a maximum of eight years. Most importantly all tigresses were exposed to the Edge Effect at the Reserve boundary (see Figure 6.2).

Variability in the quality of breeding habitat, especially for those exposed to the Edge Effect, affected the overall reproductive success and survival rates of the tiger population. These observations are important lessons that show the need to monitor these parameters, for managing the re-introduced tiger population in Panna to ensure tigers' future survival there. Monitoring of such parameters, as well as counting tigers, are immensely relevant for managing smaller tiger populations everywhere in the subcontinent. It is essential that management plans incorporate measures to ensure the minimum ecological requirements for tigers to achieve optimal reproductive success and stability for the breeding population. We do not see this happening in our Tiger Reserves. We only count tigers, though camera traps are more prevalent now; but monitoring of these populations requires a great deal more than simply counting the tigers and its prey. This is where a scientific faculty becomes essential, to help put scientific information in a management perspective and create an effective management system.

Prey Availability

The female tigers' strategy is resource-oriented. They spend most of their time raising cubs. Therefore, they occupy areas where food and other resources are in abundance. Only after all such habitats are occupied, will other sub-optimal habitats be occupied. Three major ungulate prey species—nilgai, sambar and chital—form the bulk of the ungulate number and biomass in Panna. The nilgai's preference for open habitats precludes it from substituting as the principal prey for tigers in dry forest habitats. In Panna, we have seen that tigers do not kill nilgai as much as one might expect from its availability. These large antelopes, well suited for open habitat, are predated on only when visiting forested habitats also frequented by tigers. Tigers do not purposely avoid nilgai but they do not frequent nilgai habitat. Wild ungulate biomass from open and disturbed habitat does not, therefore, necessarily translate into high prey availability for tigers. Besides, neither nilgai nor sambar can become the tigers' principal food as neither can achieve the densities that chital can. On average, chital-size prey across the subcontinent contribute about 47% of the total prey biomass and in numerical terms, over 75% in high tiger density areas such as Kanha, Nagarahole and Kaziranga (Chundawat and Sharma, 2008). In Panna, chital were limited in number and also restricted in distribution; they formed only 17% of available prey biomass and almost 40% in terms of number. The role of medium-sized prey that can achieve high densities as principal food in the ecology of the tiger is an important factor and can affect the tiger's responses (such as densities, land tenure, distribution and ultimately reproductive success) significantly more than other prey species.

We observed that as far as prey availability is concerned, the Tropical Dry Forest habitat can support fairly high prey abundance—well above the metabolic need of the tiger. In areas where prey availability is above metabolic requirement, we see that tiger densities are not related to prey abundance (Figure 9.2). In such a situation, the large home range sizes in Panna may be a result of several additional factors other than prey abundance. We noticed high CVs in our prey estimate, based on distance sampling line transect surveys (see Table 4.4). This indicates that prey densities in Panna vary considerably between habitat types and one can find a similar trend in other such studies conducted in Tropical Dry Forests of the subcontinent. This suggests that this habitat is characterized by high variability in prey dispersion. I believe this heterogeneity in prey availability, along with water availability, high ratio of open forest habitat to the suitable dense forest habitat, and temperature, are definitely important factors in determining the home range sizes.

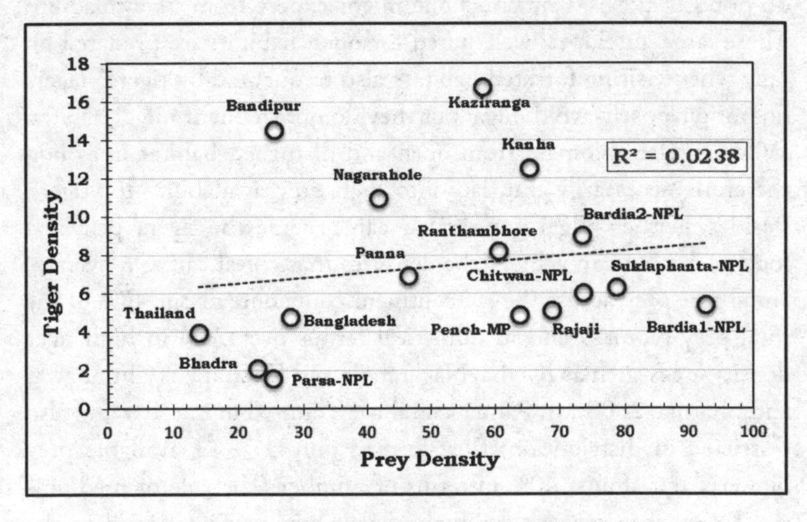

Figure 9.2 Tiger and prey densities in many tiger habitats of the subcontinent and one site in Thailand.

Space Requirements

We found that the annual home ranges (annual space) of the tigers in Panna are much larger than those known so far from other habitats of the subcontinent (Sunquist, 1981; Smith, 1984; Karanth and Sunquist, 2000; Goodrich et al., 2010; Sharma et al., 2010). This need for a larger space, 3–4 times more than those in other tropical habitats, is a significant finding because it has serious conservation implications for all Tropical Dry Forest tiger populations. We know mammal populations with larger home ranges are highly vulnerable to local extinction (Woodroffe and Ginsberg, 1998). Therefore, if larger ranges are a typical characteristic of Tropical Dry Forest habitats, it can be safely stated that tiger populations in these forests are likely to be more vulnerable to extinction. The past trends of general decline that our study results identified in Tropical Dry Forests, along with the extinctions from Sariska and Panna, strengthen the argument. On average, PAs in Tropical Dry Forests are small and tiger ranges are larger: this scale mismatch between the space need of the tiger and that which is provided by our Protected Area network makes it difficult for them to survive.

The extended dry season in Tropical Dry Forests is a key ecological driver that not only governs prey abundance and distribution directly but can change conditions that indirectly affect the prey: frequent extreme droughts take their toll by repeatedly creating sub-optimal conditions. Dispersion of key resources such as cover (including temperature regime), food and water during the dry season (an annual drought-like situation during an extremely long dry spell from October to June) and extreme drought (three to four times a decade due to failure of monsoon rains) may be important factors in Tropical Dry Forest ecology. We need to understand how wildlife populations respond to these extreme environments.

The large home ranges of Panna tigers could be one of the responses to these prevailing ecological conditions. The result is that fewer breeding territories can be accommodated in PAs in TDF, as seen in Panna. From the study, with extensive camera trapping and monitoring of the study population, we could identify a maximum of seven breeding female territories in the Reserve when the tiger population was at its peak (early 2002). This small breeding population is all that the Panna Tiger Reserve could support within its boundaries. The point here is that prey densities in Tropical Dry Forests like Panna could be very high, but habitat variability and environment characteristics can limit tiger densities and affect home range size.

Another aspect that added to the Panna tigers' vulnerability and is associated with the large home ranges, is that the territories of breeding tigers extend up to and beyond the tiger Reserve boundaries into the less protected tiger habitats outside the Park. This is where conflict rules, as tigers frequently preyed on livestock there. In the process they are exposed to the Edge Effect, created due to managerial differentiation between Protected Areas and Buffer Zones. Since most of the protected areas in Tropical Dry Forest habitats are smaller than Panna, it is likely that a similar situation exists in most of them. In such a situation, breeding tigers are not fully protected within the reserves. As mentioned earlier, we found that the survival of adult females in Panna was unusually poor (0.76). The implication of this is critical for managing a population viably in this habitat. I believe this happens because a female's behavioural response to the hostile environment that exists at the periphery is different from a male's and this makes female tigers more susceptible to the Edge Effect.

We know that male cubs undergo high mortality during dispersal as compared to females of the same age (Smith, 1993, 1984). As a result of this exposure, the dispersing males undergo a kind of a selection process, whereby only those individuals who have the knack of avoiding human-caused mortalities survive to adulthood. On the other hand, most of the young females do not undergo such an experience as they settle next to their natal area. They tend to respond to conflict directly. In complete contrast to female behaviour, we notice that males who have survived the selection process, behave timidly and avoid confrontation.

We observed that when a tigress made a kill, especially livestock, everyone in the village got to know about it. This is because they tend to be more possessive of their resources and defend them aggressively. In complete contrast to this, our monitoring of the two dominant radio-collared males revealed completely different behaviour. Both the males were timid, fed on a large amount in one go and then left the kill (not returning or settling down a few kilometres away before returning later). Females stay with the kill until it is finished completely and defend it aggressively. Males responded differently to human presence; they hid or slipped away from the scene quietly when disturbed and would usually not return to the kill site.

One observation highly relevant to providing protection to tigers in such situations was that whenever a radio-collared tiger made a buffalo kill, over 90% of the time villagers found it first, before our monitoring team could. This was in complete contrast to cow kills; over 80% of these were found first by our monitoring team. This happened because buffaloes are expensive assets and therefore always accompanied by a caretaker. The cow owners usually would not know until several days later because cows are not always accompanied or brought back to the house every day. When a buffalo has been killed by a tiger, the entire village is also likely to know and thus, poachers or their contacts in the area also hear about it soon thereafter. So, when a tiger kills a buffalo, it is highly vulnerable to poaching on two counts.

The first is from retaliatory killing. The loss of a buffalo is much greater than that of a cow—a buffalo may cost between Rs 25,000-30,000, compared to a cow that may only be worth Rs 300-1,200. In May 2006, this is what happened in Panna when we lost the last breeding Amdar female to the poisoning of a buffalo kill. Along with her went two cubs who were in their second year. Secondly, the presence of a tiger on a buffalo kill can quickly be relayed to interested parties, who can set a trap and poach the predator.

My advice to managers would be to investigate each and every buffalo kill at the earliest, so that poachers become aware that the kill is under surveillance. Actually, efforts should be made to monitor every tiger kill but this is almost impossible. However, since buffalo kills are easily detectable, they should all be monitored. Such monitoring will make it difficult for poachers to find kills that are not known to the management, so any attempt at poaching will expose them and force them to take greater risks.

We only started losing tigers to poaching in Panna with the reduction in kill monitoring. As long as we were monitoring tiger kills, the breeding tigers were secure. Within a few months of the management imposing restrictions on our monitoring, we lost two radio-collared breeding females. This curtailment of monitoring unfortunately coincided with high international demand for tiger skins. The Sariska tiger population succumbed to this in 2004 and Panna too suffered badly, finally losing its last tiger in 2009.

Size of Breeding Population

Studies have documented how exposure to the Edge Effect can make a wide-ranging species like the tiger highly vulnerable to local extinctions (Woodroffe and Ginsberg, 1998). One of the important factors that contribute to this is poaching. Regarding the impact of poaching on smaller tiger populations such as Panna, our simulations suggest that small populations supported by 7-8 breeding tigresses are not viable when poaching of breeding females cannot be ruled out.

As outlined earlier, our observations show that a combination of factors—such as smaller protected areas in Tropical Dry Forests, requirement of larger spaces, exposure to the Edge Effect and low survival of breeding females—make the Panna tiger population highly vulnerable to extinction. The 'small population syndrome', a typical characteristic of a small population, can make survival and recovery of a tiger population very difficult (Lande, 1988; Caughley, 1994). One of the encouraging observations of our simulations was that a slightly larger breeding population, of more than 13-15 females, could sustain a greater amount of human-induced mortalities. But we know that PAs in the dry forest habitats are smaller than average and cannot support so many breeding females. For this reason, I am arguing that most of the protected areas in this habitat are not large enough to play the role expected of them, which is to protect a demographically viable population. It is risky, therefore, to depend entirely on the Protected Area network for tiger conservation. This is the biggest challenge for tiger conservation authorities: how to find space for a larger breeding population outside the protected area network.

The loss of the entire tiger population from the Panna forest was the second local extinction within our most heavily guarded tiger reserves. Such losses do not augur well for the tiger's long-term viability. When breeding individuals are unsafe, it is difficult to provide stability to a tiger population. To achieve maximum reproductive success, stability of the breeding population is essential. This is an important step towards saving the tiger, especially in its Tropical Dry Forest habitat. The immediate action should be to find ways to enhance our conservation effort in the adjoining tiger habitats outside the PA network. Tiger populations such as Panna, which are small and isolated, cannot survive without an input (immigration of tiger individuals) from a neighbouring population. Creating several small-territory-size tiger populations in the neighbouring forests to provide support from the outside to the protected breeding unit can be an alternative to the large buffer habitat.

Tigers Beyond Boundaries

Since there is little possibility of increasing the size of our protected areas and recognizing the need for larger space, the tiger conservation policy in India is trying to overcome the problem by creating large buffer zones around the Tiger Reserves, as per the Wild Life (Protection) Amendment Act, 2006. This is not a new strategy. In my view, by defining in legislation how the buffer zone should be managed, we have lost the flexibility that we had earlier. In fact, the way it has been visualized, buffers could create more problems than solutions. Let me explain.

As stated in the Wild Life (Protection) Amendment Act, 2006, the buffer zone hopes to 'ensure the integrity of the critical tiger habitat' and provide habitat for dispersing individuals. It is argued that the ring of buffer habitat will act as a sink to the protected (source) population. But this is also intended as an area of 'co-existence' and the status quo is expected as far as most human activities are concerned. Thus, the biotic pressure and threat level will remain the same. As the law puts it, the buffer zones are areas 'where a lesser degree of habitat protection is required'. Herein lies the danger: when these buffer 'sinks' turn into ecological traps, they may act contrary to their intended role. Instead of strengthening protection for the source population, they could hasten its demise.

If the habitats within the buffer are improved to the point where they become attractive to tigers (with improved and better cover, water and prey availability), animals from the source habitat may start using these areas with increased frequency. This sounds like an encouraging and attractive scenario, but the problem is that the tigers are not aware of the risks involved in using a habitat with lesser degree of protection (Delibes et al., 2001; Gundersen et al., 2001). Moreover, the density-dependent habitat selection dynamic is affected when the fittest breeding individuals find sink habitats attractive because of its perceived quality. In density-dependent habitat selection, the fittest animals occupy the best suited habitat. This is a serious and realistic possibility. We see celebratory media reports of females with cubs sighted or photographed in sink areas, hailing this as the result of a successful conservation programme. But whenever I read this I worry about the female's survival in these attractive sinks, especially if she is part of the protected breeding population of a core protected area.

An attractive sink can turn into an ecological trap, when two different mortality probabilities are operating on the same population—one, when it is inside the protected habitat, and the other when it is in the less protected 'buffer area' with its greater biotic interference. In such a scenario, movement from the source habitat can reduce the population size due to the poor survival of breeding populations in the attractive sink. This can ultimately affect the viability of the source population (Delibes et al., 2001; Gundersen et al., 2001).

Whenever I talk about this scenario during my presentations, the concept of a buffer is vehemently defended by suggesting that the conservation work being done in buffers provides protection to the tigers as well as to the core. I would agree if tiger survival in buffers was as good as in the core. But we have to be aware of the dangers when tiger survival is lower than the core. These sink habitats can turn into ecological traps. I am not against the buffer concept per se, not as it is presently conceived and managed. If I want to protect a vulnerable core I will need a buffer as strong and hard as the shell of an egg—not a porous and weaker ring. I would rather have a narrower ring of buffer but one that is better protected than the core.

Can we afford the possibility of our protected populations being surrounded by ecological traps, when our tigers are already highly threatened? The risk is too high. We are aware of the reality of such a possibility since it contributed to the recent extinction of Panna's tigers in 2009. Any conservation plan would be counter-productive if it exposed the tiger to such high risk. Panna's 580 km^2 core is now surrounded by a 1000 km^2 buffer with over fifty villages. I am not confident that such a large buffer can have the same level of protection as the core.

Alternatively, our conservation goal could be to find space for a minimum number of breeding females that can withstand poaching pressure and ensure stability for the population. Since increasing the size of the core area (CTH) is not an available option and, as the buffer is associated with vulnerability of the targeted species, we need to find new ways. We need to move away from the old practices and develop new strategies to save the last remaining tigers in Dry Forest Habitats. At present, all our conservation eggs are in one, old, basket; there is only a single model in India, based on the government-managed Protected Area network. It has worked in many areas but in some aspects, this model is inadequate and is failing to achieve the desired goal. We need to develop new models that work in parallel and simultaneously to the existing system—ones that complement and bolster it.

New Models

When well protected, 13–15 breeding female territories could keep a population viable over a long period and withstand some amount of poaching pressure. But finding space for them within one site is not easy and becomes more difficult when other ecological factors are considered. For instance, not all the territories will be equal in habitat quality and provide the minimum ecological needs of a breeding individual.

Force and armed guards are not the way to deal with such social and ecological problems. Force can only deal with the criminal element that is targeting the tiger population. In a situation where increasing the size of PAs is not always possible, an alternative management strategy is required to save these populations.

To formulate comprehensive tiger conservation plans, we need basic knowledge of what characterizes a breeding habitat, where such potential habitats are located, and the ecological requirements needed for tigers to breed successfully. Our study has documented these in detail and should benefit managers who formulate such plans in these areas. We developed a resource map that identifies important tiger habitats. To achieve optimal reproductive success, it is important that all potential breeding habitats are occupied by breeding females and provide for their minimum ecological needs, ensuring their survival. It is up to the management to effectively use these resources and the knowledge bank that is now available to create a favourable environment in these critical tiger habitats.

I remember constant discussions in the 1980s on SLOSS (Single Large or Several Small); in India we took steps towards 'Single Large' areas for tigers and established a network of Tiger Reserves around this concept. But our reserves are not large enough to protect a viable population. It is time now to review this old strategy and see if we can modify and develop possibilities within the 'Several Small' realm *around* the well-established Single Large. That is, since increasing the size of the protected area is not always possible, instead of continuing to look for a single large population, we suggest creating 'Several Small Satellite (territory size) Populations' in the neighbouring landscape outside our PA network.

The basis for this approach, is the fact that tiger populations like Panna are demographically not viable on their own and their viability is dependent on inputs from neighbouring populations (Akçakaya et al., 2007). Since most such populations are isolated and have no neighbouring populations, we need to create a series of satellite breeding populations around them. This will create a localized meta-population structure. We know that the meta-population structure increases the persistence of a population (Akçakaya et al., 2007). Tigers in this situation will benefit from a meta-population approach which constitutes a more relevant conservation strategy. Applying this concept for tiger conservation within a geographical area not only provides an alternate path, but builds an adaptive system to achieve our original goals, which have been hampered in the past by single large populations not being viable and stable on their own. Some of these

Several Small Satellite or 'S³ populations', when strategically located as stepping stones, should also encourage successful movement between two larger populations.

This strategy provides an alternate approach to the existing conservation plan and is not designed to eliminate or replace the present system. It is proposed as an additional strategy to complement the existing conservation effort. Its origin is based on the meta-population concept and the opportunities available within the present legal framework of the country.

Meta-population and 'Core and Buffer'

Meta-population is defined as a set of discrete populations of the same species, in the same general geographical area, that may exchange individuals through migration, dispersal or human-mediated movement (Akçakaya et al., 2007). An important characteristic of the meta-population structure is the geographically discrete set of populations, where mixing of individuals between populations is always less than within the population. On the other hand, the core and buffer populations are panmictic populations (where each individual has an equal chance to interbreed with every other individual), which is very different from meta-population. However, the 'core and buffer' structure is erroneously referred to as a meta-population structure in the 2006 amendment to our Wild Life Protection Act. Application of the meta-population concept is highly misplaced in the law.

Each of the discrete populations within the meta-population has its own demographic dynamic, thus creating its own demographic characteristics. These populations can also undergo extinction and re-colonization. Survival of these populations is dependent on movement from neighbouring populations. For example, in the Himalayas, snow leopard habitat is above the tree-line but these are surrounded at many places by lower altitude forested habitat. Such isolated snow leopard populations survive in these fragmented habitats by using the forested habitats to move between two populations. Camera trap photographs of snow leopards in the forested habitats (leopard habitat) show this movement but also generate excitement for the wrong reasons (i.e. snow leopard presence sometimes recorded in forest habitat). A similar situation occurs in Mongolia, where snow leopard habitat is surrounded by large plains or desert. We know snow leopards use these desert habitats to move between two mountains. Tigers in a similar situation can use surrounding, poor quality forest and agricultural space to move between two breeding populations, provided such populations are available to it. In these circumstances, the distance between two breeding populations will be a relevant criterion, though it will be different for female and male tigers. It is generally believed that only the male component of a tiger population disperses, but we have seen examples of female dispersal in India.

There are many potential tiger habitats available outside the protected area network, albeit often in smaller units; these are presently not well utilized for wildlife or biodiversity conservation. Using such wildlife-impoverished forest areas, the S^3 Population vision has the potential to restore several such sites to support a small number of breeding units (1-3 female territories) as satellites around a main core population. When established strategically between two tiger reserves, some of these satellite populations can work as 'Stepping Stone' habitats. These stepping stones will connect the two larger populations and make the corridor viable. Such an approach will create a nested meta-population structure, where a local meta-population is nested within larger inter-connected populations of tiger Reserves (Figure 9.3). Instead of trying to manage thousands of square kilometres of tiger habitat corridors, the protection of only a fraction of the area (1-3 territories) will resurrect the connectivity. Managing inter-connected small populations within small fragments is a logistically feasible approach that can provide necessary security to breeding females. The 'Several Small' strategy can run parallel to the existing 'Single Large' approach and provide external support and opportunities to explore new conservation models without altering the existing Protected Area model.

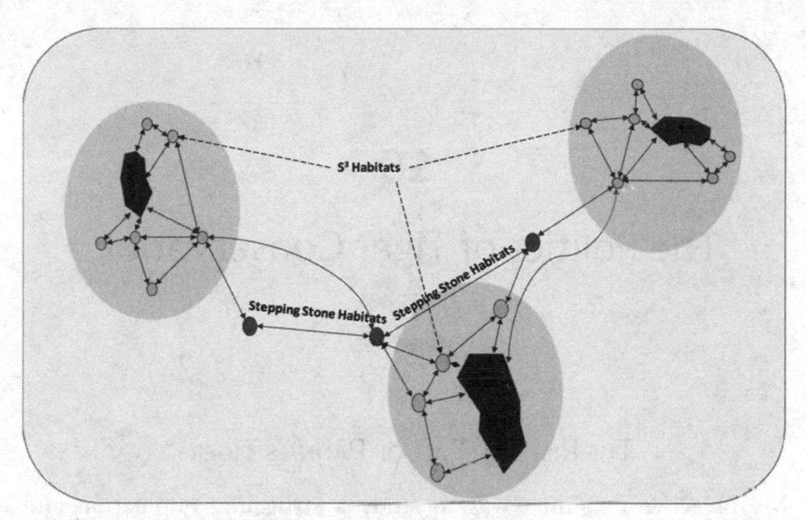

Figure 9.3 Several satellite-territory-sized populations around tiger Reserves will create a localized meta-population structure as the Stepping Stone populations will connect with other such populations to create a nested, larger meta-population structure.

10

The Politics of Tiger Conservation

The Rise and Fall of Panna's Tigers

My objective in Panna was to study a struggling population and gain some understanding of why Tropical Dry Forest tigers are so vulnerable. But I never thought that I would witness a local extinction there. The population made a rapid recovery from 1996, reaching a record high in 2002. At that time everything looked very promising. However, the speed at which we lost more than 30 tigers in the space of 4 years was even more startling. The response of the Reserve authorities, flatly denying any problems and countering with misinformation, intimidation and ad-hominem attacks was traumatic. In this chapter I examine issues of institutional apathy and the politics that were responsible for the loss of an entire thriving tiger population in Panna. We need to understand the causes and the impact of such apathy in order to avoid repetitions.

It was not only the authorities' reactions that surprised us, but also those of colleagues and friends as well as some national and international organizations who remained distant spectators. No one likes to be part of a failure and this is why for India it is important to have successful programmes so that the national and international communities continue to support and partner its tiger conservation mission. The international community still looks forward to a better future for tigers in India despite its many problems. The brilliant recovery of the original Panna tiger population in the late 1990s and the successful relocation and restoration in 2008, both excited the world community. It is such events that bring support and vigour to a conservation programme.

There were only a few friends like the late Fateh Singh Rathore, Belinda Wright, Valmik Thapar and Faiyaz Khudsar who openly came out in our support. Mike Birkhead, who made the BBC film 'Tigers of the Emerald Forest' in 2002–03, was so moved to find that all the tigers he had filmed had died, that he decided to make not one but two campaign films supporting our effort. In the process, he got into trouble with the authorities, almost getting banned from filming in India. Support from these friends gave us the strength to continue to fight until the last male tiger disappeared in February 2009. After I submitted our report titled 'Missing Tigers of Panna'—on the disappearance of tigers which we were monitoring—in early 2005, I was publicly labelled 'anti-system' and accused of having a 'hidden agenda' by Dr Rajesh Gopal, then head of the NTCA. As the system closed ranks, it became clear that it would be very hard for me to pursue research work in tiger areas in future.

Back in the mid-1990s when I first arrived at Panna, things were very different. I was welcomed warmly. My association with the WII might have helped, but mostly, it was because of the wonderful P.K. Chawdhry, the Panna Field Director at the time. He took me and Mr Pabla, my colleague at WII and former officer-in-charge when Panna National Park was first established, into the Reserve to explore the possibilities for a tiger study. I had already made up my mind to work in a Dry Forest habitat. Ranthambhore was ruled out because it was a big tourist destination, and Panna won over Pench and Tadoba due to its terrain and the promised access to elephants for monitoring. But the overall enthusiasm shown by the Reserve management clinched the decision. Close co-operation between the research team and the management was a crucial element for the recovery of a dwindling tiger population from only 10-15 tigers in 1995, to a flourishing 35 tigers by the end of 2001. The research, the tigers and the management, all benefitted from this positive working environment. Little did we realize that this success was contingent on a certain individual. Things changed drastically once Mr Chawdhry was transferred. Support for our research vanished, leading to a hostile work environment where our fieldwork became a struggle and the tigers suffered.

The Beginning

When Neel Gogate joined me in Panna as a research student to carry out fieldwork, the Park authorities recommended two of their best trackers for our team. Their field skills, combined with Neel's experience and some training in surveying techniques for the local staff, allowed us to assemble one of the best research teams I have ever worked with.

Our field monitoring abilities and dedication impressed the Field Director so much that he gave us radios for communication, in case we came across any illegal activities in the Park. We became an integral part of the system, working in tandem with the Park officials.

Once, in peak summer of 1997, the collared tigress Baavan (F-123) had injured her foot, and was unable to make a kill for almost two weeks. Her health had deteriorated, along with her three young cubs. Neel called me to say that if food was not provided to the mother and her cubs, they would perish. Most people on the WII faculty, of which I was a part, asserted that we should not interfere with natural processes—if she died, so be it. This may sound strange now but at the time it was a legitimate and prevailing view—a reflection of less desperate times. However, Baavan was one of only two adult females in the Reserve. The other was already past her prime, unlikely to live long, so the Park officials along with our research team decided to provide food to the ailing Baavan and her cubs. She recovered quickly, going on to contribute over 20 tigers to the Reserve population through her cubs and cubs' cubs. She was key to the remarkable recovery of Panna's tigers till 2002.

There were other instances where the research team and the Park management came together. When our first radio-collared tiger F-01 died, its carcass was found close to a village, next to two livestock kills it had made. By the time we got to the site, the carcass had decomposed completely because of the monsoon humidity and warmth. We suspected poisoning. This was a wake-up call for us and the Park officials as we realized the importance of investigating kills as early as possible, especially at the periphery. From this time onward, they provided us with elephants to investigate every known kill that was made by a collared tiger. On a few occasions we actually found evidence of poisoning but were able to bury the carcasses in time. Soon, it became known locally that it was possible to find those who did such mischief. After this, we never saw another mortality due to poisoning. The constant monitoring of kills in sensitive areas using elephants helped reduce tiger mortality due to human-related threats. When breeding individuals were provided such safety, the results were amazing and the resulting recovery of the Panna tiger population, in the late 1990s, was rightly hailed as great success story.

We were fortunate that the Field Director recognized the importance of our monitoring and supported the research project. The entire staff helped in tracking tiger movements and sharing information. We really appreciated their cooperation without which we could not have achieved much in those early years.

By mid-1999, Neel returned to WII to write his report. I decided to expand the scope of the study, taking leave from WII to be in the field and continue the research work. I arrived at Panna in October 1999, when we only had three working radio-collars on tigers. We collared two new tigers and replaced collars on the existing ones. Additionally, we also radio-collared five sambar and two chital. We conducted camera trapping to estimate the tiger population with the help of Dr Karanth and the CWS in 2002 and 2003. We also tried to establish a monitoring protocol for the Park's managers as I was very keen to set up a permanent field research station for the use of other researchers in the future. The years of our own research could provide a good foundation for continuing study work and I worked towards this with hope.

Early Successes

As already mentioned, with full support of the management our monitoring eliminated human-caused mortalities, improving the tigers' survival rates. Adult females bred successfully and in just 5-6 years Panna had more than 35 tigers. This was a rare recovery amidst the doom and gloom dominating the conservation world at that time. The years between 1996 and 2001 were the best time for field research in Panna. The Park management also supported several other research projects: Yoganand K (WII) conducted research on sloth bear ecology and behaviour; Koustubh Sharma from the Bombay Natural History Society (BNHS) came to Panna to undertake an ecological study of the four-horned antelope. Furthermore, one of the range officers from the Reserve management, took study leave and joined our research team for his PhD. It was a wonderful atmosphere—the management welcomed researchers with open arms, attracting the best brains from all over the world. Well-respected biologist Dr Cliff Rice was working with Yoganand, Dr Asad Rahmani with Koustubh Sharma, and we partnered with Dr Karanth and his team. Such cooperation helped all of us enormously.

With this tiger population recovery, I became the 'blue-eyed boy' of the Forest Department and was asked to undertake similar studies in their other Reserves. National and international NGOs wanted to be part of this success story, offering support. The BBC made the award-winning documentary, 'Tigers of the Emerald Forest', about the recovery. By the end of 2004, we had collected a wealth of information on the tiger—more comprehensive than we had ever before achieved in India.

However, we were not able to continue the research as planned. How and why this happened will become clear later in this chapter. We also established a reliable prey monitoring system. Many volunteers from various parts of India helped us gather this information. We also trained the Reserve staff and many local enthusiasts in these monitoring techniques. We hoped that Panna would illustrate to India and the world how science and management working together could bring considerable conservation success. Sadly, just as this message was spreading, the Park leadership changed and the alliance fell apart.

The End of the Recovery (2001–2005)

It was amazing how fast things changed when Mr Chawdhry was transferred from Panna in 2001. A new management team under Mr Sanjay Mukhariya's leadership took over the charge of the Tiger Reserve. Within six months, the Panna tigers' fate was altered irrevocably. The growing tiger population and increased tiger sightings had made Panna a popular destination, which put pressure on the tigers and the tracking elephants. Tigress F-113 became the focus of the tiger show. Every time the research team was out tracking her, tourist vehicles would follow in convoy. Due to the heavy disturbance this caused her, we stopped tracking her during visiting hours. This meant that the Park elephants were not able to locate the tigress on a regular basis.

Unhappy with this development, the authorities curtailed our access to elephants—they were no longer available to us for monitoring purposes. By mid-2002, our monitoring was restricted to taking locations remotely from our vehicle and investigating kills on foot only after the tiger had finished feeding and left the site. We could not approach kill sites while a tiger was feeding without the safety of an elephant. Investigation was only possible on the fourth or fifth day after the kill. We were concerned by our inability to reach the kill sites at an early stage, especially in areas where tigers were vulnerable to poaching and poisoning.

We tried to communicate our concerns to the new leadership, explaining why it was necessary to monitor kills. In response to one of our letters, the Deputy Director wrote, '[A]s a manager of the Park we have to consider all aspects for the management of the Reserve. Due to increase in tourism we have procured two elephants (with calf) from Sanjay National Park, Sidhi, last year. We have to justify the procurement. Increase in income from the elephant is the only justification acceptable to the Head Office and we have achieved that this year.' We were shocked to see revenue generation cited as the new goal for park elephants, since we understood that elephants were procured for patrolling and protection purposes. We were unable to convince them of the critical need to monitor kills. In the following years, the repercussions of this change became apparent and Panna's tigers paid the price.

This change in priorities was one example of the way general protection measures were losing focus and becoming lax. We started noticing animals running loose with broken snares around their necks and we came across several ungulates killed by snares. We also found traps around waterholes with increasing frequency.

These were worrying developments that I felt should be communicated to the Park management. The Park's deputy director Mr Ambade had been a trainee student in the Wild Life Management diploma course at the WII, so I knew him. I went to his office and had an apparently cordial chat about the snare and the traps over a cup of tea. In the middle of the discussion he disappeared and after about five minutes, I got a message summoning me to the Field Director's office. Mr Mukhariya told me that I must not interfere with management and should mind my own business. Until this time, apart from the elephant access issue, we had had a good relationship, so this came as a rude shock.

One day during routine tracking we came across a waterhole with snares arranged in two rings around it. We removed all the snares and brought them to the Range Office. The office staff informed the Deputy Director and his reaction shocked us and them both. They were told that the research team is not authorized to carry out such activities. The message was clear and crisp: we were no longer friendly researchers but unwelcome outsiders for the new regime. This really changed our relationship with the staff.

The Decline

Over the next few months things did not change much and in October 2002, the first collared breeding tiger went missing. We had continued monitoring as best we could in the unfriendly environment. But when we located tigress F-111 in the same location for two successive days, we suspected that she was on a kill. Without an elephant, we were unable to check immediately. When we arrived to investigate a couple of days later, we could not get a signal from her collar. We thought that she must have finished feeding and moved on but when we reached the kill site, we found that the livestock she had killed had not been consumed completely. Suspecting that she may have been disturbed by villagers, we decided to track her down but after two days of searching, we could not receive any signal from her collar. Since there had been no human-caused tiger deaths for several years, poaching was not uppermost in our minds. We thought the radio-transmitter may have failed, so we set up camera traps in her known home-range area. However, we could not confirm her presence. Seriously worried now, we launched an intensive search. We started seeing evidence of another adult female in her territory; this was not a good sign. We spent quite some time trying to find evidence that F-111 was still alive. Even after two months of monitoring, we had no luck, not even signs of her death. She had disappeared.

Before we could recover from this loss, we received another setback through the death of her sibling F-120. In December 2002, F-120 and her two young cubs were located in an area which was not safe—near the edge of the Park near Koni village, where there had been a tiger poaching case about a decade earlier. Worried, we tracked her almost daily on foot and were relieved when she finally moved away. But a few days later she was back in the same area. By then I had had to leave for Ranthambhore for a meeting. For several days the team continued to monitor her in the area. She was moving around, so a kill was not expected, though she remained in the vicinity. We requested an elephant so that the team could check on her safety but were unable to get one. A few days later, the research team found that her collar had started transmitting the inactive signal, which continued for several hours. Worried, the team once again requested an elephant; it was only when possible mortality was mentioned that an elephant was made available, which arrived after several days. Tragically, this was too late and the team only found her dead body. She had been caught in a snare. They also found a dead sambar near her in a similar trap, along with signs of other sambar carcasses at the site. The research staff had taken photographs as evidence of the poaching incident but the Park officials confiscated the film roll and did not return it.

The death of F-120 was reported to the Panna Field Director and the Director of Project Tiger (now NTCA) at Delhi on 17 December 2002. I wrote a brief report, dated 12 January 2003, stressing the importance of this death as an example of the extreme vulnerability of Panna's tigers due to extension of their territories into peripheral areas. It re-emphasized the need to bring the peripheral areas under the Tiger Reserve management, if the breeding tigers of the Reserve were to be fully protected.

Since I was in Delhi at the time of F-120's death and could not immediately reach the Field Director, I informed Dr Rajesh Gopal, the Director of Project Tiger. Unfortunately, this turned out to be a big mistake—his intervention turned the senior officers of Panna against me. Instead of increased patrolling to contain the poaching, our research activities were targeted and the team's movements restricted. The same month I received a letter from the Reserve authorities claiming that 'research activities were having a negative effect on the Park management', so the 24-hour monitoring of collared animals was restricted to the daytime. Another letter was issued on the same date asking me to personally give a presentation to the Field Director every three months. Now, night monitoring and movement by foot, in addition to access to elephants, was completely stopped. This meant that information on tiger locations was limited to being taken remotely from vehicles on the Park's tracks during daylight hours. After several meetings with the Field Director, and a great deal of persuasion, I finally managed to convince him of the importance of our monitoring. We resumed night monitoring, albeit without written permission. This was to haunt me later. Every time we went, we had to first make an entry in a special register provided to monitor research activities. The Deputy Director regularly checked this register. Instead of keeping a check on illegal activities, our research activities became their main focus and a complete check on us was maintained.

Before things could settle there was another tiger death. The large male tiger Hairy Foot was found dead in the summer of 2003. With this death, three breeding tigers had died within one year. This dominant breeding male's body was found in a well by a member of our team. In trying to minimize the impact of this on our research activities, we took the precaution of passing the news on to the management through other sources. However, our activities were further restricted. We now had to take prior permission from the Range Officer every time we went for fieldwork. The officer was always asleep in the early morning when we needed to be in the field, so the team had to tolerate his abuse every day. We had no choice.

Despite the three tiger deaths indicating a dangerous trend, nothing changed on the ground and we continued to find a number of animals with nooses around their necks. Between November 2003 and February 2004 we documented over fifteen animals with such nooses. Many of these animals succumbed to death (see photograph). Despite spending many years in jungles, I had never seen live animals running around with snares around their necks before. I asked many

This male nilgai was caught in a trap similar to the one which killed tigress F-120. The noose was attached to a pole. The nilgai had dragged it around until it got hooked to the fence. In F-120's case, the pole got caught between two trees and she, too, had choked to death.

senior forest officers about their experiences with this. It was largely unheard of, with only a couple of sightings over 25-30 years of service. Within a period of 5-6 months, we saw fifteen.

In February 2004, the noted biologist George Schaller was planning to visit Panna to see the work we were doing. Project Tiger's Director (later Secretary of the NTCA) Rajesh Gopal, whom I first met in Kanha Tiger Reserve during a visit there, wanted to meet Dr Schaller and asked me to organize a meeting for him. I therefore invited him to Panna to meet George, and during that time we discussed and conveyed to him our worry about some of the signs that we were witnessing and the possible threat the tigers were facing. However, sharing field information with him turned out to be the second mistake we made with him. After meeting us, Dr Gopal visited the Tiger Reserve with the Reserve authorities.

The day after he left Panna on 14 February 2004, the Park management seized our research equipment and jeep, allegedly for entering the park in the night. We were charged with illegal entry into the Park. We had been conducting night monitoring for many months with complete knowledge of the authorities, keeping entry records in the register at the Park gates. But since the Field Director's last order had only been given verbally, we were caught. This was not the first time researchers had faced such opposition in India. It is a well-known management strategy to discourage and force them out.

We had no choice but to take this up with the Chief Wild Life Warden of the state. After several meetings over two months, he released the research vehicle and equipment, reissuing our permissions but with many restrictions—radio-tracking was curbed to the daytime and night-monitoring to 5 days in a month, and I had to apply to the Field Director *every* time for night monitoring and be chaperoned by a Forest Officer. By the time we secured this permission in March, it was too late to conduct the line surveys for prey estimation and camera-trapping for tiger population estimation. We were also unable to complete our village surveys. Moreover, we could not find a Forest Officer willing to accompany us. So, we got daily wage labourers instead from nearby villages. Besides, camera-trapping for the tiger census was also restricted to the daytime. Separate permissions were required for the night hours. This was most ridiculous; it was clear that they did not want us monitoring the tigers and exposing the declining population.

Furthermore, the Field Director of the Reserve issued a letter adding his own 14 additional conditions. Our research vehicle's movement was restricted to the main roads and we were no longer allowed to use wireless communication. Photography was banned except for 'research-related activities' and a copy of each photograph taken had to be submitted to the Field Director's office. We were also not allowed to keep tranquillization equipment at the camp.

By this time the disappearance of tigers in Panna had become public knowledge, bringing several concerned people to the Park. One such visitor was Ms Belinda Wright, Executive Director of the Wild Life Protection Society of India, who saw a large male sambar with a noose made from clutch wire around its neck. Alarmed by the deteriorating situation, the Wild Life Protection Society of India filed a writ petition to the Central Empowered Committee (constituted by the Supreme Court of India) in April 2004. The petition raised many concerns regarding the Park authorities and the alarming loss of tigers and their prey to poaching.

Between the time the petition was filed and it came to hearing, another tiger, F-113, went missing from Panna. Since we had removed her collar the previous year due to the excess pressure on her from the Park's tiger shows, she was not monitored on a regular basis. We received unconfirmed reports that she had been poached from a kill in April and was never sighted again. She had been the star of the tiger show conducted by the Reserve authorities and, with her death, tiger sightings dropped drastically. At the time of her death, we believe that she was raising her third litter of very young cubs.

May 2004: Consequences of the Writ

Immediately after the Writ Petition by the Wild Life Protection Society was heard by the Supreme Court's Central Empowered Committee (CEC), the Field Director's office sent us a barrage of letters. Our research once again became the target of the management's anger. The letters ordered us to do the following:

- Vacate the field camp with immediate effect.
- Return the wireless set issued by the Field Director's office and threatened us with action for using the official frequency and wireless network.
- Remove all tranquillization equipment and drugs from the camp.
- Send them a list of the research staff working in the project.
- Barred us from any photography inside the Reserve and ordered us to submit a copy of all the photos taken in the past.
- One letter claimed that we had not employed enough staff and the team was not large enough for monitoring, ordering us to hire a minimum of four field staff. We already had five field staffers for monitoring.
- We were also asked to provide details of how many animals were radio-collared and when (important information already known to management and available in the form of progress and annual reports previously submitted).
- Pay deposit fees of Rs 1,70,000 for past elephant use (2000–2003). No breakdown provided.
- Another letter directed us to deposit the money within ten days, threatening legal action if not done.

The Central Empowered Committee visited Panna in May 2004 for a field inspection and submitted its interim report. It looked into all the issues raised in the petition and found them to be accurate, making the following observation:

> The increase in the number of animals reported to have been caught in the snares and the alarm over disappearance of tigers is cause for grave concern. There have been violations of the provision of the Wild Life (Protection) Act, 1972 and the order of the Hon' able Supreme Court dated 14/2/2000…

It further noted that the Reserve had been mismanaged and senior supervision found 'woefully lacking'. Our research project was ascribed an important role in providing inputs to the Park management. Lastly, the committee suggested that guidelines be framed within two months for better co-ordination and cooperation between researchers and the management. All research projects were put on hold until then. The state authority promptly took this opportunity to suspend our tiger research project, just a day after the report was submitted on 24 May 2004. Other research projects were not affected.

Panna had lost four resident tigers, including three breeding females, out of a total of seven breeding females. It was heading towards extinction. But the management seemed to be more occupied with their inquiry against our project. The Chief Wild Life Warden of the state was concerned about permissions for our field camp—why I was inviting my scientific friends, why I was using elephants and why I was taking photographs. This letter was faxed to me at Delhi on 18 June and expected me to be present at Panna to meet him by 21 June 2004.

I responded to the questions in detail but nothing happened for several months. Between June and December 2004, I wrote several letters, drafting protocols for research in Protected Areas and coordination with Park authorities, as requested by the CEC, but received no response. Pursuing the restoration of research permission, making calls and meeting the Chief Wild Life Warden multiple times did not help. There was no movement for nearly six months.

I received another letter in January 2005 demanding explanations about the benefits of tiger research for the Tiger Reserve management, the reasons for night monitoring and 'illegal entry' into the park, the use of wireless sets, non-payment of elephant usage fees, and why fresh permissions were required to continue research when nine years of study were already over.

I wrote back in detail, also writing to the Madhya Pradesh Forest Minister and the Chief Secretary requesting their intervention to save a precious wildlife habitat. After a lot of persuasion, research permission was granted on 29 January 2005. But this only restored the old permission which was due to expire in less than two months, in March 2005. The previous restrictions on monitoring and photography remained. There were still no protocols or guidelines in place.

The CEC visited Panna again in February 2005 and submitted a second report. The Committee was alarmed by the persistent decline in tiger numbers and suggested an immediate assessment of the population through camera traps. It also noted that the management was continuing to carry out activities forbidden by the Supreme Court and causing serious damage to wildlife habitats by extensive burning and creating wide view lines on either side of the major tourist roads. In its conclusion the CEC said, 'Panna is showing signs of Sariska'. They stressed the need for immediate action before it was too late for any recovery.

While we had been shut out of the Reserve as researchers, we continued gathering information on known tigers through tourist guides and other visitors. Two of the tigers still had active radio-collars. But many of the other tigers we knew had not been seen for months. As soon as our permission was restored in January we returned to the field, conducted a quick assessment of the tiger population and initiated a line survey for prey estimation. By the end of March 2005, before our permission expired, we could only complete a part of the line surveys because the Park staff refused to accompany us as required. Without them we could not do the line survey.

Even so, we were stunned by our assessment of the tiger population. In the last two-and-a half years (since the death of F-111 in 2002) Panna had lost 9 breeding tigers out of the eleven known to us. This represented almost the entire breeding population of the Reserve. It was a huge setback. More worrying was the fact that there had been no record of cubs surviving to adulthood in the last two years, whereas in early 2002 all seven breeding females had cubs. In all, only two or three adult female tigers survived.

We compiled all this information in a report titled 'Missing Tigers of Panna'. It listed all the known tigers, with photographs for identification, and documented their history and listed those that had died, survived or gone missing as far as we could ascertain. It was circulated widely, even personally handed over to the Director of Project Tiger and the Chairman of the National Board for Wild Life. Copies were also distributed to the MOEF, the Madhya Pradesh

Chief Minister, the Forest Minister, Chief Secretary, Principal Chief Conservator of Forests, Chief Wild Life Warden and the Field Director of Panna Tiger Reserve. We hoped to wake the authorities up to the seriousness of the situation.

The Indian Express Article

Based on our report, *The Indian Express* carried a front-page article with the headline NOW 30 TIGERS GO MISSING FROM MP'S SHOWCASE SANCTUARY. This was the first major tiger expose after Sariska. On 12 March 2005, Rajesh Gopal, the Director of Project Tiger, responded to the article:

> **Hidden Agenda**
>
> Apropos of the recent coverage on Panna, regarding missing tigers (IE, March 6), the report does not reflect the true picture since the Tiger Reserve Management has recently estimated more than 30 tigers. This can always be verified. The researcher who was quoted in the report has based this report on a collar study undertaken by him almost a decade back. Considering the longevity of tigers and their innate tenurial behaviour to move away from natal areas, the possibility of such tigers being present in the habitat does not seem to be well-founded. The researcher, like many others who have done breast-beating in the media over tigers, also appears to have a hidden agenda. It is learnt he has set up an NGO near the tiger Reserve recently to further his cause, which perhaps warrants an anti-system posture to gain credibility. Alas, these are the woes of wildlife conservation today!
>
> —Rajesh Gopal, IGF & director, Project Tiger, New Delhi

Although Dr Gopal was in full possession of all the facts, he misled the reader into thinking that my study was out of date and attacked me personally. At the very least, our claims warranted a measured response instead of flat denial. Strangely, when I had met him personally to hand over this report, he appeared concerned and immediately dictated a letter asking for an investigation. Whether it was actually sent and carried out, I do not know.

The television and print media covered the report extensively because the Sariska extinction in 2004 was fresh in everyone's mind. This was also the time when the Environment Investigation Agency, a reputed UK NGO, and the Wild Life Protection Society of India had exposed the illegal trade of tiger and leopard skins in Tibet. The huge seizures made in India, Nepal and Tibet alarmed the conservation community across the world. The impact of this on India's tiger population was similar to that of the tiger bone trade that hit India in the early 1990s. Sariska fell first. Yet when our report found twenty tigers missing from Panna, the Indian authorities were unmoved, despite worldwide concern.

At least in the case of Panna, we had blown the whistle well before all the tigers disappeared. Extinction in Sariska had happened quietly and almost unnoticed. Authorities there also tried to shrug it off as misreporting, claiming the tigers had gone 'to the hills and will return'. In January 2005, *The Indian Express* exposed the complete loss of tigers from Sariska Tiger Reserve. But as late as February, Rajesh Gopal was claiming to the press that reports on missing tigers were 'baseless, false and intended to malign the government' (*Tehelka*, 19/01/2013) and 'there are still tigers in the area. Maybe, they have moved away due to tourist disturbance' (*The Indian Express*, 13/02/2005).

The extinction was confirmed beyond doubt by the CBI in March that year. After this Project Tiger's Director and the rest of the government had to accept the reality.

Panna still had 10–12 tigers and it would have been possible to restore the population to its previous glory had timely action been taken. But 'shoot the messenger' was again the action of choice for the authorities.

Fresh Census

The media pressure from the expose did push the authorities to order a fresh special census, to take place over one week in March 2005. MP Forest Officer Asim Srivastava (then the Field Director of Bandhavgarh Tiger Reserve) was invited to conduct the census as an independent person. It was entirely upon him to present the true situation and save the remaining tiger population from extinction. In 2005, India still used to conduct tiger census based on pugmark impressions.

Hundreds of Pugmark Impression Pads (PIPs) were created on paths in the park. PIPs are large patches of soft dust created on well-travelled routes of the tiger. When a tiger walks over them, it leaves behind a clear impression of its pugmark. It was believed that individual tigers could be identified from these pugmark impressions.

For this occasion, the number of PIPs created were more than 10 times the usual number—2,200 in the 540 km^2 area. In spite of this large number, only about 30 pugmarks could be obtained from them. Impressions from tracks and waterholes were also added to the tally, contrary to normal protocol. Despite this unusually intensive census operation, less than 70 impressions could be collected. This was far less than the previous censuses.

Based on these pugmark impressions, Asim Srivastava's team concluded that there was no loss of tigers; in fact they found an extra tiger in the Park. The census reconfirmed the presence of 34 tigers that were counted in the previous census and added one more to the tally. After all Project Tiger's director had already announced before the census that Panna had 'more than 30 tigers'.

But the results were in fact scary and worse than we had expected. The map that showed the locations of the pugmark impressions was revealing. We still had two tigers with working radio-collars and our team was tracking them, as our permission had not expired when the census was conducted. We knew their exact movement and locations during the census. Clearly, pugmark impressions of these radio-collared animals were counted many times over—13 different adult tigresses within the territory of one tigress, F-123, and 9 adult male tigers within the territory of M-125. All the impressions were from within these two ranges. It was a massive cover-up. Overlap between a few males was possible but 9 in one area was unheard of and 13 tigresses within one tigress's territory would certainly rewrite all known tiger natural history. The most worrying information from this operation was that almost all the signs came from only 25% of the Reserve; the rest of the Park revealed no tiger presence at all. We estimated that in all there may not have been more than 8 or 9 tigers left in Panna.

For the first time we felt that extinction for this population was a definite possibility. Even now, a decade later, writing this line sends a chill down my spine and gooseflesh appears. We were traumatized by this thought; I could not sleep properly for weeks. Apart from myself, Fateh Singh Rathore, former Field Director of the Ranthambhore National Park and Nitin Desai of the Wild Life Protection Society of India attended as observers of this census and we all registered our objections to the figure given by Asim Srivastava. Shri Fateh Singh's presence during the census was a huge support to our campaign. Not many openly came forward in support in the way that he did. He had predicted that not only would they find all the claimed tigers but one or two additional ones, too. This is exactly what happened. He knew that they would throw this figure at us and we would have to disprove it. A young support group also came, led by Faiyaz Khudsar and Dharmendra Khandal. At such times, having such strong backing around us was very helpful.

After this census the state authorities aggressively dismissed our claims about the missing tigers in Panna. On 9 April 2005, the Chief Wild Life Warden told the Hindi daily *Nav Bharat* that the situation in Panna was quite satisfactory. Upon being questioned about the missing tigers he responded that '[the situation] has been blown out of proportion by one individual and his claims are baseless.' The State Forest Minister said that 'the entire controversy about Panna and its declining tiger population had been generated by a disgruntled researcher' (*The Hindu,* 11 April 2005). Karan Thapar reported that the Secretary of the MOEF 'claimed that stories about tigers disappearing and ensuing crisis are gross exaggeration [...] they were put out by so-called experts who are not scientists but are seeking publicity' (*Hindustan Times,* 3 April 2005).

But the media slammed this controversial census and under pressure, the Forest Department of MP invited the Wild Life Institute of India to review the census results. The WII team asked the Reserve authorities to collect more pugmark impressions. The collection of pugmark impressions was extended for another month but they still could not muster enough evidence.

However, the authorities at all levels were adamant and, refused to accept the loss of tigers and the fact that the situation demanded immediate remedial actions. Our findings were repeatedly rejected as sour grapes. We had high hopes from the CEC reports. The high level committee was not happy with the situation and sent a follow-up letter to the MP Chief Secretary on 28 March 2005, repeating their concern that the 'Panna tiger population does not follow Sariska's example...' They requested that an 'Action Taken Report' be filed before them 'at the earliest.'

The response from the MP State Principal Secretary (Forest) stated that they will 'take such action as is deemed appropriate' but 'to compare Panna with Sariska is unwarranted and unduly alarmist.' He declared that the CEC's observations '[were] not backed by evidence' and '[did] not seem appropriate for a senior level committee appointed by the Supreme Court.' He accused them of quoting a 'disgruntled researcher [who is] reported to be a close associate of one of the members.' This was an astonishing reply and a remarkable aspersion to come from a Chief Secretary to a high-level Supreme Court committee.

Intimidation and Harassment

Every time a report appeared, there would be retaliations against us. The CEC's follow-up letter led to enquiries into land purchases and fabricated offences during the filming of the BBC documentary between 2002 and 2003. Ironically, I was accused of withholding information on poaching, and threatened with prosecution and more. Things took a dark turn when I received an anonymous phone call while driving to Delhi from Panna. I was warned that two police officials would stop me on the road at Nowgaon and that I must cooperate.

I feared that something illegal had been planted in my car, as it was always parked on the main road, easily accessible to outsiders.

After receiving the call, I stopped the car and searched inside and out, even under the bonnet. Only when sure that nothing had been planted did I resume my journey. This was not paranoia, as earlier we had found illegal wildlife items hidden in the building where we were staying.

We were indeed stopped by a man from the Subsidiary Intelligence Bureau, along with his friend. They questioned me about tiger poaching and hinted at my possible role in it because we knew the whereabouts of the collared tigers. They probed us about our funding sources and other personal details. Initially, he seemed to be playing the 'bad cop' but gradually turned into a 'good cop' at the mention of the name of one of my students, Neel Gogate. The cop had seen tigers with him several years ago. We were let go, and afterwards the officer must have spoken to him and heard our side of the story. Even before we reached Delhi, the cop called me to apologize. He even asked me to inform him about any leads on poaching in Panna, promising he would try his best to catch the poachers.

After this incident, I was more careful, washing and inspecting my car every day. A few months later I received another mysterious early-morning call asking whether I had gone for a walk on my Madla property, a piece of land I had on the banks of the river Ken. I asked him who he was and why he was asking this. He identified himself as my well-wisher, insisting that I go there. Since I was not in the vicinity, I asked one of my staff to check it out. They found two large bags full of antlers. The possession of such wildlife items was illegal, so the nervous staffer threw the bags into the monsoon-swollen river.

Such harassment was not only directed at us—even some of the elephant mahouts and members of the research team were taken into custody, and threatened and questioned for days. Not only were we failing to save the remaining tigers, but this had created an unsafe environment for our staff and colleagues as well as ourselves.

However, the disturbing incident with the intelligence officers had a positive impact. We shared information related to the poachers of F-113 with them, which resulted in an arrest in July 2005. A resident of Chhatarpur, this poacher admitted to trading in eight tigers and over thirty leopard skins and body parts, most of them from Panna. The arrest was proof that poaching was rampant in the area, again putting the spotlight on Panna. As media pressure mounted, Park authorities continued to hit back—this time with a Revenue Recovery Certificate, demanding pending elephant fees within 24 hours and threatening legal action would be taken. The amount claimed was totally arbitrary with no justification. On the same day my permission for extending research in Panna was denied 'keeping in view the technical and administrative difficulties'. I was also dropped from the State Advisory Board for Wild Life.

But the print media campaign was hotting up and Mr Harish Salve, then amicus curiae to the Supreme Court for environmental matters, filed a petition in the Supreme Court regarding the disappearance of tigers from Panna Tiger Reserve. The MP Forest Department's counter-affidavit, instead of addressing the petition's issue of tiger disappearance again focused on me, accusing me of instigating the two petitions, even though I did not have a hand in them, of having 'deep commercial interests', and stating that 'certain violations and grave negligence' had been committed during my research which had received 'huge financial assistance from foreign agencies.'

Even the WII, whose faculty I had been on until 2003, joined the bandwagon. Since it was included in the affidavit, I learnt that its director, Mr P R Sinha (also a government Forest Officer) had sent a letter to the Chief Wild Life Warden of MP stating that the WII had withheld my pension benefits due to various alleged misdemeanours. I was not even aware that I qualified for a pension and had never been informed directly of this nor of any 'misdemeanour' worthy of stopping it. There was certainly no reason for the Director of WII to share my pension status with the Chief Wild Life Warden of Madhya Pradesh. But this was used to malign and pressurize me. I was advised that I should respond to clear such allegations, so I filed an intervention application and thereby became a party to the case. More than ten years later, the matter is still sub-judice.

We were not the only ones to be targeted. Between December 2005 and January 2006, Valmik Thapar—a member of the Supreme Court's

CEC and MP's Wild Life Advisory Board—received letters from the new field director of Panna regarding newspaper articles purportedly written by him concerning the missing tigers. One letter requested him to provide details of poaching within 10 days. Mr Thapar took the matter to the State's Chief Secretary, Mr Vijay Singh and later received a conciliatory letter from the Forest Secretary, although it ended with veiled threats about the 'high and mighty' attitudes of people like him.

Post-2006: The Cover-Up Continues

In January 2006, not having visited for many months, Joanna and I returned to the Panna Tiger Reserve. Since we no longer had research permission, we wanted to enter as tourists. But on arrival at the gate we were refused entry, even as normal fee-paying visitors. This was a rude and embarrassing shock for both parties, as the gatekeeper and the other staff had worked and lived with us for many years at the camp. I saw some of them quietly walking away from the scene. We felt very sorry for inadvertently putting them in this awkward situation. We had never imagined such a scenario. The instruction to prevent our entry was never given in writing.

During one of the hearings on Harish Salve's petition, the Supreme Court asked the MP Forest Department to submit the WII report reviewing the special census conducted in March 2005. In response, the Director of WII submitted a two-line letter claiming that the pugmarks collected during the census were of too poor a quality to ascertain the number of tigers. Yet Asim Srivastava's count from the same pugmarks was not questioned. WII had shrugged off its responsibility. But, concerned by the facts presented by the amicus curiae, the Honourable Supreme Court asked for another assessment, this time using camera traps. WII was already planning to conduct a pan-India tiger assessment using camera traps, so Panna became one of the first sites and the census was conducted during April–May 2006.

In the first week of May, yet another tigress with one of her two cubs was found dead, later confirmed as poisoned. She was one of only two adult females that were known to be surviving in the area. Although this occurred during the census, these mortalities were ignored in WII's report. Even more reprehensible was the fact that these dead tigers were included in the estimation count and the report was submitted to the Supreme Court by the MP Forest Department.

The accompanying letter from the WII director was very carefully worded. It presented the picture as favourably as possible, mentioning 'a healthy tiger population in the study area'. The decline was artfully camouflaged in statistical jargon. So once again, although the data clearly indicated a serious decline (to those who wanted to see), the report and figures projected a healthy status of tigers in Panna.

If the tiger and cub mortalities had been included, the WII census would have shown a density of around 3.7 tigers per 100 km^2. This was an almost 50% decline from the 2002 estimation (6.94 per 100 km^2). The WII data also showed that tigers were missing from almost 40% of the Reserve. Despite these facts, the report had suggested that there was no significant decline because the 2006 estimate was within the confidence limit of the 2002 estimate.

The data from the WII report supported our contentions but the covering letter from the Director gave a completely contrary picture. We argued this in the court, but to no avail and with no support. It was somewhat galling therefore, to find that one year after the Panna tigers' extinction in 2009, Rajesh Gopal, then Secretary of the NTCA, and the WII faculty, published the very same data with a different interpretation, claiming that these figures actually gave evidence of the decline.

I was able to identify all the individuals in the WII census images. There were three females, two cubs and four males. One of these females and her two cubs were those who died during the census period. One female was the ageing Baavan and the other was her daughter. This indicated a very desperate situation: Baavan was well past her prime and we doubted that she could raise another litter, so her young daughter was the only hope.

The all-India tiger number was announced in May 2007 and this revealed a serious decline, the worst figures being from Madhya

Pradesh. Attention shifted to this and Panna was forgotten for some time.

In November 2007, I visited Panna several times and saw little evidence of tigers and none of the females. This was confirmed by tourist guides who were going into the park almost every day. They could only confirm the presence of two males. I wrote to the MP Chief Wildlife Warden and Principal Chief Conservator of Forests, drawing their attention to the 'grave extinction risk to the existing population,' and urging them to take 'action on a war-footing.'

In January 2008, the NTCA sent an official team comprising Mr P.K. Sen, ex-Director Project Tiger and Mr Ravi Singh, Secretary General, WWF-India to report on the status of tigers in Panna. But nothing concrete resulted: their report appreciated the good work being done there, although it also expressed some concern about the tiger numbers and suggested yet another camera-trapping assessment. It should not require an outsider to point out when the situation is dire. It is the responsibility of the Reserve and higher supervising authorities to keep track of the situation and take remedial measures when necessary. If they did that, there would be no need for any of us to interfere in their work.

By now, in early 2008, we were pretty sure that Panna was home only to male tigers. In fact, in the tourist world Panna was dubbed the 'bachelor park.' Travel Operator For Tigers (TOFT) wrote a letter to the Chief Wildlife Warden of MP, pointing out that only males survived in the Reserve and urged action. The issue was even raised in the Lok Sabha as a Parliamentary question in March 2008. But despite this being public knowledge, the authorities continued to deny the problem.

2008: The Persistent Denials

The authorities were aware of the problem but not ready to accept it, as that would mean holding someone accountable. This was apparent from a communication from the Chief Wildlife Warden of MP in May 2008: worried by the fallout of the crisis, he requested permission from the Government of India to translocate two female tigers to the Panna

Tiger Reserve from elsewhere in the state. It was abundantly clear that the Panna tiger population was in a serious state and required a rescue operation similar to Sariska. Yet despite the 'paucity of females and cubs', in the same letter, the Chief Wildlife Warden insisted that the Panna Tiger Reserve had not witnessed any decline of tigers since its creation in 1981.

In spite of the emergency, it took the NTCA several months to respond to the MP Government. They gave favourable consideration to the request for translocation only in September 2008. But the NTCA put forward four names, including mine, for a monitoring committee to oversee the operation. This raised another controversy: the then Addl. Principal Chief Conservator of Forests of MP, H.S. Pabla, requested that my name be excluded on the grounds that I had 'filed PILs against the State Govt' (factually untrue) and that I had 'biased perceptions about Panna Tiger Reserve'.

Whose perceptions were biased? In June 2008, the leading wildlife magazine *Sanctuary Asia* published our two opposing views (Vol. XXVIII No. 3) in an article, 'Panna's Tigers: Have They Gone The Sariska Way?' Joanna and I wrote 'Nothing Is Gained by Denial' on the possibility and evidence of only one male tiger remaining. Mr Pabla insisted that 'Nothing Is Lost in Panna': 'I assure the world that the tiger density in this park has never been better'. Yet his own office was requesting tigers for reintroduction to Panna, and this denial exposed the reactions of the system. There had been so many opportunities to set it right, but all energy was spent denying the problem and shooting the messenger. A mere 6 months later came the official confirmation that Panna had not a single tiger left. Sadly, it was not I who had been suffering from biased perceptions.

The tragedy is that this extinction need never have happened. Had the first census operation under Asim Srivastava or the later review of it by WII been conducted honestly, there would have been enough time to avert it. Even later, there was another opportunity when the WII conducted its camera trap estimate. The authors of the WII report were justifiably well known in their respective fields of statistics and population ecology. How could they not see the problem? My shock stems from the realization that they probably did. But, as mentioned above, at the crucial moment their data was presented to the Supreme Court *in support* of the authorities' contention that there was no decline in Panna. It was only four years after the extinction of the Panna tigers that the very same data from this 2006 report was presented in a scientific journal to show the occurrence of poaching and decline. The about-face interpretation was as follows:

Excerpts from the WII's technical report and cover letter from the Director of WII, P.R. Sinha, to the Panna Field Director to enable the State Government to file affidavit to the Honourable Supreme Court:

> We also have conducted camera trapping exercise covering an area of 185 km^2 in Panna National Park. The estimated density of tiger in this area is 4.9 (SE 0.96) tigers per 100 km^2. Number of tiger in the study area of 185 km^2 with a confidence limit of 95% comes to 9 (range- minimum 8 tigers to a maximum of 15 tigers). Viewed in the context of the All India situation this is reasonably good density and indicates a healthy tiger population in the study area.

The letter also mentioned the results:

> [S]o far as comparability of our studies with past study done by Karanth et al in (2004) is concerned, it would not be out of place to mention here that their study covered an area of 418 km^2 of the park and estimated a population density of 6.94 (SE 3.23) tigers per 100 km^2. They estimated a population of 29 over 418 km^2 with a range from 10-48 tigers (at 95% confidence limit). Such wide variance in population estimation is not a very useful tool for monitoring a population. It is also relevant to point out here that our density estimate over 185 km^2 has low CV of 16% compared to their CV of 46.54%. Thus our estimates are more precise and fall with the range of estimates of tiger estimation given by the aforesaid study.

Four years later, after the Panna tigers went extinct, the same information from this 2006 report was published under the name of the NTCA Member Secretary Dr Rajesh Gopal and the WII scientists who had authored the report, giving a completely different perspective. This paper appeared in *Oryx* with the following abstract:

> We evaluated the status of tigers *Panthera tigris* and their prey in Panna Tiger Reserve using occupancy surveys, camera-trap mark-recapture population estimation, and distance sampling along foot transects, in 2006. ...The best model incorporating individual heterogeneity (Mh) estimated the tiger population to be 9 – SE 2. (4.2 tigers per 100 km^2). Both occupancy and density indicated a decline of the tiger population in the Reserve... Since our survey in 2006 tiger status in Panna has deteriorated further because of poaching... In late 2008 there was a single male tiger left in Panna but he has not been seen since January 2009... Panna, along with Sariska Tiger Reserve, exemplifies the vulnerability of small, isolated tiger populations to local extinctions caused by poaching, even in areas with suitable habitat and sufficient prey.*

None of the authors raised this voice at the time of the report's presentation in the Supreme Court. If only they had, the Panna tigers might have been saved. The intellectual duplicity pains me. The tigers were lost as the authors remained quiet when the data was used to show a 'healthy' population, and then they publish the same information taking credit for identifying the decline—*after* the extinction. Our system allows little to no accountability, so even at as high a level as the Supreme Court very little can be expected.

In October 2008, perhaps anticipating the serious fallout of another extinction during his tenure, the NTCA Member Secretary suddenly recognized the Panna tiger population as 'alarmingly low' and requested urgent action from the Field Director to improve protection and secure the Park. Once again he requested camera-traps to be deployed 'at the earliest', with the assistance of the WII, who had themselves had several opportunities to save the situation over the last few years. It is hard not to think that this action was cosmetic and more to do with saving oneself from being held accountable. It might have had some meaning and effect if it was taken in 2004 or after the 2005 census, but by the last quarter of 2008 it was too late.

---

* Gopal et al., Oryx 2010: 44(3), 383–389.

The last tiger of Panna's original population. Note the markings on his eyebrow; you will recognize him as one of Baavan's cubs (see photo on p. 98).

A 'Brainstorming Workshop' in Khajuraho was hurriedly organized on 9 December 2008 to which even I was invited. It was called 'Protection Strategies That Need to Be Followed in the Reserve'. Delegates were asked to visit the park the day before in order to 'appreciate the field situation'. Joanna could not help but privately remark on the irony of one visit being considered sufficient for such appreciation while my 9 years of continuous presence and research was not. The Field Director and other officials continued *even then* to deny that Panna was heading the Sariska way, so little was achieved by this meeting.

The Cover-up

Several newspapers were reporting the presence of only one or possibly two male tigers in Panna. But the Forest Department has a strict linear hierarchy, so when the higher authorities openly say nothing is lost in

Panna, it is difficult for the lower staff to contradict the bosses. To divert media attention, the park's staff fabricated a false report of seeing a tigress and two cubs. This was not the first time such distracting claims had been made of female sightings as a counter to the 'bachelor park' appellation. Images of pugmarks, they claimed, appeared to show two old tiger tracks, one larger forepaw (the mother) and the smaller hind paw pugmark (one cub), alongside a fresher leopard track (the second cub). A retired Chief Wildlife Warden visiting the Reserve also confirmed the mother cub claim as a fact. It was amazing how ugly it had all become. If there was a resident female and cubs in the park, evidence of their presence would have been apparent regularly—not just once and never again. In spite of intensive monitoring on foot with elephants and camera traps, no confirmation of the sighting was possible. One can only read this as a final and desperate attempt by the management to obfuscate the truth.

WII once again came to Panna to assess the tiger status—their third such visit during the crisis. Their interim report found no camera captures of tigers in the Reserve. But this was not enough to settle the question of extinction. Clearly they still hoped for a miracle, and a larger team was sent with fifty cameras, distributed extensively throughout the Reserve. After more than 20 days of continuous camera-trapping, there was still no definite evidence of a tiger. However, no final report containing these results was published. Indeed, till this day I have not come across a report specifically confirming the total extinction of the tiger population in Panna. Even in late January 2009, the WII and other authorities were still talking of possibly 'one to three tigers in the area' even while claiming that they had 'never denied the problem' and admitting that the situation '[was] not good, with hardly any signs of tiger cubs.'

The Re-introduction of Tigers in Panna

Finally, tigers were brought to Panna from Pench, Bandhavgarh and Kanha Tiger Reserves. Four females and one male tiger were successfully trans-located from 2009 onwards. This recovery of a tiger population is nothing less than fantastic and the achievements unimaginable. One highlight of this recovery was the rehabilitation of two captive-reared tigresses into the wild. In the seven years since the first re-introduction of a female, the tiger population in Panna has crossed 30. It is almost close to the peak of 2002. The recoveries between 1996–2001 and later 2009–2016 have one common factor: leadership. The field team remained more or less the same but the leadership of Shri P.K. Chawdhry in the late '90s and Shri R. Sreenivasa Murthy during the reintroduction made all the difference. The Panna story clearly shows what is possible when there is effective leadership and what happens when such leadership is missing. The system unfortunately depends on individual brilliance, which is hard to find.

Panna: A Repeat of Sariska

The loss of the entire tiger population in Panna is a shocking tale. Could there be any reasonable explanation for how another one of India's most protected tiger areas lost its tigers? The reason it happened in the Sariska Tiger Reserve, according to the Tiger Task Force, was because of 'management breakdown' and an 'increase in poaching... combined with extremely faulty and negligent conduct of tiger census in the Reserve.' This loss was revealed to the world in December 2004. Was nothing learnt from this shame? All of it was repeated in Panna. The Sariska debacle went relatively unnoticed while it was happening. In Panna, a spotlight was shining on the whole episode. Panna's repeat of Sariska was made worse by the fact that every step of the six-year decline was documented and publicized by the media, conservationists, scientists, NGOs and even the Supreme Court's Central Empowered Committee. In addition to these, a few others had cried themselves hoarse with warnings in an attempt to awaken the relevant authorities to their duties, but all failed.

Why can't we stop this? We have the expertise, the money, political will (no prime minister of India will say he does not want to save the national animal), public support, legal support, and an animal is deeply embedded in our cultural heritage. Then why are we failing?

The Failures of the Forest Department

In many countries, wildlife habitats are owned by private individuals, corporates, communities, and government and non-government agencies. This can make conservation a very complicated task because of multiple ownerships. But in India, the Forest Department owns and manages all the wildlife habitats, so technically it should be a much easier task. However, when the sole management system of Indian forests fails to function, it has a far-reaching impact. The problem arises from the policies followed by the Forest Department, which may have worked in the 1960s and '70s but they are no longer appropriate in the twenty-first century. Threats have changed, the pressure on forest land has grown, and the modus operandi of the poachers has advanced but our management has not grown beyond its age-old 'waterhole, watch tower, building forest chowkies (guard posts), managing fire lines with a beat guard' system established in the1860s. The way the laws are implemented creates anti-conservation sentiments and the department is also seen in some quarters as an anti-development agency. One of the main causes is the isolated, closed way in which it operates.

The protracted Panna saga is an example of how the cadre works, how it closes ranks and misuses the powers vested in it. When senior leadership behaves like this, it trickles down to the bottom of the system and the system fails to work. When I received funds from outside India for my research project, I was tagged as 'anti-establishment'. The authorities try to use whatever means possible to silence those who raise their voice against system failures. To fight for accountability, one is compelled to take up the issue personally. I had no personal enmities, but felt the system should respond and fix responsibility. If they did that there would be no need for a whistle-blower to intervene; the system itself would ensure that such offences do not recur and when they do, the responsible official is disciplined appropriately.

For four years I tried hard to make the point that Panna had lost almost 80% of its tiger population and that immediate intervention was required to halt the process; it had no effect. The department continued to remain in denial, claiming Panna had 34 tigers. As a result of this denial, no effective measures were taken to halt the decline. Even when only a couple of males survived and the Reserve had lost all the females, the authorities continued to take shelter by lying and misquoting reports. Finally, when it reached a point at which there was every danger of losing the last tiger any time, a request was made to introduce two females but even then the reason given was a skewed sex-ratio, not a reduced population!

It was sad to see the desperate attempts made to deny the loss of the tigers. It is only when the higher authorities accept the reality that the full truth can come out into the open. Once it is out in the open, everyone from the wildlife guards to the Chief Minister of the state will be able to discuss the issue openly and in this way, solutions may be found. But when the leadership continues to lie and deny facts, we cannot expect the field staff to go against their bosses' view. These bosses must have made over fifteen visits to Panna Tiger Reserve, since we first complained. Every time they arrived they would first announce the number of tigers in the Reserve. Only after this did they go on their 'fact-finding mission', and obviously could not figure out how many tigers were actually there. What this must do to staff morale! To top it all, they blamed us for destroying the staff's morale and accused us of maligning the IFS cadre when we were merely pointing out the facts.

Sometimes the system works—if a teak tree is cut, an inquiry happens, accountability is fixed and the responsible officer is punished. One can find many examples where the corrupt or negligent officers were punished. However, this is a simpler equation. With tigers the reality is different. It is not that every tiger death should be laid at the manager's door but when the whole population goes missing as in Sariska and Panna, it is important to fix accountability as a deterrent to poor management. When this problem was diagnosed after Sariska, nothing was done, so history was repeated in Panna. Since nobody was held accountable in Panna, how many more places will lose tigers before we learn?

It is not only tigers that suffer—a similar event happened in

Karera. This area once held 20 to 26 breeding Great Indian Bustards (GIB), one of the most highly endangered species the world. When the BNHS found that the population was declining to precariously low levels, they wrote to the authorities. After a lot of pressure the Chief Wildlife Warden visited the Sanctuary. However the local manager lined up dozens of people to impress the boss and claim that there were over forty GIBs in the sanctuary. Ignoring the information based on field research, the leadership chose to believe this fiction and the frustrated BNHS research team could do little to save the birds. Soon the state lost all the GIBs in Karera. Was anybody held responsible? No.

We saw a repeat of this in Panna and, the tigers are lost forever. With the successful re-introduction of tigers everyone forgot about the extinction and its causes. When these events and their reasons are so poorly recognized and understood, there can be no confidence that they will not be repeated in the future. Blame for the loss is variously apportioned now—a male-biased sex ratio, bandit activities, and stress among females that led them to abandon their territories, are often cited. Actually, the biased sex ratio was a *result* of the decline, not the cause in itself, and the 'bandit' issue came up in 2006–07, after much of the decline had already occurred. The bandits were not responsible for the poaching of tigers but their presence was used effectively as an excuse.

In fact, the real causes still remain unaddressed. High female mortality, which we had explained in earlier chapters, was one of the main reasons. At the time of writing this book, another adult female from the reintroduced population was found dead in a snare. This is the sixth or seventh female from this new population that has died in as many years. History repeats itself—once again we are witnessing high female mortality. We have not done much to address this problem because it was not recognized by any of the committees set up to look into the causes and fix accountability for the loss. We have ignored the science.

Whichever way one looks at the loss, a systemic failure that prevented timely action, denial, and failure to understand the real causes for the decline allowed extinction to happen. Sadly, little has changed, but I do hope that these early signs we are now witnessing again will be taken seriously.

In the following chapter I provide solutions to some of the important biological, ecological and system-related problems affecting tiger conservation.

11

Saving Tigers

For the telling, I may have simplified the story about the complete loss of tigers in Panna and how our system failed them. But in fact, it is a very complex scenario. Showing how the system is failing tigers is not to denigrate the Forest Department; many excellent officers are part of its ranks and, of course, it does much that is positive for conservation. Unfortunately, these officers often struggle as the system does not encourage the best personnel to function effectively. For 30-40 years we have seen tiger populations decline, and current management action is not able to maintain and restore them in most places. Our successes are few and not as widespread as one would like to see. This has worried conservationists for decades.

When we lost tigers in Panna and Sariska we did not lose everything that these Reserves protected; we lost only tigers. When Panna was losing its tigers, senior officers of the state assured us that they were doing their best. Maybe they were, but it was worrying as their 'best' was not enough to save the tigers. We need strategies that will not only save the habitat and tigers' prey, but also the tigers themselves. Unfortunately, generally speaking, our present management continues to use the same methods that it has been using for decades and these are proving inadequate.

The Need to Revamp Indian Conservation

Many of the protected areas are not large enough to protect a viable population of large-ranging animals like tigers and elephants. We have identified this scale mismatch in Tropical Dry Forest habitats as one of the reasons for the tiger's vulnerability there. Protected Area management also needs to reflect and examine what has worked and what is not working. This does not mean that they should stop what they are doing entirely because much has worked for the habitat and building the tigers' prey base. But they do need to formulate management actions that can also work for tigers. Given the nature of the present system, new and innovative ideas may not all arise from within, so it would be good to see management officials opening their arms and minds to new thoughts from outside their cadre. Many of us may be critical of management approaches but these critiques do provide an alternate perspective. Unfortunately, for the most part, any comments on management actions—however constructive—are received defensively as though the commentator is only out to denigrate their actions and achievements.

Trying to indicate where Reserve management is failing and to open a discussion on how problems can be fixed can therefore be a frustrating process. Whenever pressure builds on managers to do something different, they double down on actions already under way that have not worked for decades. Sometimes I wonder whether they really do believe that some of us are just scaremongers and 'disgruntled' individuals.

Often their main defence strategy is denial, which is hard not to see as a sign of incompetence or lack of sincerity. How could one believe, with so much evidence provided during the seven years of the Panna episode, that there was not one individual officer who could understand the gravity of the situation? If they really did not see what was coming, then the problem is even more serious. We were shocked by the lack of action and reaction to the Sariska and Panna extinctions. But it seems to be a pattern in our conservation history. There are other similar examples—Asiatic lions, the Indian rhino and hard-ground barasingha. These species were allowed to drop to as low as 50 or less and only then was action taken. Their subsequent recovery also shows the ability of the system to achieve its conservation goal when desired. I only hope that we do not let tigers reach such a dire level. Panna is still not free from the threats that doomed the earlier population. I fear that they have not been properly understood.

Tiger conservation under Project Tiger has now completed almost four decades. But sadly for wild tigers, they continue to face the very same problems that were identified in the 1970s, when Project Tiger was launched. Management is still playing catch-up with poachers, rather than finding an effective system to counteract them. Catching criminals with dead animal body parts is not helping tigers, and we continue to lose tigers every week. This is leading us to the same precarious predicament that the lion and the rhino once faced. We need to be two steps ahead of these gangs of poachers and traders. The old stratagems worked in the '70s and early '80s, stabilizing the tiger population within a protected area system. But they are no longer proving adequate.

The Way Forward

We need to create an environment where the population can grow and occupy a larger landscape. The loss of distribution range is an early sign of extinction risk. An increased tiger presence in this greater landscape will help reverse the trend.

This argument is based on science but there is also a political reason why tiger/leopard presence can actually help us manage conflict in the larger landscape in the long-term. Peaceful co-existence is sustainable only in areas where there are tigers and leopards because their presence encourages good practices. These good practices have evolved over time and help minimize conflict. There are still many areas—as was the case in Panna—where communities live comfortably with tigers, with minimal conflict on either side. But an absence of tigers and leopards breaks this important link and this disconnect creates a situation where 'bad practices' take precedence. The good practices of the past fade away and are forgotten. This results in heightened conflict. In the absence of tigers or leopards, a new generation of humans grows up without the experience of how to live with them. If and when they do reappear as a result of successful conservation programmes, the human reactions can be violent, and the conflict engendered appears unmanageable. As a way forward, we must see this conflict as a journey and work in a way where we make it comfortable for both tigers/ leopards and the communities who share the same space. We need to identify the good and bad practices and work towards creating an environment where a peaceful equilibrium can be found. So removing a 'problem' animal (other than a man-eater) may not help over the long term; in reality it complicates many conservation issues (Athreya et al. 2011).

We have reached a point where we now worry about the tiger's very existence. A fragile equilibrium has been broken. Now, our conservation successes are resulting in tigers dispersing and recolonizing some areas but the communities have, to a large extent, lost the experience and tolerance of living with carnivores. We need to focus on conflict with a more pragmatic perspective, not only see it as a threat to the tigers and aim to eliminate it. With assistance, today's communities can find their own balance and relearn a compatible coexistence that allows both carnivores and humans to flourish. Tiger presence is an essential component to achieve this equilibrium.

We need a conservation vision that takes full advantage of our successes, but it appears that even for this we are not prepared. In 40 years of tiger conservation, very little research has been done within the administrative system. As a result, our understanding of the numerous chronic problems has not changed. It is still based on individual experience. Scientific information can help the management make appropriate and informed decisions. But since the leadership of reserves is sourced from diverse disciplines, the management's priority tends to shift with every leadership change. It is guided by past experience and personal instinct rather than science or system memory. This lack of regard for science occurs at the very highest levels, even in academic environments: a director of the WII (a forest officer) once told me that he could write the same thesis on tigers in a few hours that I would come up with after ten years of research. Indeed, it was this attitude that delayed my research proposal for several years, although things have changed since then. However, most of the wildlife studies are short-term and the number of crucial long-term studies is negligible. Natural history observations and two-year studies are no replacement for thorough and systematically conducted long-duration research. When management decisions are based on instinct and personal experiences, it brings about discontinuity in management actions and allows individual whims and fancies to outweigh well-informed management strategies based on scientific knowledge. Other than ecological and biological research, management-oriented research that reviews the efficacy of the existing management is urgently required to bring changes and guide future management actions.

The most recent all-India tiger census shows only a small gain over the figure of 1972, the year Project Tiger was launched. Throughout this period, the denial and obfuscation of true tiger numbers has been a key factor in the tigers' decline. One of my biggest concerns is the total intolerance to criticism and the inability to appreciate or accept independent research results, especially when it comes to population figures. Figures are contested even when they come from within their own system. A large body of the research is conducted by NGOs and independent individuals, and this has created a growing pool of expertise outside the system. Instead of taking advantage of this expertise, current management practice does not provide enough space for it to make a positive contribution.

I have put together a few points that I believe need to be addressed to bring about change and to make our management system more effective and professional. It is not just about science, but also about improving and strengthening our management system.

Remove Ad-Hocism: Modifying Annual Plans of Operation

Tiger Reserves need a system that encourages or institutionalizes access to available research in protected areas and takes full advantage of the growing body of professionals with expertise in the relevant areas. Most of the management plans for protected areas are not based on scientific knowledge. Areas are managed through APOs that encapsulate only a year-long vision, and this dependence does not represent a professional approach.

In India, wildlife management is entirely governed by APOs. The way APOs are prepared encourages ad-hoc practices and militates against continuity. We know that Field Directors of tiger Reserves come from different backgrounds such as forestry, social forestry, soil conservation etc. and their past experiences guide the manner in which many of these APOs are formulated. However, the actions they propose are not always desirable for a wildlife area because science is not behind some of these prescriptions, leading to a mismatch between what is required and what is implemented. Once, a field director of Panna decided to use his soil conservation skills and dug trenches into a huge landscape to increase the soil moisture. He left Panna in a couple of years and the whole landscape was left scarred, with little effect on the soil and no follow-up action. I also remember a few limping nilgai from that year. Thus, APOs are also not always consistent with the overall park management plan and this creates management instability.

Since we are so dependent on these APOs to bring change, they also need to survive frequent administrative changes at various levels. I suggest two possible strategies to overcome this problem and create a system memory—one could be to create a ten-year management plan, including ten APOs that would remain undisturbed by whoever comes in as field director, regardless of their background. They will be obliged to follow the already prepared management APOs. To avoid rigidity, a monitoring and evaluation mechanism must be built into the approach to provide some flexibility for the implementing officer. Alternatively, the tenure of field directors could be increased to a five-year period and the first year made to overlap with the previous regime. A vision for the new five-year plan would be formulated by the new person during this time. The overlap will not only ensure continuity and bring stability to the system, but also improve accountability. The new leader's tenure will be assessed based on the successful implementation and achievement of his proposed goals. Monitoring must be a key aspect. Such changes can generate a strong system memory, which is absent in the current system, leading to widespread ad-hocism.

Review of the Existing Management System

The country's wildlife management system typically moves from one crisis to another, fire-fighting the current one, and forgetting and not learning from earlier crises. To protect tigers from the menace of poaching and various other threats, it needs to be creative. There is plenty that can done to make the existing system more effective by reviewing our everyday management practices.

I remember reading about the horrific poaching incident in the Tadoba area, where a tiger's body was found cut up into several large pieces. The photographs were horrifying. On another occasion, two tigers were found trapped in a snare—one was rescued and then held in captivity while the other died. The photos of the tiger carcass still attached to the leg-hold trap were equally disturbing. Such incidents are worrying because they clearly tell us that we have not done enough to control poaching, which is happening at a regular frequency. They highlight tigers' vulnerability and indicate how urgently we need to take steps to change this. We do not want the Panna and Sariska debacle to be repeated anywhere else.

Combating Poaching

Working with tigers for more than two decades, I have learned a thing or two; one of these is the fact that the poaching threat to tigers will never die away. Although the management may recognize this, it hardly seems to reflect in their long-term planning or management plans.

The two poaching cases from Tadoba exemplify the two different types of poaching threats that the management has to deal with and they need separate strategies to deal with these two different crimes. The case where two tigers were found caught in a snare (one died, the other was rescued and sent to captivity) is a result of poaching by an organized professional network. The second, where the tiger was cut into several pieces, represents unorganized poaching that is not targeted specifically towards tigers or leopards, though they are quite often the unfortunate casualties. The most likely explanation for this latter case is that the snare was set for a tiger prey and when the tiger was found caught in it, the person panicked and tried to dispose of the carcass. Possibly, he had set the trap—a snare or an electric trap—at the edge of his crop field, and wanted to hide the evidence far away. Since a whole tiger would have been difficult to get rid of, it was probably cut into pieces and thrown away.

This second kind of poaching is rampant but should be easier to deal with because, in general, the people involved in such cases are not criminal or professional poachers. I would even describe them as innocent law offenders, because they may not be aware of the consequences of killing a wild animal, let alone a tiger. Recognizing this, we should deal with them with sensitivity—7 years' imprisonment is certainly not the answer for such offenders. Counselling and force alone also will not work; social and economic solutions may help but mainly, constant vigilance is required against such crimes. Vigilance not only within the boundary of PAs but in all areas that tigers can use. Only this will result in effective protection.

It would be a mistake to think that an untrained forest or game guard could do this job. Appropriate expertise and skills are required to make an efficient, vigilant squad to deal with this menace, because it is chronic in nature and widespread. I remember a conversation with my father, who was posted as a Divisional Forest Officer in Madla in the mid-1960s, in which he recounted more than fifty cases of tiger and leopard deaths due to poisoning or snaring during his three-year tenure. In the past four decades, we have failed miserably in developing special skills of the forest staff. We still pursue foot patrols, shows of strength or force, and the beat-guard system of patrolling our forests. We seem to be willing to spend a huge amount of funds on special Task Forces. Deployments of such groups tend to catch only firewood collectors, grazers, MFP collectors, or innocent villagers who happen to be at the wrong place at the wrong time. This only generates antipathy toward wildlife conservation efforts.

How many tiger poachers have we caught through such exercises? Our approach is usually a knee-jerk reaction to the problem. When a tiger is found in a trap, there would be a desperate order directing all field staff to go out on patrol every day to find traps. Such orders ignore the fact that many of them may not even have seen traps in their lifetime, while those who have may not know how and where to look for them. The whole exercise would be like finding a needle in a haystack, even if equipped with metal detectors. After a week or two, things would calm down and status quo would prevail once again, until years or months later, when another trapping comes to the limelight.

In all these years, we could have created specialized faculties (sections) within our management system—one for public relations, one for protection measures, one for law enforcement, one for scientific wildlife management and one for administration—all devoted entirely to their specialized fields, professional and effective in their functioning. Imagine a squad of just ten people working only to find traps for ten years: they would develop into one of the best trap-finders in the world. Developing such human resources must be built into the system to achieve the professionalism required to protect tigers. Such a skill-set, once developed, can be shared with others to recreate other such groups elsewhere. The problem with our system today is that someone trained in a specialized skill required for wildlife management could be posted in soil conservation.

The other problem with our existing anti-poaching or protection measures that use force is that we consider every person who enters the park (for collecting wood, MFP, grazing, or any other reason) as a potential poacher. There is a tendency to be high-handed in dealings with them. This certainly does not foster friendly relations in the neighbourhood. In the current environment, friendly relations with the people who live in and around the tigers' habitat is essential; wildlife management needs a more human face. The combination of unfriendly relations and unprofessional vigilance makes the entire anti-poaching effort incompetent. While the management continues its age-old strategies, we continue to lose tigers. It is very frustrating for those of us on the periphery, seeing the tiger's sad plight right in front of our eyes and yet being powerless to do anything about it.

Poaching by organized crime is where management will need help from other agencies (including NGOs) because the threat comes from an organized network run by smart people who operate in various states. Dealing with this threat requires a completely different strategy.

This poaching is market-driven and that is where the problem lies. It may not appear to be such a major threat when the demand is not there. But when the market demand is high, it can and will remove tigers from our protected tiger habitats with such efficiency that they will be gone before we realize it. We saw this in the early 1990s in the form of the tiger bone trade, and again in 2003–04 when demand for tiger skin skyrocketed. Both times we lost a huge chunk of our tiger population. All the gains that we had made almost came to zero. To some extent, the illegal trade menace can be fought away from the forests because the kingpins live among us in urban areas.

In the past four decades, Project Tiger (now NTCA) has created over forty tiger Reserves. We now conduct the All-India Tiger Assessments, and the government of India dedicates larger amounts of money exclusively to tiger conservation alone (US $25–30 million a year). We have had two successful re-introductions, and have more personnel per tiger, more equipment, more funds for patrolling, increasing number of chowkies (guard posts), new roads, new watchtowers and waterholes that have been constructed and proposed. We also have management plans for some of the tiger Reserves (though most still run on the ad-hoc APOs); we are talking about filling vacancies; we have employed retired army personnel in order to establish a Special Tiger Force (US $100 million for five years), and we now have the Wild Life Crime Bureau to assist the Forest Department's anti-poaching effort. We must not forget eco-development, village relocation, eco-tourism guidelines, and Rapid Response Units. The list is long. The world conservation community that met in Delhi was definitely impressed by this list. The question is, how effective are these measures in protecting tigers beyond PA boundaries? We know where the truth lies—for some it is in the ever-increasing number of tigers over the last one decade; for others perhaps, it lies more in the increasing number of deaths that central India is witnessing.

Tigers need a more professional management system and they need this change to happen now.

Increase in Conviction Rates: Database On Criminal History

The early 1970s were the most significant time in conservation history in India. The Wild Life Protection Act (1972) was enacted but, decades later, it still suffers from an implementation problem. The low rate of conviction in the trial courts is one of the reasons. Currently, tiger conservation authorities spend millions of rupees on protection measures but when the alleged poachers are caught and prosecuted, very little is done to make sure that the guilty are properly punished. As a result, the same few poachers commit crimes, get bail, move on and commit a crime again somewhere else (sometimes under a different identity). In many cases, their criminal history goes back as far as 20 to 25 years. Each of these cases is dealt with independently, without any awareness of the criminal record or history of the offender. We need a database that keeps track of the criminal records of every wildlife offender. Once this database is created, wildlife crime cases can be argued in court with the help of the crime history. This has happened occasionally and with great results, but we must make it a routine. The death of tigress F-120 underlined this desperate need. The people who were arrested and prosecuted for killing the tigress had been released a few weeks earlier from an old poaching case.

Proper allocation of funds can help solve this problem. At the moment there is too much focus on protection and not enough on prosecution. More funds are required for the hiring of specialist lawyers to help the management successfully prosecute offenders. Forensic investigations need serious improvement too. New technologies are available, and we must bring in expert agencies to conduct forensic investigation. We know that between the state police forces and the state forest departments, many poachers have been caught—in some cases, multiple times. Since there is no centralized database for wildlife crimes, however, poachers get bail easily in the absence of criminal history. This database must also have interstate connectivity. At present, the best databases and information are in the NGO sector, where conservationists have stepped in to fill the gap.

Each tiger state must initiate a project under which it hires a team of lawyers to collate all the wildlife crime records within the state and build a comprehensive database. From this list, the top fifteen or twenty cases of repeat and major offenders could be identified—the biggest fish in the game—and legal support provided to the prosecution, wherever possible, to argue the cases in court. Arguing by expert lawyers is important here, and we may need to introduce some necessary changes in the system to allow this to happen. In fact, multiple experts within the legal strategy are a must. While some lawyers are familiar with the Wild Life Act they may not be equally adept in criminal law, and those who are regular criminal lawyers do not always possess the requisite experience in wildlife laws. A combination of the two would be required to deal with major criminal cases in courts, especially at the trial level. It may be necessary to work for changes within the system to allow this unique approach to take shape. It is unfortunate that we spend millions of rupees on protection and yet, when an alleged criminal is caught, the case is often left to the public prosecutor to pursue and they may not have the requisite expertise or incentives to fight such cases. In many instances, the public prosecutors or their assistants fail to attend the courts and the wildlife officials have to handle the situation. In such circumstances the officials rely on their instincts and experience rather than expertise in the law. I suspect that the management authorities and police may have caught perhaps 60-70% of all professional poachers, but only a few have been locked away and most are free to continue indulging in wildlife crimes or illegal trade. Unless our law is looked upon as a threat by these criminals, we will not be able to reduce poaching.

To achieve the goal of increasing the conviction rate, a detailed survey of all cases relating to wildlife is urgently required to create a comprehensive database. This database will provide valuable information on the exact number of pending cases as well as their various stages of trial, identify repeat offenders and quantify the volume of poaching incidents. Besides this, it will also help prioritize the important cases needing urgent attention and legal help. A few successes would certainly help deter offenders and streamline the existing difficulties in dealing with wildlife cases.

Genetic Profiling

Genetic profiling of the entire tiger and leopard populations to control illegal trade in wildlife products is another strategy. It is necessary to develop a completely detailed genetic profile of the tiger and leopard populations of all the tiger Reserves and its surrounding tiger habitats. When a genetic material (skin or other body part) is seized, the identity of the main source population can be easily established from these samples. The purpose of this profiling is to determine the main areas where poachers are operating, so one can track the poachers' activities. With this database, it will become relatively simple to fix accountability and help us focus our efforts more effectively to prevent the crime, rather than catch the poacher after the tiger's death.

We cannot depend on random interceptions and chance seizures. The 'guns, guards and ex-army' approach that we have pursued so far is simply not working on its own; it needs an overhaul. Serious strategic planning with several simultaneous approaches and the development of intelligence-led enforcement is required. Some of the following suggestions show how we can improve that.

A More Professional Management

Wildlife management in the twenty-first century requires very different skills, ranging from an ability to communicate well to the expertise to efficiently find traps (not only in the forest but beyond the boundary and in crop fields). I once listed all the different work a forest guard does over a year and it came to over forty odd jobs! Protection was one of them. But also he has to make roads, clear and burn fire lines, clean waterholes, conduct census work, firefight, help in polio eradication, build and repair chowkies, construct new structures such as watch towers, patrol and protect his beat, and so on—before his attention could be turned to protection work. Is it possible for a beat guard, even with two unskilled daily-wage assistants, to protect tigers after discharging all these duties? To expect the skills required for all forty jobs from one person—that too with minimal training—is hardly a professional approach. We must re-evaluate this. There are several ways this can be set right without needing more staff. The same work could be done with much greater efficiency if the guards were trained for specific duties, broadly divided into public relations, protection measures, law enforcement, scientific wildlife management, and administration.

There are various studies that document how anthropogenic pressure declines from edge to core. Boundaries create the Edge Effect, and to address the overwhelming pressure on the edges we must intensify our protection measures. Currently, for management purposes, Protected Areas are divided into beats and these are almost evenly distributed throughout a Protected Area. These beats were delineated decades ago with commercial forestry in mind; however, this design is not suited for wildlife management. This is because threats on each of these beats are different and the skills required for appropriately managing these beats will be different. A realignment of our beats is needed. For example, we can create a higher density of smaller beats along the borders and relatively larger beats in the middle. In our management plan for each beat, we must identify what skills are required and set an objective for each unit according to its need. We can group units in various skill categories and only trained personnel suited for the job should be posted in the relevant beats. This will create a team of professionals within the system. Strategies currently in use need urgent review for an effective conservation effort.

In my list of the numerous odd jobs undertaken by wildlife managers, forestry does not find a prominent place as a required skill for managing a wildlife population. Comparing the skill sets required for tiger conservation with those we currently have within the management cadre, there is a huge mismatch. The management must review the skills of cadres and fill the gaps on a regular basis. Academic work on the skill sets required for managing different types of protected areas like tiger Reserves or bird sanctuaries is also urgently needed. Currently, the wildlife wing suffers from this lack of specialized skills. The new cadre option has been debated for decades but has always remained on the backburner. Billy Arjan Singh tried his best to get it through and was heavily criticized, but he knew the benefits of such a change. We could also learn a few lessons from New Zealand of the 1980s, where they created a completely new conservation department and saved many species from the brink of extinction. In India, now is the right time to make such a change; our economy is growing and pressures on natural resources from developmental activities are higher than ever before. We need a management that can keep pace with our development and work in a direction that ensures our ecological security along with economic well-being.

To summarize, I see a crying need for four different sets of skills to create a more professional cadre:

1. Law enforcement (policing and specialized prosecution)
2. Administration
3. Wildlife science/manager
4. Public relations with local communities

Forestry is not incompatible with wildlife management, but the latter encompasses much more. Forestry is just a small part of wildlife management. So, a field director of a tiger Reserve can be from any of the above fields, equipped with excellent managerial skills, but they should lead a specialized team of four independent directors. A team built with these four forms of expertise would create a professional wildlife cadre with the ability to deal with today's circumstances, covering more disciplines than just commercial forestry, social forestry or soil conservation.

Facilitating Wild Life Research

We must also recognize the importance of conservation science and the impact of long-term research projects. If we look at some of the long-term research projects such as those in Chitwan, the Russian Far-East, Nagarahole, and snow leopard research and conservation work in Rumbak and Uley in Ladakh and in Kibbar in Spiti, they show that the presence of a researcher not only generates a knowledge-base, it also creates conservation-friendly sentiments among the local community with whom they interact and work. But we must not confuse the use of technology with science. Camera traps, telemetry, drones and GIS are technological tools that are used by science. But merely obtaining pictures from camera traps will not help build scientific understanding. We need trained personnel with a research background to gather ecological and biological information appropriately and place it within a management perspective. So far, we have failed to create a system that supports independent research in the country. The general belief among managers is that they know all there is to know about tigers or, for that matter, any other wildlife. Thus, it is very hard to earn the management's goodwill for a research project, which is crucial for its success. Research permissions can be retracted at any moment and the researchers can face prosecution as soon as this goodwill is lost. In the absence of science, our management strategies will continue to depend on individual whims as in the past. If we wish the management of our PAs to be the best in the world, we must encourage wildlife research and provide protection to our young environment champions. Without them we will not be able to understand the value of these natural resources.

Moratorium on Civil Construction

Why is it that we continue to construct forest chowkies (guard posts)? How come such basic requirements have not been fulfilled after forty years? Nobody is against staff welfare and other needs, but a balance is required. The government cannot fund the construction of these new structures forever. Activities like building new roads, check dams, machans and chowkies every year not only take away a huge chunk of funds meant for the tiger but also time away from patrolling. The concretization of our national parks is against the ethos and objectives for which they were created in the first place. Expenditure under these civil and purchase heads must be limited to a percentage of the budget allocation.

Revisit SLOSS

In reality, it would be preferable to have several pathways that run parallel to the existing conservation model. Since the buffer requirement has now been mandated in the Wild Life Protection Act, much of the flexibility of the past is lost. Earlier, 'core' and 'buffer' were management tools and the tiger Reserve had the flexibility to define and manage these zones according to its requirement. But since the court order in 2012, all Reserves have had to notify and fix the buffer zones around the protected areas, with little scope for modifications.

Our conservation successes are mainly dependent on the exclusionary model. This model attempts to keep the human-animal conflict at arm's length—it does not solve it. This approach is tiring and cannot be sustained over the long run. In a conflict someone will lose out eventually, and when one side has a tiger or an elephant, a frog or a sal tree, we know who will surely be the loser. We need to change this. We need new approaches and innovative ideas to make this conflict-ridden journey more comfortable for both tigers and human communities. Unfortunately, within the rigid framework of our PA-based exclusionary model, little can be done.

Over several decades, we have forgotten the debate over SLOSS (Single Large or Several Small). In India, we opted for the Single Large model for tiger conservation but were not able to create large viable populations at many places. Alternatively, where there are no possibilities for a Single Large viable population within the CTH of a tiger Reserve, we have no choice but to create Several Small populations around the Single Large population that is not viable on its own. Cumulatively, these satellite populations can prop up the large population. I have explained this in greater detail in Chapter 10. We should see this model as an opportunity to use such places to engage the local communities in wildlife conservation instead of making them a battleground where both tigers and the locals vie for survival.

Conflict does not only exist between the wildlife and local communities, but also between those two groups and Forest Department policies. If we wish to resolve this conflict, we must create an environment where the communities fight the destructive forces from our side of the fence. It is not only the Forest Department's job, but all of ours. For decades, the MOEF (the guardians of tigers) has been giving away thousands of square kilometres of tiger habitat for mining, dams, highways and other industrial development. The worst part is that these habitats will be lost forever without bringing much benefit to the local communities as they are not the primary beneficiaries in most such cases. The fight to save the tiger is our responsibility and must be shared; these small satellite habitats can be ideal places to achieve this.

When it is widely recognized that the welfare of tigers in the non-protected tiger habitats is entirely dependent on the goodwill of local people, why not genuinely involve them in this endeavour and save the tiger by developing that goodwill? Why not give some of the space being doled out for industrial or agricultural development to the primary stakeholders of a tiger conservation initiative—the local communities and tigers? Such a change will make the conflict-ridden journey a little more tolerable for both.

'S^3 population' or Several Small Satellite Populations

The long-term viability of some of the tiger populations like that of Panna Tiger Reserve will be highly compromised if we continue to depend entirely on smaller protected areas or CTHs and ignore the role of tiger habitats outside the protected area boundary in tiger conservation. To make a population like Panna viable and self-sustaining, new management strategies must focus on this greater landscape. In Chapter 10 I have explained how for several decades we have been losing tiger populations from smaller protected areas in Tropical Dry and Tropical Moist Deciduous forests. Various population viability models have demonstrated and re-emphasized that small populations are highly vulnerable, particularly to the poaching of breeding females. We need to create new metaphorical baskets for our tiger 'eggs', since our present model based on the PA network cannot always achieve its conservation goal. The Several Small model, explained in the following sub-section, beyond the PA boundary is an exciting new approach which can complement and bolster the existing system.

Panna as a S^3 case study

Increasing the size of the protected area to include 13–15 females' territories is not always possible within one continuous space (these territories can support a population of 70–80 tigers of all ages and sexes, as shown in an earlier chapter). A larger population of breeding females can sustain poaching threats, but we have to find spaces for them outside the protected areas. In such a situation, instead of looking for a single large population in isolation, we can achieve our conservation goal by creating several discrete Small Satellite Populations or S^3 populations on the lines of the single species meta-population concept. From our analysis we have seen that the Panna population is demographically not viable on its own and its survival is dependent on inputs from neighbouring populations. When there are no neighbouring populations to support the existing CTH population, a geographically localized meta-population structure (elaborated in chapter 10) can increase the survival probability or persistence of the main population through dispersal and immigrations. This meta-population approach of creating S^3 populations will make a more relevant conservation strategy. Applying the meta-population concept for tiger conservation within a localized geographical area not only provides an alternate path but builds an adaptive system. That is, when strategically located as Stepping Stones, some of these S^3 populations will encourage successful movement between two larger populations. This will create a nested meta-population structure (Figure 9.3), where several geographically localized meta-populations will be connected with each other, creating a larger viable meta-population. Using only a fraction of tiger habitat, these Stepping Stone populations will revive their connectivity. Managing inter-connected small populations within small fragments is a logistically feasible approach that can provide the necessary security to breeding females. An S^3 tiger population will be small (tiger territory size) but will require intensive monitoring of just a couple of breeding individuals using radio-collaring (as done for the reintroduced tigers). The habitat that connects S^3 populations to each other and to the main source population is only to provide passage habitat for the dispersing tigers. Inter-connected with the main core, the satellite populations will form a larger, viable breeding population with reduced extinction risk. This strategy will not replace the existing system but will rather work as an additional effort, complementing the work being done within the tiger Reserve boundary.

A network of S^3 populations can open up opportunities for developing various conservation models and providing opportunities to use tiger conservation as an effective development tool for the local communities. Legally, we do not envisage S^3 populations as protected areas but rather as development areas—areas managed for community benefits outside the National Park and Wild Life Sanctuary network system. This model of conservation has the ability to address many of the issues and threats presently afflicting protected tiger populations (Table 11.1) . The intention is to capitalize on the immense expertise and funds available outside India's present conservation model. Our S^3 population strategy is also suggested as a practical way to provide tiger conservation on a landscape level. This idea has been discussed for decades but with very little progress.

Purpose of the S^3 populations

Our conservation goal for this concept would be to ensure the demographic viability of the tiger population in the local geographical area. The primary beneficiaries would be the local communities, along with tigers, who would get additional breeding spaces. In the current model, tiger conservation is the driving force for tiger Reserves, but in the S^3 population approach it is replaced by revenue generation to benefit local communities. Of course, tiger conservation remains the final destination. This is the subtle change that is incorporated in this alternate approach.

Formulation of the S^3 Approach

Consider the S^3 populations areas as nothing but buffer habitats. Instead of a conventional ring of sink habitat (buffer) around a protected area, the S^3 population will create a series of discrete habitats, some of which will act as Stepping Stones. This is the main difference from the existing model. For example, the straight line distance from Panna to Bandhavgarh is about 150 km, but if we could create two Stepping Stone populations it would divide this distance into three sections of fifty kilometres each. The probability of successful dispersal could be greatly increased by such an intervention. This will revive the connectivity between Panna and Bandavgarh by creating two conservation development areas of 80–120 km^2. Instead of spreading our effort thin across thousands of square kilometres, we can be more effective by concentrating only on two small spaces.

The S^3 populations will act as true sink populations that can experience local extinctions and recolonization repeatedly. The dispersal and immigrations between these populations and their population dynamics will ensure better survival possibilities for the entire population. Each S^3 population can be a stand-alone entity run independently by different management establishments. It will provide freedom to each management unit to devise its own unique conservation plan without wavering from the common conservation goal. A recent survey of tiger Reserves in central India has found that almost 45% of the total turnover of the tourism industry brings direct economic benefits to the local communities. Eco-tourism could be enlisted as a conservation model to benefit the local community. This should help engage the local communities to actively partner in tiger conservation efforts and enable them to stand fully on our side of the fence.

Moreover, through this initiative we can rebuild tiger populations, restore the habitat quality of tiger habitats, restore connectivity, create larger breeding populations and generate economic benefit for the local communities.

These S^3 population habitats can be territory-sized habitats for one or two females distributed in the neighbouring forested landscape. The restoration of tiger habitat as well as preparing the communities for having tigers in the neighbourhood would be an integral part of this initiative. These areas should support discrete populations located away from other breeding populations, but at a distance that can be covered by a dispersing tiger over a short period of time. This will reduce mortality risk during dispersal from one conservation area to another and improve connectivity between populations.

In Situ Conservation Breeding population (ISCB)

In addition to S^3 populations, ISCB or breeding of individuals in captivity can be established with the aim to ensure genetic security of the main source population (of the tiger Reserve) and a source for founder populations in the restoration of S^3 and Stepping Stone populations. Every year, many tigers are captured from the wild and taken into captivity. These include problem individuals, dispersing individuals and abandoned cubs. Not only is this an additional depletion of wild tigers, but it is also a lost opportunity for us. Studies on leopards and tigers suggest that problem animals should not be relocated in the wild. But every wild tiger is a precious genetic resource and we should do everything possible to give these animals the chance to contribute to the wild population. ISCB will provide this opportunity. A large and wild (but fenced) environment (10–15 km^2) can house a few problem individuals. The subsequent generations born in this wild (but fenced) area can be used as founder populations to re-populate the S^3, Stepping Stone and main populations, or to release new generations to populate the larger landscape. This important strategy is proposed not only as a source for founder populations but also to ensure the continued existence of breeding individuals representing the same pool of the main source population. If we had had such a programme, we may never have lost the original gene pool of Panna and all the unique genetic variations those animals may have possessed.

The ISCB must not be confused with safari parks on the lines of the Gir lion safari or the Bannerghatta tiger safari. It should not be managed like the latter because the objectives of the two are very different. The ISCB can be made an integral and active part of the entire tiger conservation plan of the landscape.

For both S^3 and ISCB populations, we should take advantage of the expertise, conservation interest and funds available outside the government setup through public-private partnership (PPP) initiatives.

An Example of Public-Private Partnership

Since the goal is to provide economic benefit to local communities, the new approach intends to generate funds from tiger conservation and pass on all the profits to them. In this example, funds are sourced from tourism, with the area managed as a tiger tourism destination and not as a protected area. A non-profit conservation company comprising of all stakeholders—conservationists, promoters, local community representatives and the Forest Department officials—will supervise the conservation programme.

To run its operations the company will include a professional team of wildlife managers and other subject experts as needed. Its primary role would be to restore and rebuild tiger habitats, and prey and tiger populations in the conservation area, supervise community development works and raise its own funds. It will also assist the Forest Department in protecting the tiger habitat. It could have a separate, small but highly-skilled team of professionals for managing the ISCB programme. To fund its conservation programme the company will charge an entry fee.

The Economics of a Non-profit Conservation Company

At present, the government of India alone spends an annual US$ 400–2,500 per sq. km. (50% contributed each by the central and state governments + other sources) on the management of tiger Reserves. Based on this figure, we estimate that an area of 100 km^2 will require a minimum of Rs 1.6 crore annually (@ Rs 63/US$) or US$ 2,54,000 for its management.

Since we are only proposing low-impact tourism activities to generate funds, a formula based on one room (double occupancy) per 2.5 km^2 was developed. This accounts for forty rooms within a 100 km^2 conservation area. Since the experience will be completely unique, we propose a fee of Rs 3,600 or US$ 57 per person for a full day.

Based on the above-proposed fee structure, we estimate the following revenue prospects for Stepping Stones after four to five years of operations:

1	Total Rooms	40
2	Total Seven months of operation (210 days)	210x40 = 8,400 rooms
3	Occupancy @ 50%	4,200 rooms occupied
4	Total number of visitors	8,400 visitors
5	@ Rs 3,600/visitor/day entry fee	Rs 3 crore or US$ 4,80,000
6	Funds required for management	Rs 1.6 crore or US$ 2,54,000
7	Income after management expenses	Rs. 1.4 crore or US$ 2,23,000
8	Additional income from other sources	Rs 27 lakh or US$ 43,000
9	Fee to Forest Department for use of land @ Rs 10,000–50,000/km2	Rs 10–50 lakh per year
10	Total revenue in hand for conservation & community development	Approx. Rs 11.7 million or US$ 186,000
11	Revenue from the sales of exclusive rights to the tour operator for four lodges @ Rs 20 lakh/year.	Rs. 8 million or US$ 127,000

This fund (which is approximately Rs 1.17 crore) along with Rs 80 lakhs from the sale of exclusive rights will go to community welfare schemes providing healthcare, education, drinking water, livestock insurance, health insurance, and skill development programs for the community and management staff.

In addition to this, this model would generate 200–230 jobs (direct employment by the management and lodges) and another 100–150 jobs would be created indirectly by the non-profit company managing the habitat. These jobs would generate an income of approximately eighty lakhs to a crore for the local community (almost Rs 80,000–1,00,000 per km^2). Indirect beneficiaries are not included in this figure. Currently, we are spending about US$ 2,500/km^2 on tiger conservation alone with no benefits going to the local communities. In this model, we can generate almost twice of what we are spending (US$ 6,400/km^2) and give almost half of the income (US$ 3,130/km^2) to the communities.

Table 11.1 Role of Stepping Stones in Mitigating Threats to Tigers

Threats to protected tiger populations	*Effect*	*Impact of S^3 populations*
Poaching	Increases mortalities, increases extinction threat	Offsets excess mortalities and enhances viability of the population
Small population and protected area size	Increases extinction threat	Reduced extinction risk, provides an alternate approach and creates a larger viable population
Isolation and fragmented population	Compromises long-term viability	Develops connected populations, increases genetic and demographic viability
Poor connectivity	Genetic loss due to inbreeding and genetic drift	Restores connectivity, improves genetic integrity
Loss of prey and quality of tiger habitats	Compromises viability	Restores tiger habitat and prey populations

Threats to protected tiger populations	*Effect*	*Impact of S^3 populations*
Increased tourism pressures	Disturbance	Reduced pressure on a single source population
Little benefit to local communities	Anti-tiger/ conservation sentiments	Provides direct benefits to local communities and makes them a partner in tiger conservation. Uses conservation as a development strategy.

In summary, Table 11.1 identifies threats that are afflicting tiger populations and their effects on the tiger population, based on the literature review and our findings. It also indicates how the S^3 approach can address these threats. The S^3 population strategy can create a larger breeding population—without increasing the protected area size—by creating several territory-size breeding populations within a larger landscape around an already existing source population. It will bring benefits to local communities through its tiger conservation initiatives. By providing direct financial benefits to the community for local development, the Stepping Stone model will make them an active conservation partner. In addition to conservation and community development work, this approach will generate revenue from forest that otherwise lies underutilized.

CONCLUSION

Since launching its unique conservation initiative Project Tiger in 1973, India has had plenty of successes, but also some failures. Creating a network of Protected Areas stabilized the population decline. When we compare India's achievement with other tiger range countries, India certainly has achieved substantially more. But many of us are still critical and not satisfied with this achievement because with our political will, legal support system, funds made available for tiger conservation, expertise, infrastructure built over the last four decades and support from the masses—India could have done better. If we wish to improve our tally of tiger numbers, we need to focus on the habitat outside PAs and restore its quality so that tigers can reoccupy it. Failure to do so will wipe out the successes that we are witnessing in the increasing number of dispersals from our successful protected populations. We must be prepared and have plans ready to take advantage of these hard-earned successes.

After almost half a century of tiger conservation under Project Tiger, it is now time for a critical review and to start looking for new approaches that incorporate more inclusive conservation models. I strongly believe that the success of our conservation efforts will depend on how well we perform outside our Protected Area network in the next few decades. Here lies an opportunity, where public and local communities can become active partners in conservation.

Epilogue

Since we lost all the tigers in Panna in 2009, the authorities have introduced a founder population from three other Tiger Reserves in Madhya Pradesh. Initially, two females from Kanha and Bandhavgarh and one male from Pench Tiger Reserve were sourced. Subsequently, a few more were added to this founder population. The recovery of the population from zero to over thirty in eight years has been remarkable.

The field staff under Mr Sreenivasa Murthy's leadership worked tirelessly to ensure that the founder population remained here in the Tiger Reserve after release. Animals that strayed were brought back and somehow the authorities were able to hold these introduced tigers within the Reserve. It was an enormous task tracking some of these runaway tigers and bringing them back to Panna. At times, they employed measures that were not quite in line with established international protocol but fortunately they were successful. This founder population has since settled, and bred successfully.

Currently, seven to eight tigers are radio-collared and monitored in Panna Tiger Reserve. There are three monitoring teams for each individual tiger and each take eight-hour shifts of monitoring round the clock, 24 hours x 365 days. In addition to this, now all the elephants are employed in tracking these tigers. The cost of this monitoring is huge—a rough estimate would peg it over US$ 100,000 or nearly seven million rupees per year. The restoration of the tiger population is a significant achievement, but my worry is that the causes of Panna's extinction have not been properly recognized and, thus, not addressed. Therefore, the possibility of history repeating itself remains.

Poaching and the presence of bandits is still blamed for the 2009 extinction and we ignore the real reason this population is so vulnerable. In 2002–04 when we were losing tigers in Panna, poaching was also taking its toll on other tiger populations. Maybe many more tigers were poached there but populations like Corbett and Kanha did not succumb to the poaching in the way Sariska and Panna did. In the last eight years we have lost seven adult females even from this monitored and re-introduced population, one from the very same spot where two previous tigers were taken. We must address this high adult female mortality effectively, otherwise the Panna population will continue to be vulnerable to extinction.

Young tigers are dispersing into neighbouring forests; these are encouraging signs for this landscape. Male and female tigers both have dispersed to Uttar Pradesh and established a breeding unit there. One male successfully travelled to Bandhavgarh. Tigers from Panna Tiger Reserve are seen in every direction, even in areas that do not have forest connectivity, indicating that tigers can disperse through all sorts of landscape. Even so, Panna's Tiger Conservation Plan must incorporate a larger landscape vision. We need these plans to take advantage of the successful restoration and breeding.

Creating several neighbouring populations is a necessity, but it needs a landscape approach. Linear projects are a big threat for such an approach. Already the number of tigers killed on the roads appears to be increasing. These mortalities reduce successful dispersal and hamper connectivity. Our fight to save natural habitats for their natural inhabitants is unending.

With great effort and expense the tiger population was restored in Panna but it is now threatened once again by the proposed damming of the river Ken, as part of the ill-conceived Ken-Betwa river-linking project. The reservoir threatens to inundate nearly 100 km^2 of the tiger Reserve and divide the larger forest landscape into two fragments. Such isolation will add to the tiger's vulnerability. If the project goes ahead, the future for tigers in Panna and the Bundelkhand landscape will certainly be extremely bleak.

But the battle to save tigers will continue!

Bibliography

Ackerman, B. B., F. G. Lindzey, and T. P. Hemker. 1984. "Cougar Food Habits in Southern Utah." *Journal of Wildlife Management* 48: 147–55.

Akçakaya, H. R., G. Mills, and C. P. Doncaster. 2007. "The Role of Metapopulations in Conservation." *Key Topics in Conservation Biology*, 64–84. https://doi.org/10.1002/jcp.22422.

Anderson, J.D. 1982. "The Home Range: A New Nonparametric Estimation Technique." *Ecology* 63: 103–12.

Athreya V., M. Odden, J. D. C. Linnell, K. U. Karanth. 2011. "Translocation as a tool for mitigating conflict with leopards in human-dominated landscapes of India." *Conservation Biology* 25:133–141.

Bagchi, S., S. P. Goyal, and K. Sankar. 2003. "Prey Abundance and Prey Selection by Tigers (Panthera Tigris) in a Semi-Arid, Dry Deciduous Forest in Western India." *Journal of Zoology* 260: 285–90.

Baker, R.R. 1978. *The Evolutionary Ecology of Animal Migration*. London: Hodder and Straughton.

Balme, G. A., R. Slotow, and L. T. B. Hunter. 2010. "Edge Effects and the Impact of Non-Protected Areas in Carnivore Conservation: Leopards in the Phinda-Mkhuze Complex, South Africa." *Animal Conservation* 13 (3): 315–23.

Barlow, A, C. McDougal, J. Smith, B. Gurung, S. Bhatta, S. Kumal, B. Mahato, and D. Tamang. 2009. "Temporal Variation in Tiger (Panthera Tigris) Populations and Its Implications for Monitoring." *Journal of Mammalogy* 90 (2): 472–78.

Benson, John F., M. J. Chamberlain, and B. D. Leopold. 2006. "Regulation of Space Use in a Solitary Felid: Population Density or Prey Availability?" *Animal Behaviour* 71 (3): 685–93. https://doi.org/10.1016/j.anbehav.2005.08.005.

Biswas, S., and K. Sankar. 2002. "Prey Abundance and Food Habit of Tigers (Panthera Tigris Tigris) in Pench National Park, Madhya Pradesh, India." *Journal of Zoology* 256: 411–20.

Borgan, Ornulf. 2005. "Estimator, Kaplan-Meier." *Encyclopedia of Biostatistics*. London: John Wiley and Sons.

Brander, A. 1923. *Wild Animals in Central India*. Dehradun: Natraj Publishers.

Broomhall, L. S., M. G. L. Mills, and J. T. du Toit. 2003. "Home Range and Habitat Use by Cheetahs (Acinonyx Jubatus) in the Kruger National Park." *Journal of Zoology* 261 (2): 119–28. https://doi.org/10.1017/S0952836903004059.

Buckland, S.T., D. R. Anderson, K. P. Burnham, J. L. Laake, D. L. Brochers. 1993. *Distance Sampling: Estimating Abundance of Biological Populations*. Chapman & Hall. London.

Buckland, S.T., D. R. Anderson, K. P. Burnham, J. L. Laake, D.L. Brochers, L. Thomas. 2001. *Introduction to Distance Sampling: Estimating Abundance of Biological Populations*. Oxford: Oxford University Press.

Burnham, K.P., Anderson, D.R. and Laake, J.L. 1980. "Estimation of Density from Line Transect Sampling of Biological Population." *Wildlife Monographs* 72: 3-202.

Burt, W.H. 1943. "Territoriality and Home Range Concepts as Applied to Mammals." *Journal of Mammalogy* 24: 346–52.

Carbone, C., S. Christie, K. Conforti, T. Coulson, N. Franklin, J. R. Ginsberg, M. Griffiths, et al. 2001. "The Use of Photographic Rates to Estimate Densities of Tigers and Other Cryptic Mammals." *Animal Conservation* 4: 75–79.

Caughley, G. 1994. "Direction in Conservation Biology." *Journal of Animal Ecology* 63: 215–44.

Chakrabarti, Stotra, Y. V. Jhala, Sutirtha Dutta, Qamar Qureshi, Riaz F. Kadivar, and Vishwadipsinh J. Rana. 2016. "Adding Constraints to Predation through Allometric Relation of Scats to Consumption." *Journal of Animal Ecology* 85 (3): 660–70. https://doi.org/10.1111/1365-2656.12508.

Chamberlain, M.J., L. M. Conner, and B. D. Leopold. 2002. "Seasonal Habitat Selection by Raccoons (Procyon Lotor) in Intensively Managed Pine Forests of Central Mississippi." *American Midland Naturalist* 147: 102–8.

Champion, H. G., and S. K. Seth. 1968. *The Revised Survey of the Forest Types of India*. New Delhi: Manager of Publications. Govt. of India.

Chapron, G., D. Miquelle, A. Lambert, J. Goodrich, S. Legendre, and

J. Clobert. 2008. "The Impact on Tigers of Poaching versus Prey Depletion." *Journal of Applied Ecology* 45 (6): 1667–74.

Chawdhry, P.K. 1997. "Management Plan for Panna National Park (Period 1997-98 to 2006-07)."

Chesson, J. 1978. "Measuring Preference in Selective Predation." *Ecology* 59: 211–15.

Chundawat, R. S. and N. Gogate, 2001. "Saving Tigers in Dry Tropical Habitats." In *Saving Wild Tigers*, edited by V. Thapar. New Delhi: Permanent Black.

Chundawat, R. S., N. S. Gogate, and A. J. T. Johnsingh. 1999. "Tigers in Panna: Preliminary Results from an Indian Tropical Dry Forest." In *Riding the Tiger: Tiger Conservation in Human-Dominated Landscape*, edited by P. Jackson, J. Seidensticker and S. Christie. London: Cambridge University Press.

Chundawat, R. S., and J. Van Gruisen. 2009. "Panna's Last Tiger? Sariska II- How the Management System Fails to Protect Our Wildlife." New Delhi: Wildlife Research and Conservation Trust.

Chundawat, R. S., and K. Sharma. 2008. "Tiger Prey in a Tropical Dry Forest: An Assessment of Abundance and Biomass Estimation Derived from Distance Sampling." *Bombay Natural History Society* 105 (1): 35–43.

Chundawat, R. S., K. Sharma, N. Gogate, P. K. Malik, and A. Tamim Vanak. 2016. "Size Matters: Scale Mismatch between Space Use Patterns of Tigers and Protected Area Size in a Tropical Dry Forest." *Biological Conservation* 197: 146–53. https://doi.org/10.1016/j.biocon.2016.03.004.

Craft, Meggan E., E. Volz, C. Packer, and L. Ancel Meyers. 2011. "Disease Transmission in Territorial Populations: The Small-World Network of Serengeti Lions." *Journal of the Royal Society* 8 (59): 776–86. https://doi.org/10.1098/rsif.2010.0511.

Damania, R., J. Seidensticker, T. Whitten, G. Sethi, K. Mackinon, A. Kiss, and A. Kushlin. 2008. "A Future for Wild Tigers." Washington, DC: The International Bank for Reconstruction and Development / The World Bank and Smithsonian's National Zoological Park.

Debroy, S. 1996. "Halting the Decline of the Tiger." *Journal of Wildlife Research* 1 (2): 224–28.

Delibes, M., P. Gaona, and P. Ferreras. 2001. "Effect of an Attractive Sink Leading into Maladaptive Habitat Selection." *American Naturalist* 158: 277–85.

Dey, A. and P. Naveen. 2013. "Ranthambore Tiger Stride 220 Km to Madhya Pradesh." *Times of India*, April 25 2013. https://timesofindia.

indiatimes.com/city/jaipur/Ranthambore-tiger-strides-220km-to-MP/articleshow/19719121.cms

Dinerstein, Eric, Colby Loucks, E. Wikramanayake, J. R. Ginsberg, E. Sanderson, J. Seidensticker, J. Forrest, et al. 2007. "The Fate of Wild Tigers." *AIBS Bulletin* 57 (6): 508. https://doi.org/10.1641/B570608.

Dixon, K. R. and J. A. Chapman. 1980. "Harmonic Mean Measure of Animal Activity Areas." *Ecology* 61 (5): 1040–44.

Eisenberg, J. F. and J. Seidensticker. 1976. "Ungulates in Southern Asia: A Consideration of Biomass Estimates for Selected Habitats." *Biological Conservation* 10: 293–308.

Flyod, J.J., L.D. Mech, and P. A. Jordan. 1978. "Relating Wolf Scat Contents to Prey Consumed." *Journal of Wildlife Management* 42: 528–32.

Forsyth, J. 1889. *The Highlands of Central India: Notes on Their Forests and Wild Tribes*. London: Chapman & Hall.

Gilpin, M.E., and M. E. Soule. 1986. "Minimum Viable Population: Processes of Species Extinction." In *Conservation Biology: The Science of Scarcity and Diversity*, edited by M.E. Soule, 19–34. Saunderland, MA: Sinauer Associates.

Ginsberg, J. R. 2001. "Setting Priorities for Carnivore Conservation: What Makes Carnivores Difficult?" In *Carnivore Conservation*, edited by J. L. Gittleman, S. M. Funk, and D. W. Macdonald, 498–593. London: Cambridge University Press.

Gittleman, J. L. 1989. *Carnivore Behaviour, Ecology and Evolution*. Chapman & Hall. London.

Gittleman, J. L., and P. H. Harvey. 1982. "Carnivore Home-Range Size, Metabolic Needs and Ecology." *Behavioral Ecology and Sociobiology* 10 (1): 57–63.

Goodrich. 2010. "Human-Tiger Conflict: A Review and Call For Comprehensive Plans." *Integrative Zoology* 5 (4): 300-312. https://onlinelibrary.wiley.com/doi/pdf/10.1111/j.1749-4877.2010.00218.x

Goodrich, J. M., L. L. Kerley, E. N. Smirnov, D. G. Miquelle, L. McDonald, H. B. Quigley, M. G. Hornocker, and T. McDonald. 2008. "Survival Rates and Causes of Mortality of Amur Tigers on and near the Sikhote-Alin Biosphere Zapovednik." *Journal of Zoology* 276 (4): 323–29. https://doi.org/10.1111/j.1469-7998.2008.00458.x.

Goodrich, John M., D. G. Miquelle, E. N. Smirnov, L. L. Kerley, H. B. Quigley, and M. G. Hornocker. 2010. "Spatial Structure of Amur (Siberian) Tigers (Panthera Tigris Altaica) on Sikhote-Alin Biosphere Zapovednik, Russia." *Journal of Mammalogy* 91 (3): 737–48. https://doi.org/10.1644/09-MAMM-A-293.1.

Gopal, Rajesh, Q. Qureshi, M. Bhardwaj, R. K. Jagadish Singh, and Y. V. Jhala. 2010. "Evaluating the Status of the Endangered Tiger Panthera Tigris and Its Prey in Panna Tiger Reserve, Madhya Pradesh, India." *Oryx* 44 (03): 383–89. https://doi.org/10.1017/S0030605310000529.

Gopal, Rajesh, S. P. Yadav, A. Majumder, and G. Areendran. 2014. "Global Tiger Atlas: A Collaborative Compilation by Global Tiger Forum."

Gottelli, D., J. Wang, S. Bashir, S. Durant. 2007. "Genetic Analysis Reveals Promiscuity among Female Cheetahs." *Proceedings of the Royal Society of London: Biological Sciences* 274: 1993–2001. https://doi.org/10.1098/rspb.2007.0502.

Grant, J. W. A., C. A. Chapman and K. S. Richardson. 1992. "Defended versus Undefended Home Range Size of Carnivores, Ungulates and Primates." *Behavioral Ecology and Sociobiology* 31: 149–61.

Gundersen, G., E. Johannessen, H. P. Andreassen, and R. A. Ims. 2001. "Source-sink Dynamics: How Sinks Affect Demography of Sources." *Ecology Letters* 4 (1): 14–21.

Halvorson, William L., and C. Eastin. 1999. "How Shall We Then Manage?" *The National Park Service's Management Policy in the 21st Century* 16 (3): 77–90.

Harestad, A.S., and T.L. Bunnell. 1979. "Home Range and Body Size: A Reevaluation." *Ecology* 60: 389–402.

Harihar, A., B. Pandav, and S. P. Goyal. 2009. "Density of Leopards (Panthera Pardus) in the Chilla Range of Rajaji National Park, Uttarakhand, India." *Mammalia* 73 (1): 68–71.

———"Responses of Leopard Panthera Pardus to the Recovery of a Tiger Panthera Tigris Population." *Journal of Applied Ecology* 48: 806–14.

Hayward, M. W., W. Jedrzejewski, and B. Jedrzewska. 2012. "Prey Preferences of the Tiger Panthera Tigris." *Journal of Zoology* 286: 221–31.

Hedrick, P. W., R. C. Lacy, F. W. Allendorf, and M. E. Soule. 1996. "Directions in Conservation Biology: Comments on Caughley." *Conservation Biology* 10: 1312–20.

Heezen, K. L., and J. R. Tester. 1967. "Evaluation of Radio Tracking by Triangulation with Special Reference to South African Woodland/Savanna Ecosystem." *Wildlife Monographs* 44: 124-141.

Hemley, G., and J. Mills. 1999. "The Begining of the End of Tigers in Trade." In *Riding the Tiger: Tiger Conservation in Human-Dominated Landscapes*, edited by J. Seidensticker, S. Christie, and P. Jackson. London: Cambridge University Press.

Herfindal, I., E. B. Nilsen, R. Andersen, J. D. C. Linnell, and J. Odden. 2005.

"Prey Density, Environmental Productivity and Home-Range Size in the Eurasian Lynx (Lynx Lynx)." *Journal of Zoology* 265: 63–71.

Hines, J. E. 2002. "SCATMAN Version 2.0." usgs-pwrc. http://www.mbr-pwrc.usgs.gov/software.

Hobbs, N. T. 1996. "Modification of Ecosystems by Ungulates." *Journal of Wildlife Management* 60 (4): 695–713.

Hojnowski, C. E., D. G. Miquelle, A. I. Myslenkov, S. Strindberg, E. N. Smirnov, and J. M. Goodrich. 2012. "Why Do Amur Tigers Maintain Exclusive Home Ranges? Relating Ungulate Seasonal Movements to Tiger Spatial Organization in the Russian Far East." *Journal of Zoology* 287: 276–82.

Horev, Aviad, R. Yosef, P. Tryjanowski, and O. Ovadia. 2012. "Consequences of Variation in Male Harem Size to Population Persistence: Modeling Poaching and Extinction Risk of Bengal Tigers (Panthera Tigris)." *Biological Conservation* 147 (1): 22–31. https://doi.org/10.1016/j.biocon.2012.01.012.

Hornocker, M.G., H. B. Quighley, D. G. Miquelle, and K. S. Quighley. 1995. "Siberian Tiger Project: Progress Report." Moscow, Idaho.

Hunter, L. T. B. 1998. "The Behavioural Ecology of Reintroduced Lions and Cheetahs in the Phinda Resource Reserve, Kwazulu-Natal, South Africa." Diss. Universiteit van Pretoria: 1–206. http://www.carnivoreconservation.org/files/thesis/hunter_1998_phd.pdf.

Jackson, P., and E. Kempf. 1994. "Wanted Alive! Tigers in the Wild AWWF Species Report." Gland, Switzerland.

Jarman, P.J. 1974. "The Social Organisation of Antelope in Relation to Their Ecology." *Behaviour* 48: 215–457.

Jathanna, D., K. U. Karanth, A. J. T Johnsingh. 2003. "Estimation of Large Herbivore Densities in the Tropical Forets of Southern India Using Distance Sampling." *Journal of Zoology* 261: 285–90.

Jedrzejewski, W., K. Schmidt, H. Okarma, and R. Kowalczyk. 2002. "Movement Pattern and Home Range Use by the Eurasian Lynx in Bialowieza Primeval Forest (Poland)." *Annales Zoologici Fennici* 39: 29–41.

Jewell, P. A. 1966. "The Concept of Home Range in Mammals." *Symposium of Zoological Society of London* 18: 188–100.

Jhala Y. V., R. Gopal and Q. Quereshi. 2008. "Status of Tigers, Co-Predators and Prey in India." New Delhi.

———2015. "The Status Of Tigers In India 2014." National Tiger Conservation Authority, New Delhi & The Wildlife Institute of India,

Dehradun. http://projecttiger.nic.in/WriteReadData/LetestNews/Document/Tiger%20Status%20booklet_XPS170115212.pdf

Jhala, Y. V., Q. Quereshi, J. Vettakevan, J. Borah, and U. Kumar. 2010. "Intensive Population Monitoring and Study of Tiger Dispersal in Kanha Tiger Reserve (Phase IV)." Dehradun: Wildlife Institute of India.

Jhala, Y. V., Q. Quereshi, and P. R. Sinha. 2011. "Status of the Tigers, Co-Predators and Prey in India." Dehradun: National Tiger Conservation Authority and Wildlife Institute of India.

Johnsingh, A.J.T. 1983. "Large Mammalian Prey-Predator in Bandipur." *Bombay Natural History Society* 80: 1–57.

Johnsingh, A. J. T., H. S. Panwar, and W. A. Rodgers. 1991. "Ecology and Conservation of Large Felids in India." In *Wildife Conservation: Present Trends and Perspectives for 21st Century*. Tsukuba and Yokohama, Japan: Proceedings of the International Symposium on Wildlife Conservation in Tsukuba and Yokohama, Japan.

Johnson, D. H. 1980. "The Comparison of Usage and Availability Measurement for Evaluating Resource Preference." *Ecology* 61: 65–71.

Joslin, P. 1973. "The Asiatic Lion: A Study of Ecology and Behaviour." Diss. University of Edinburgh.

Jotikapukkana, Sukanda, Åke Berg, and A. Pattanavibool. 2010. "Wildlife and Human Use of Buffer-Zone Areas in a Wildlife Sanctuary." *Wildlife Research* 37 (6): 466–74. https://doi.org/10.1071/WR09132.

Kaplan, E. L. and P. Meier. 1958. "Nonparametric Estimation from Incomplete Observation." *Journal Of The American Statistical Association* 53 (282): 457-481.

Karanth, K. U. 1991. "Ecology and Management of the Tiger in Tropical Asia." In *Wildlife Conservation: Present Trends and Perspectives for the 21st Century*, edited by M. Maruyama et al. Tokyo, Japan: Japan Wildlife Research Centre.

———1993. "Predator-Prey Relationships among Large Mammals in Nagarhole National Park." Diss. Mangalore University.

———1995. "Estimating Tiger Panthera Tigris Populations from Camera-Trap Data Using Capture-Recapture Models." *Biological Conservation* 71: 333–38.

———2001. *Tigers*. Grantown-on-Spey, Scotland: Colin Baxter Ltd.

Karanth, K. U. and J. D. Nichols. 2002. *Monitoring Tigers and Their Prey: A Manual for Researchers, Managers and Conservationists in Tropical Asia*. Dehradun: Natraj Publishers.

Karanth, K. U. and B. M. Stith. 1999. "Prey Depletion as a Critical Determinant of Tiger Population Viability." In *Riding the Tiger: Tiger Conservation in Human-Dominated Landscape*, edited by J. Seidensticker, S. Christie, and P. Jackson. London: Cambridge University Press.

Karanth, K.U. and M. E. Sunquist. 1987. "Tigers in India: A Critical Review of Field Censuses." In *Tigers of the World: The Biology, Biopolitics, Management and Conservation of an Endangered Species*, edited by R. L. Tilson and U. S. Seal. Park Ridge, New Jersey: Noyes Publication.

———1992. "Population Structure, Density and Biomass of Large Herbivores in the Tropical Forests of Nagarhole (India)." *Journal of Tropical Ecology* 8: 21–35.

———1995. "Prey Selection by Tiger, Leopard and Dhole in Tropical Forests." *Journal of Animal Ecology* 64: 439–50.

———2000. "Behavioural Correlates of Predation by Tiger (Panthera Tigris), Leopard (Panthera Pardus) and Dhole (Cuon Alpinus) in Nagarahole, India." *Journal of Zoology* 250 (2): 255–65. https://doi.org/10.1017/S0952836900002119.

Karanth, K.U., and R. Gopal. 2005. "An Ecology-Based Policy Framework for Human – Tiger Coexistence in India." In *People and Wildlife: Conflict or Coexistence?*, edited by Rosie Woodroffe and Simon Thirgood, 273–387. London: Cambridge University Press.

Karanth, K. U., R. S. Chundawat, J. D. Nichols, and N. S. Kumar. 2004. "Estimation of Tiger Densities in the Tropical Dry Forests of Panna, Central India, Using Photographic Capture–recapture Sampling." *Animal Conservation* 7 (3): 285–90. https://doi.org/10.1017/S1367943004001477.

Karanth, K. U., N. S. Kumar, J. D. Nichols, W. A. Link, and J. E. Hines. 2004. "Tigers and Their Prey: Predicting Carnivore Densities from Prey Abundance." *Proceedings of the National Academy of Sciences of the United States of America* 101: 4854–58.

Karanth, K. U., and J. D. Nichols. 1998. "Estimation of Tiger Densities in India Using Photographic Captures and Recaptures." *Ecology* 79: 2852–62.

Karanth, K. U., J. D. Nichols, N. S. Kumar, W. A. Link, and J. E. Hines. 2004. "Tigers and Their Prey: Predicting Carnivore Densities from Prey Abundance." *Proceedings of the National Academy of Sciences of the United States of America* 101 (14): 4854–58. https://doi.org/10.1073/pnas.0306210101.

Karanth, K. U., J. D. Nichols, J. Seidensticker, E. Dinerstein, J. L. D. Smith, C. McDougal, A. J. T. Johnsingh, R. S. Chundawat, and V. Thapar. 2003. "Science Deficiency in Conservation Practice: The Monitoring of Tiger

Populations in India." *Animal Conservation* 6: 141–46. https://doi.org/10.1017/S1367943002004000.

Karanth, Kriti K., L. M. Curran, and J. D. Reuning-Scherer. 2006. "Village Size and Forest Disturbance in Bhadra Wildlife Sanctuary, Western Ghats, India." *Biological Conservation* 128 (2): 147–57. https://doi.org/10.1016/j.biocon.2005.09.024.

Karanth, Krithi K., J. D. Nichols, K. U. Karanth, J. E. Hines, and N. L. Christensen Jr. 2010. "The Shrinking Ark : Patterns of Large Mammal Extinctions in India," *Proceedings of the Royal Society of London: Biological Sciences*. https://doi.org/10.1098/rspb.2010.0171.

Kawanishi, Kae. 2002. "Population Status of Tigers (Panthera Tigris) in a Primary Rainforest of Peninsular Malaysia." Diss. University of Florida.

Kelly, M. J., T. M. Caro, M. K. Laurenson, C. D. Fitzgibbon, D. A. Collins, S. M. Durant, G. W. Frame, and B. C. R. Bertram. 1998. "Demography of the Serengeti Cheetah (Acinonyx Jubatus) Population: The First 25 Years." *Journal of Zoology* 244: 473–88.

Kenney, J. S., J. L. Smith, A. M. Starfield, and C. W. McDouglas. 1995. "The Long-Term Effects of Tiger Poaching on Population Viability." *Conservation Biology* 9: 1127–33.

Kerley, L. L., J. M. Goodrich, D. G. Miquelle, H. B. Quigley, M. G. Hornocker, and E. N. Smirnov. 2003. "Reproductive Parameters of Wild Female Amur (Siberian) Tigers (Panthera Tigris Altaica)." *Journal of Mammalogy* 84: 288–98.

Khan, J. A. 1996. "Factors Governing the Habitat Occupancy of Ungulates in Gir Lion Sanctuary, Gujarat, India." *International Journal of Ecology and Environmental Sciences* 22: 73–83.

Khan, J. A., R. Chellam, W. A. Rodgers, and A. J. T. Johnsingh. 1996. "Ungulate Densities and Biomass in the Tropical Dry Deciduous Forests of Gir, Gujarat, India." *Journal of Tropical Ecology* 12: 149–62.

Kleiman, D.G. and J.F. Eisenberg. 1973. "Comparisons of Canid and Felid Social Systems from an Evolutionary Perspective." *Animal Behaviour* 21: 637–59.

Kokko, H., and W.J. Sutherland. 1998. "Potimal Floating and Queing Strategies: Consequences for Density Dependence and Habitat Loss." *American Naturalist* 152: 354–66.

Koppikar, B.R., and J.H. Sabnis. 1976. "Identification of Hairs of Some Indian Mammals." *Bombay Natural History Society* 73: 5–20.

Kothari, A., S. Suri, and N. Singh. 1995. "Conservation in India: A New Direction." *Economic and Political Weekly*: 2755-2766.

Kumar, Ashok, and Belinda Wright. 1999. "Combating Tiger Poaching and Illegal Wildlife Trade in India." In *Riding the Tiger: Tiger Conservation in Human-Dominated Landscapes*, edited by J. Seidensticker, S. Christie, and P. Jackson. London: Cambridge University Press.

Kumar, N. Samba. 2000. "Ungulate Density and Biomass in the Tropical Semi-Arid Forest of Ranthambhore, India." Diss. Pondichery University.

Laake, J.L., S.T. Buckland, D. R. Anderson and K.P. Burnham. 1994. *Distance: User's Guide*. Fort Collins: Colorado State University.

Lancia, R.A., J. D. Nochols, and K.H. Pollock. 1994. "Estimating the Number of Animals in Wildlife Populations." In *Research and Management Techniques for Wildlife and Habitat*, edited by T. Bookhout. Bethesda, Maryland: The Wildlife Society.

Lande, R. 1988. "Genetics and Demography in Biological Conservation." *Science* 241: (1455–1460).

Laurance, W. 2013. "Does Research Help to Safeguard Protected Areas?" *Trends in Ecology & Evolution* 28 (5): 261–66.

Lindstedt, S. L., B.J. Miller, and W. Buskirk. 1986. "Home Range, Time and Body Size in Mammals." *Ecology* 67 (2): 413–18.

Linkie, Matthew, G. Chapron, D. J. Martyr, J. Holden, and N. Leader-Williams. 2006. "Assessing the Viability of Tiger Subpopulations in a Fragmented Landscape." *Journal of Applied Ecology* 43 (3): 576–86. https://doi.org/10.1111/j.1365-2664.2006.01153.x.

Litvaitis, J. A., J. A. Sherburne, and J. A. Bissonette. 1986. "Bobcat Habitat Use and Home Range Size in Relation to Prey Density." *Journal of Wildlife Management* 50: 110–17.

Logan, Kenneth A., and L.L. Sweanor. 2001. *Desert Puma: Evolutionary Ecology and Conservation of an Enduring Carnivore*. Washington, DC: Island Press.

Majumder, A., S. Basu, K. Sankar, Q. Qureshi, Y. V. Jhala, P. Nigam, and R. Gopal. 2012. "Home Ranges of the Radio-Collared Bengal Tigers (Panthera Tigris Tigris L.) in Pench Tiger Reserve, Madhya Pradesh, Central India." *Wildlife Biology in Practice* 8 (1): 36–49. https://doi.org/10.2461/wbp.2012.8.4.

Manly, B. F. J., L. L. McDonald, and D. L. Thomas. 1993. *Resource Selection by Animals: Statistical Design and Analysis for Field Studies*. London: Chapman & Hall.

Martin, Kathy. 1998. "The Role of Animal Behavior Studies in Wildlife Science and Management." *Wildlife Society Bulletin (1973-2006)* 26 (4): 911–20. http://www.jstor.org/stable/3783570.

Marzluff, John M., J.J. Millspaugh, P. Hurvitz, and M. S. Handcock. 2004. "Relating Resources to a Probabilistic Measure of Space Use: Forest Fragments and Steller's Jays." *Ecology* 85 (5): 1411–27. https://doi.org/10.1890/03-0114.

McDonald, D.W. 1983. "The Ecology of Carnivore Social Behaviour." *Nature* 301: 379–84.

McDougal, C. 1977. *The Face of the Tiger*. Rivington Books.

——— 1987. "The Man-Eating Tiger in Geographical and Historical Perspective." In *Tigers of the World: The Biology, Biopolitics, Management and Conservation of an Endangered Species*, edited by R. L. Tilson and U. S. Seal. Park Ridge, New Jersey: Noyes Publication.

McLoughlin, P. D., L. R. Walton, M. A. Ramsay, H. D. Cluff, and P. C. Paquet. 2004. "Hierarchical Habitat Selection by Tundra Wolves." *Journal of Mammalogy* 85: 576–80.

McNab, B.K. 1963. "Bioenergetics and the Determination of Home Range Size." *American Naturalist* 97: 133–40.

Mech, D.L. 2002. "A Critique of Wildlife Radio-Tracking and Its Use in the National Parks: A Report to the U.S. National Park Service." The Biological Resources Division of the U. S. Geological Survey. http://npshistory.com/publications/wildlife/radio-tracking-2002.pdf

Merrick, Melissa J., and J. L. Koprowski. 2017. "Should We Consider Individual Behavior Differences in Applied Wildlife Conservation Studies?" *Biological Conservation* 209 (May): 34–44. https://doi.org/http://dx.doi.org/10.1016/j.biocon.2017.01.021.

Miller, M., M. Weber, D. Neiffer, B. Mangold, D. Fontenot, and M. Stetter. 2003. "Anesthetic Induction of Captive Tigers (Panthera Tigris) Using a Medetomidine-Ketamine Combination." *Journal of Zoo and Wildlife Medicine* 34: 307–8.

Mishra, H. 1982. "The Ecology and Behaviour of Chital (Axis Axis) in the Royal Chitwan National Park, Nepal: With Comparative Studies of Hog Deer, Sambar and Barking Deer." Diss. University of Edinburgh.

Mohr, C.O. 1947. "Table of Equivalent Population of North American Small Mammals." *American Midland Naturalist* 37: 223–49.

Mondol, K., S. Gupta, S. Bhattacharjee, Q. Qureshi, and K. Sankar. 2012. "Response of Leopards to Re-Introduced Tigers in Sariska Tiger Reserve, Western India." *International Journal of Biodiversity and Conservation* 4 (5): 228–36. https://doi.org/10.5897/IJBC12.014.

Mountfort, G. 1981. *Saving the Tiger*. New York: Viking Press.

Mukherjee, S., S. P. Goyal, and R. Chellam. 1994a. "Refined Techniques for the Analysis of Asiatic Lion Panthera Leo Persica Scats." *Acta Theriologica* 39: 425–30.

——— 1994b. "Standardisation of Scat Analysis Techniques for Leopard (Panthera Pardus) in Gir National Park, Western India." *Mammalia* 58: 139–43.

Nichols, J. D. and K. U. Karanth. 2002. "Statistical Concepts: Estimating Absolute Densities of Tigers Using Capture-Recapture Sampling." In *Monitoring Tigers and Their Prey: A Manual for Researchers, Managers and Conservationists in Tropical Asia*. Dehradun: Natraj Publishers.

Nichols, J.D. 1992. "Capture-Recapture Models: Using Marked Animals to Study Population Dynamics." *BioScience* 42: 94–102.

Nowell, K. and P. Jackson. 1996. *Wild Cats: Status Survey and Conservation Action Plan*. Gland, Switzerland: IUCN.

Odden, Morten., P. Wegge, and T. Fredriksen. 2010. "Do Tigers Displace Leopards? If so, Why?" *Ecological Research* 25: 875–81.

Otis, D. L., K. P. Burnham, G. C. White and D. R. Anderson. 1978. "Statistical Inference from Capture Data on Closed Animal Populations." *Wildlife Monographs* 62: 1–135.

Pabla, H.S. 1984. "Panna National Park - Prospects and Problems."

Panwar, H. S. 1982. "What to Do When You've Succeeded: Project Tiger Ten Years Later (Panthera Tigris, India)." *Ambio* 11: 330 37.

——— 1987. "Project Tiger: The Reserve, the Tiger and Their Future." In *Tigers of the World: The Biology, Biopolitics, Management and Conservation of an Endangered Species*, edited by R. L. Tilson and U. S. Seal. Park Ridge, New Jersey: Noyes Publication.

Patil, N., N. S. Kumar, A. M. Gopalaswamy, and K. U. Karanth, 2011. "Dispersing Tiger Makes a Point." *Oryx* 45: 472–75.

Pen, Ido, and F. J. Weissing. 2000. "Optimal Floating and Queuing Strategies: The Logic of Territory Choice." *The American Naturalist* 155 (4): 512-526. https://doi.org/10.1086/303338.

Penteriani, V., M. Ferrer, and M. M. Delgado. 2011. "Floater Strategies and Dynamics in Birds, and Their Importance in Conservation Biology: Towards an Understanding of Nonbreeders in Avian Populations." *Animal Conservation* 14 (3): 233–41. https://doi.org/10.1111/j.1469-1795.2010.00433.x.

Powell, R. A., J. W. Zimmerman and D. E. Seaman. 1997. *Ecology and Behavior North American Black Bears: Home Ranges, Habitat and Social Organization*. London: Chapman & Hall.

Powell, A. 1957. *Call of the Tiger*. London: Robert Hale Limited.

Powell, R.A. 2000. "Animal Home Ranges and Territories and Home Range Estimator." In *Research Techniques in Animal Ecology: Controversies and Consequences*, edited by L. Boitani and T. K. Fuller. New York: Columbia University Press.

Prater, S. 1988. *The Book of Indian Animals*. Bombay: Bombay Natural History Society.

Qureshi Q., R. Gopal, S. Kyatham, S. Basu, A. Mitra, Y. V. Jhala. 2006. "Evaluating Tiger Habitat at the Tehsil Level." *Project Tiger Directorate, Govt. of India, New Delhi and the Wildlife Institute of India*, Dehradun.

Qvarnström, A., and E. Forsgren. 1998. "Should Females Prefer Dominant Males?" *Trends in Ecology & Evolution* 13 (12): 498–501. http://www.ncbi.nlm.nih.gov/pubmed/21238407.

Rangarajan, M. 2001. *India's Wildlife History: An Introduction*. New Delhi: Parmanent Black.

Rettie, W. James, and F. Messier. 2000. "Hierarchical Habitat Selection by Woodland Caribou: Its Relationship to Limiting Factors." *Ecography* 23 (4): 466–78. https://doi.org/10.1034/j.1600-0587.2000.230409.x.

Reynolds, J. C., and N. J. Aebischer. 1991. "Comparison and Quantification of Carnivore Diet by Faecal Analysis: A Critique, with Recommendations, Based on a Study of the Fox Vulpes Vulpes." *Mammal Review* 21: 97–122.

Rodgers, W.A., and H.S. Panwar. 1988. "Planning a Wildlife Protected Area Network in India: Vol. I & II." Dehradun: Wildlife Institute of India.

Rolstad, J., B. Loken, and E. Rolstad. 2000. "Habitat Selection as a Hierarchical Spatial Process: The Gree Woodpecker at the Northern Edge of Its Distribution Range." *Oecologia* 124 (1): 116–29.

Rosenzweig, M.L., and Z. Abramsky. 1986. "Centrifugal Community Organization." *Oikos* 46: 339–48.

Sahgal, B., and V. Thapar. 1996. "Tiger 2000, 1000 Days to Save the Tiger." *Sanctuary Asia* 16: 24–43.

Saltz David. 1994. "Reporting Error Measures in Radio Location by Triangulation: A Review." *Journal of Wildlife Management* 58 (1): 181–84.

Sandell, Mikael. 1989. "The Mating Tactic and Spacing Patterns of Solitary Carnivores." In *Carnivore Behaviour, Ecology and Evolution*, edited by Gittleman, J.L. London: Chapman & Hall.

Sanderson, G. 1912. *Thirteen Years among the Wild Beasts of India*. Edinburgh: John Grant.

Sanderson, E., E. Dinerstein, C. Loucks, E. Heydlauff, A. Wiikramanayake, G. Bryja, J. Forrest, J. R. Ginsberg, et al. 2006. "Setting Priorities for the Conservation and Recovery of Wild Tigers: 2005-2015." In *Tigers of the World (Second Edition)*. Cambridge, MA: Academic Press.

Sankhala, K.S. 1978. *Tiger!: The Story of the Indian Tiger*. Dehradun: Natraj Publishers.

Say, L., D. Pontier, and E. Natoli. 1999. "High Variation in Multiple Paternity of Domestic Cats (Felis Catus L.) in Relation to Environmental Conditions." *Proceedings of the Royal Society of London: Biological Sciences* 266: 2071-74.

Schaller, G. B. 1967. *The Deer and the Tiger: A Study of Wildlife in India*. Chicago: Chicago University Press.

Sebastian, S. 2005. "A Dead Tiger Tells a Tale, Solves a Mystery." *The Hindu*, April 30 2005. http://www.thehindu.com/2005/04/30/stories/2005043009860500.htm

Seidensticker, J. 1986. "Large Carnivores and the Consequences of Habitat Insularization: Ecology and Conservation of Tigers in Indonesia and Bangladesh." In *Cats of the World: Biology, Conservation and Management*, edited by S.D. Miller and D. D. Everett D.D. Washington, DC: National Wildlife Federation.

Seidensticker, J., M.E. Sunquist, and C. McDougal. 1990. "Leopards Living at the Edge of Royal Chitwan National Park, Nepal." In *Conservation in Developing Countries: Problems and Prospects*, edited by J. C. Daniel and J. S. Serrao. Bombay: Bombay Natural History Society.

Seidensticker, J. 1997. "Saving the Tiger." *Wildlife Society Bulletin* 25 (1): 6-17.

Seidensticker, J., M. G. Hornocker, W. V. Wiles, and J. P. Messick. 1973. "Mountain Lion Social Organization in the Idaho Primitive Area." *Wildlife Monographs* 35 (35): 3–60.

Sharma, Koustubh, R. S. Chundawat, J. V. Gruisen, and A. R. Rahmani. 2013. "Understanding the Patchy Distribution of Four-Horned Antelope Tetracerus Quadricornis in a Tropical Dry Deciduous Forest in Central India." *Journal of Tropical Ecology* 30 (01): 45–54. https://doi.org/10.1017/S0266467413000722.

Sharma, R. K., Y. V. Jhala, Q. Qureshi, J. Vattakaven, R. Gopal, and K. Nayak. 2010. "Evaluating Capture-Recapture Population and Density Estimation of Tigers in a Population with Known Parameters." *Animal Conservation* 13 (1): 94–103. https://doi.org/10.1111/j.1469-1795.2009.00305.x.

Sharma, S., Y. V. Jhala, and V. B. Sawarkar. 2005. "Identification of Individual Tigers (Panthera Tigris) from Their Pugmarks." *Journal of Zoology* 267: 11–18.

Sharma, Sandeep, T. Dutta, J. E. Maldonado, T. C. Wood, H. S. Panwar,

J. Seidensticker, and C. Wood. 2013. "Forest Corridors Maintain Historical Gene Flow in a Tiger Metapopulation in the Highlands of Central India." *Proceedings of the Royal Society: Biological Sciences* 280: 1–9.

Sinclair, A. R. E., S. Mduma, and J. S. Brashares. 2003. "Patterns of Predation in a Diverse Predator-Prey System." *Nature* 425 (6955): 288–90. https://doi.org/10.1038/nature01934.

Singh, Randeep, and A. Majumder. 2013. "Interbirth Interval and Litter Size of Free-Ranging Bengal Tiger (Panthera Tigris Tigris) in Dry Tropical Deciduous Forests of India." *European Journal of Wildlife Research* 59 (5): 629-636. https://doi.org/10.1007/s10344-013-0713-z.

Smith, B. R., and D. T. Blumstein. 2013. "Animal Personality and Conservation Biology: The Importance of Behavioral Diversity." In *Animal Personalities*, edited by C. Carere and D. Maestripieri. Chicago: University of Chicago Press.

Smith, J. L. D. 1984. "Dispersal, Communication and Conservation Strategies for the Tiger (Panthera Tigris) in Royal Chitwan National Park, Nepal." Diss. University of Minnesota.

———1993. "The Role of Dispersal in Structuring the Chitwan Tiger Population." *Behaviour* 124: 165–95.

Smith, J. L. D., and C. McDougal. 1991. "The Contribution of Variance in Lifetime Reproduction to Effective Population Size in Tigers." *Conservation Biology* 5: 484–90. https://doi.org/10.1111/j.1523-1739.1991.tb00355.x.

Smith, J.L.D., C. McDougal. and M. E. Sunquist. 1987. "Land Tenure System in Female Tigers." In *Tigers of the World: The Biology, Biopolitics, Management and Conservation of an Endangered Species*. Park Ridge, New Jersey: Noyes Publication.

Springer, J.T. 1967. "Some Sources of Bias and Sampling Error in Radio-Triangulation." *Journal of Wildlife Management* 43: 926–35.

Starfield, A. M., and A. L. Beloch. 1986. *Building Models for Conservation and Wildlife Management*. New York: Macmillan Publishing Company.

Stearns, S. C. 1992. *The Evolution of Life Histories*. Oxford: Oxford University Press.

Stracey, P. D. 1968. *Tigers*. New York: Arthur Barker Ltd.

Sunquist, M. E., K. U. Karanth, and F. Sunquist. 1999. "Ecology, Behaviour and Resilience of the Tiger and Its Conservation Needs." In *Riding the Tiger: Tiger Conservation in Human-Dominated Landscapes*, edited by P. Seidensticker, J., Christie, S. & Jackson. London: Cambridge University Press.

Sunquist, M.E. 1981. "The Social Organization of Tigers (Panthera Tigris) in Royal Chitawan National Park, Nepal."

Sunquist, M.E., and F. Sunquist. 1989. "Ecological Constraints on Predation by Large Felids." In *Carnivore Behaviour, Ecology, and Evolution*, edited by J. L. Gittleman. Ithaca: Cornell University Press.

——— 2002. *Wild Cats of the World*. Chicago: University of Chicago Press.

Tamang, K.M. 1979. "Population Characteristics of the Tiger and Its Prey." In *International Symposium on Tiger, India, February 22-24 1979: Papers, Proceedings and Resolutions*. New Delhi: Project Tiger.

Thapa, Shova, and D. S. Chapman. 2010. "Impacts of Resource Extraction on Forest Structure and Diversity in Bardia National Park, Nepal." *Forest Ecology and Management* 259 (3): 641–49. https://doi.org/10.1016/j.foreco.2009.11.023.

Thapar, V. 1999. "The Tragedy of Indian Tiger: Starting from Scratch." In *Riding the Tiger: Tiger Conservation in Human-Dominated Landscapes*, edited by J. Seidensticker, S. Christie, and P. Jackson. London: Cambridge University Press.

Thapar, V. and F. Singh. 1989. *Tigers: The Secret Life*. London: Elm Tree Books.

Thapar, V. 2001. *Saving Wild Tigers*. New Delhi: Permanent Black.

Thomas, L., S. T. Buckland, K. P. Burnham, D. R. Anderson, J. L. Laake, D. L. Borchers, and S. Strindberg. 2002. "Distance Sampling." In *Encyclopaedia of Environmetrics*, edited by A. El-Shaarawi, and W. W. Peigorsch. London: John Wiley & Sons.

Thompson, W.L. 2004. "Future Direction in Estimating Abundance of Rare or Elusive Species." In *Sampling Rare or Elusive Species*, edited by W.L. Thompson. Washington, DC: Island Press.

Walston, Joe, J. G. Robinson, E. L. Bennett, Urs Breitenmoser, Gustavo A. B. Fonseca, J. Goodrich, M. Gumal, et al. 2010. "Bringing the Tiger Back from the Brink—The Six Percent Solution." *PLoS Biology* 8 (9): 6–9. https://doi.org/10.1371/journal.pbio.1000485.

Wegge, P., M. Odden, C. Pokharel, and T. Storaas. 2009. "Predator-Prey Relationships and Responses of Ungulates and Their Predators to the Establishment of Protected Areas: A Case Study of Tigers, Leopards and Their Prey in Bardia National Park, Nepal." *Biological Conservation* 142 (1): 189–202.

Wegge, P., C. Pokheral, and S. R. Jnawali. 2004. "Effects of Trapping Effort and Trap Shyness on Estimates of Tiger Abundance from Camera Trap Studies." *Animal Conservation* 7: 251–56.

Wemmer, C., J. L. D. Smith, and H.R. Mishra. 1987. "Tigers in the Wild: The

Biopolitical Challenges." In *Tigers of the World: The Biology, Biopolitics, Management and Conservation of an Endangered Species*, edited by R. L. Tilson and U. S. Seal. Park Ridge, New Jersey: Noyes Publication.

White, G. C., and R. A. Garrot. 1990a. *Analysis of Radio Tracking Data*. San Diego: Academic Press.

Wikramanayake, Eric. D., E. Dinerstein, J. G. Robinson, K. U. Karanth, A. Rabinowitz, and D. Olson. 1999. "Where Can Tigers Live in the Future? A Framework for Identifying High Priority Areas for the Conservation of Tigers in the Wild." In *Riding the Tiger: Tiger Conservation in Human-Dominated Landscapes*, edited by J. Seidensticker, S. Christie and P. Jackson. London: Cambridge University Press.

Wikramanayake, Eric. Dinerstein, J. G. Robinson, K. U. Karanth, A. Rabinowitz, D. Olson, T. Mathew, et al. 1998. "An Ecology-Based Method for Defining Priorities for Large Mammal Conservation: The Tiger as Case Study." *Conservation Biology* 12 (4): 865–78.

Wikramanayake, Eric, M. C. Knight, E. Dinerstein, A. Joshi, B. Gurung, and D. Smith. 2004. "Designing a Conservation Landscape for Tigers in Human-Dominated Environments." *Conservation Biology* 18 (3): 839–44.

Williams, C. L., and J. J. Johnston. 2004. "Using Genetic Analysis to Identify Predators." *Sheep and Goat Research Journal* 19: 85–88.

Wilson, D.E. and Mittermeier, R.A. 2009. *Handbook of the Mammals of the World: Carnivores*. Barcelona: Lynx Edicions.

Wilson, K. R., and D. R. Anderson. 1985. "Evaluation of Two Density Estimators of Small Mammal Population Size." *Journal of Mammalogy* 66: 13–21.

Wolf, Max, and F. J. Weissing. 2012. "Animal Personalities : Consequences for Ecology and Evolution" *Trends in Ecology & Evolution* 27 (8): 452-461.

Woodroffe, R., and J. R. Ginsberg. 2000. "Ranging Behaviour and Vulnerability to Extinction in Carnivore." In *Behaviour and Conservation*, edited by L. M. Gosling and W. J. Sutherland,. London: Cambridge University Press.

Woodroffe, Rosie, and J. R. Ginsberg. 1998. "Edge Effects and the Extinction of Populations Inside Protected Areas." *Science* 280: 2126–28.

Worton, B J. 1989. "Kernel Method for Estimating the Utilization Distribution in Home Range Studies." *Ecology* 70 (1): 164–68.

Yoganand, K. 2005. "Behavioural Ecology of Sloth Bear (Melursus Ursinus) in Panna National Park, Central India." Diss. Saurashtra University, Rajkot, India.

Zabel, C. J., K. Mckelvey, and J.P. Ward. 1995. "Influence of Primary Prey on Home-Range Size and Habitat-Use Patterns of Northern Spotted Owls (Strix Occidentalis Caurina)." *Canadian Journal of Zoology* 73: 433–39.

Zar, J. H. 1984. *Biostatistical Analysis*. Jersey: Englewood Cliffs.

Zimmerman, J. W. 1990. "A Critical Review of the Error Polygon Method." *International Conference on Bear Research and Management* 8: 251–56.

Acknowledgements

I cannot thank my wife, Joanna Van Gruisen, enough for making my English readable and still keeping my Indian expressions intact. She accompanied me in the field and her vast understanding of Indian jungle life was of tremendous help to me every day. It was not easy for me to get over my anger and frustration over what had happened in Panna and this reflected in every draft of the book. This is where Joanna's help as a moderator was skilful. She was my most rigorous reviewer and I am grateful to her for the many hours she spent editing the several drafts. Also, by taking on the enormous workload of running the Sarai at Toria for a couple of years, she gave me enough time to work on the book. This book would not have been possible without her help.

I am also very thankful for the effort of Kartikeya Jain, the editor assigned to me by Speaking Tiger, especially for alerting me to the repetitions and for improving the readability of the manuscript by scrutinizing it with his layman's eyes.

Encouragement from friends and colleagues like Pradip Krishen, Valmik Thapar, Supriya Mukherjee, and Mahesh Rangarajan was forceful enough to motivate me to write the book. I am really grateful to all who have encouraged and inspired me to write this book.

I also wish to thank Koustubh Sharma, Abi Tamim Vanak, Neel Gogate, Manu Mathai, and Ullas Karanth and his organization—who have worked with me in the field in various capacities. Koustubh Sharma and Qamar Quereshi were especially helpful to me during the analysis, and I am most grateful to them.

The fieldwork would not have been possible without the help and commitment of the field research team. They worked tirelessly and laboured every day to help me collect information for the project. I feel very fortunate to have had such a wonderful team. My special thanks go to Late Kalyan Singh Yadav, Sataru, Banshgopal Yadav, Suresh Yadav, Hargovind Yadav, Mahadev Yadav and to our family cook, Dhan Bahadur Thapa, who was an integral part of our field team. The time and experience I shared with them was exceptional and I will always remain grateful for their unflinching dedication.

I would also like to thank friends and colleagues—Belinda Wright, P.K. Chawdhry, Dr P.K. Malik, Toby Sinclair, Debbie Banks, Amanda Bright and John Seidensticker for their help and encouragement. Paola Manfredi, Valmik Thapar, Asad Rahmani, B.C. Choudhary and Abi Tamin Vanak also went through the draft, providing constructive inputs. Vikram Soni gave the title suggestion and I am grateful to him for settling the deliberations on this.

Dr. P.K. Malik and his veterinary colleagues were invaluable to the project and I thank them deeply for their care and expertise. The project was supported by several other organizations in many ways. I am grateful to all the concerned individuals of these organizations, including the Global Tiger Patrol (UK), The National Fish and Wildlife Foundation (Save the Tiger Fund) USA, Wildlife Conservation Society (USA), U.S. Fish and Wildlife Service, Ranthambhore Foundation, The Centre for Wildlife Studies, Bangalore and of course, the Wildlife Institute of India for financial and logistical support to the research project. Finally, thanks to the Government of Madhya Pradesh for the permissions.

I also wish to thank my late mother, my brother Shimmujee, and my three sisters and their families, for their encouragement and support.

Index